MW00608927

**Mathematical Methods
in
Continuous and Discrete
Systems**

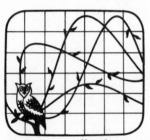

HRW
Series in
Electrical and
Computer Engineering

M. E. Van Valkenburg, Series Editor

Mathematical Methods in Continuous and Discrete Systems

by

SHLOMO KARNI and WILLIAM J. BYATT

Department of Electrical and Computer Engineering
The University of New Mexico

Holt, Rinehart and Winston

New York   Chicago   San Francisco
Philadelphia   Montreal   Toronto   London
Sydney   Tokyo   Mexico City
Rio de Janeiro   Madrid

Other books by S. Karni and W. J. Byatt:

S. Karni, NETWORK THEORY: ANALYSIS AND SYNTHESIS (1966).
————NETWORK THEORY (1973) pirated Russian edition.
————INTERMEDIATE NETWORK ANALYSIS (1971).

W. J. Byatt, INTRODUCTORY ENGINEERING FIELD THEORY. (with M. D. Bradshaw) (1967).

Copyright © 1982 CBS Publishing
All rights reserved

Address correspondence to:
383 Madison Avenue, New York, NY 10017

Library of Congress Cataloging in Publication Data

Karni, Shlomo, 1932–
　　Mathematical methods in continuous & discrete systems.

　　Includes bibliographies and index.
　　1. Electric engineering—Mathematics.　I. Byatt,
William J.　II. Title.
TK153.K38　　　　510′.246213　　　　81-6705
ISBN 0-03-057038-7　　　　　　　　　AACR2

Printed in the United States of America

234　　038　　987654321

CBS COLLEGE PUBLISHING
Holt, Rinehart and Winston
The Dryden Press
Saunders College Publishing

Preface

One of our intentions in writing this text is to enable students to see that applications of linear algebra, complex variables, and transform methods to the analysis of continuous and discrete systems in electrical engineering will do much to unify their point of view. Typically, students in electrical engineering are exposed to some of these topics during their upper division studies in circuit analysis, control theory, and advanced engineering mathematics. However, we have observed that most students do not entirely grasp, for example, the interrelationships among matrices, eigenvalues, and differential equations. Distributed systems, such as electromagnetic waves or solid-state phenomena, described by partial differential equations, are viewed as sinister, to be avoided if possible. Discrete signals are seen as collections of numbers contained in computer printouts.

During the past several years, we have taught a senior course in the Department of Electrical and Computer Engineering at the University of New Mexico in which we cover matrices, complex variables, and transforms of continuous and discrete signals and their applications to electrical engineering. We make no apology for teaching the applications of mathematics in a department dedicated to electrical and computer engineering: There can be no disagreement that educated students within the discipline must be able to apply mathematics in order to model, analyze, and synthesize electrical systems. Therefore, we stress applications of mathematics. Our classroom notes, tested over the years, have resulted in this text, and the reaction of students to the material has been gratifying.

The first chapter covers matrices and introduces matrix differential equations, with applications to topology and to state variables, among others. In order to understand thoroughly the inversion of Laplace, Fourier, and Z-transforms, a knowledge of integration in the complex plane is not only helpful, but essential. For that reason Chapter 2 contains a discussion of complex variables and contour integration. There are applications to electrostatic problems and to diffusion theory.

Chapters on Laplace and Fourier transforms and their inversions then follow, with applications to solid state, circuits, the wave equation and transmission lines, and filter theory, as well as to AM and FM communications. The final chapter, on the analysis of discrete signals, introduces and illustrates the Z-transform and the discrete Fourier transform. The appendices provide supplementary material on the delta function, Fourier series and integrals, Bessel functions, and pairs of transforms.

The problems at the end of each chapter often include extensions of material covered in the text, both in theory and in application. We hope that these will challenge the student to do further work.

We wish to thank our students who, over several years, have offered helpful comments on the presentation of this material and added to its clarity. In particular we acknowledge the help of Avi Zisman, of IBM, Burlington, Vermont, and Edwin Tucker of the Los Alamos National Laboratory, Los Alamos, New Mexico. We are grateful to our friends and colleagues, Professor Edward Angel and Dr. Samuel Stearns, for helpful discussions. Professor Peter Dorato, chairman of the Department of Electrical and Computer Engineering at the University of New Mexico, encouraged us in our efforts.

Albuquerque, New Mexico   Shlomo Karni
October 1981   William J. Byatt

Contents

Mathematical Methods
in
Continuous and Discrete
Systems

CHAPTER 1

Determinants, Matrices, and Linear Algebraic Equations

1.1 INTRODUCTION

Systems of linear algebraic equations occur very frequently in various branches of engineering and science, and their study is fundamental. Although it is assumed that the reader has had some exposure to certain topics in this chapter, we start with simple cases in order to review, and at times illustrate, additional aspects.

Consider the two linear equations

$$a_{11}x_1 + a_{12}x_2 = b_1$$
$$a_{21}x_1 + a_{22}x_2 = b_2 \tag{1.1}$$

where the a's and the b's are given constants. The unknowns x_1 and x_2 can be found by substituting one unknown from one equation into the other, with the results

$$x_1 = \frac{a_{22}b_1 - a_{12}b_2}{a_{11}a_{22} - a_{12}a_{21}}$$

and

$$x_2 = \frac{a_{11}b_2 - a_{21}b_1}{a_{11}a_{22} - a_{12}a_{21}} \tag{1.2}$$

The denominator in Equation 1.2 is conveniently designated as the determinant of order 2

$$D_2 = \begin{vmatrix} a_{11} & a_{12} \\ a_{21} & a_{22} \end{vmatrix} = a_{11}a_{22} - a_{12}a_{21} \tag{1.3}$$

By the same rule, the numerators in Equation 1.2 can be written as determinants of order 2

$$\begin{vmatrix} b_1 & a_{12} \\ b_2 & a_{22} \end{vmatrix} = a_{22}b_1 - a_{12}b_2$$

and

$$\begin{vmatrix} a_{11} & b_1 \\ a_{21} & b_2 \end{vmatrix} = a_{11}b_2 - a_{21}b_1$$ (1.4)

Hence Equation 1.2 can be rewritten in the form

$$x_1 = \frac{\begin{vmatrix} b_1 & a_{12} \\ b_2 & a_{22} \end{vmatrix}}{\begin{vmatrix} a_{11} & a_{12} \\ a_{21} & a_{22} \end{vmatrix}} \qquad x_2 = \frac{\begin{vmatrix} a_{11} & b_1 \\ a_{21} & b_2 \end{vmatrix}}{\begin{vmatrix} a_{11} & a_{12} \\ a_{21} & a_{22} \end{vmatrix}}$$ (1.5)

known as *Cramer's rule*. The same rule, properly defined and applied later, holds for determinants of higher order.

Example 1.1 Use Cramer's rule to find i_1 and i_2 in the circuit shown in Figure 1.1, where element values are in ohms.

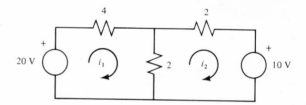

FIGURE 1.1   Example 1.1.

The two loop equations are

$$6i_1 - 2i_2 = 20$$
$$-2i_1 + 4i_2 = -10$$

$$\therefore D_2 = \begin{vmatrix} 6 & -2 \\ -2 & 4 \end{vmatrix} = 24 - 4 = 20$$

$$\therefore i_1 = \frac{\begin{vmatrix} 20 & -2 \\ -10 & 4 \end{vmatrix}}{D_2} = \frac{80 - 20}{20} = 3 \; amperes$$

$$\therefore i_2 = \frac{\begin{vmatrix} 6 & 20 \\ -2 & -10 \end{vmatrix}}{D_2} = \frac{-60 + 40}{20} = -1 \; ampere$$ ∎

Let us consider the geometrical (spatial) meaning of Equation 1.1 and its solution. In a two-dimensional space, i.e., a plane, with coordinate axes x_1 and x_2 as shown in Figure 1.2, Equation 1.1 represents two lines that intersect [Figure 1.2(a)] provided

$$\begin{vmatrix} a_{11} & a_{12} \\ a_{21} & a_{22} \end{vmatrix} \neq 0$$ (1.6)

If the determinant in Equation 1.3 vanishes, i.e.,

$$\begin{vmatrix} a_{11} & a_{12} \\ a_{21} & a_{22} \end{vmatrix} = 0$$ (1.7)

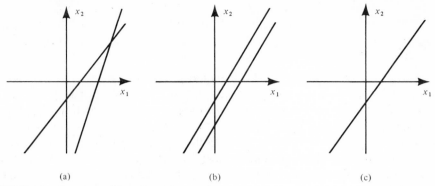

(a)   (b)   (c)

FIGURE 1.2   Geometry of Equation 1.1.

then

$$\frac{a_{11}}{a_{21}} = \frac{a_{12}}{a_{22}} \tag{1.8}$$

which, in turn, indicates that the two lines are parallel. They are *distinct* [Figure 1.2(b)] if, in addition to Equation 1.8, we also have

$$\frac{a_{11}}{a_{21}} \neq \frac{b_1}{b_2} \tag{1.9}$$

The two lines are parallel and *coincident*—i.e., they merge into a single line [Figure 1.2(c)]—if, in addition to Equation 1.8, we also have

$$\frac{a_{11}}{a_{21}} = \frac{b_1}{b_2} \tag{1.10}$$

Finally, viewed from the existence of solution, we say that in Figure 1.2(a) there is a unique solution and Equations 1.1 are *consistent*. In Figure 1.2(b) there is no solution, and Equations 1.1 are *inconsistent*. In Figure 1.2(c) there are infinitely many solutions: The equations are consistent but *redundant* and any arbitrarily chosen value of x_1, say, will yield a corresponding value of x_2 on that line.

Example 1.2   Find the value(s) of x for which the following system of equations is (a) consistent, (b) inconsistent, (c) redundant:

$$2I_1 + 3I_2 = -4$$
$$6I_1 + 9I_2 = x$$

Since $2/6 = 3/9, D_2 = 0$, as in Equation 1.7. Therefore the system is inconsistent if $3/9 \neq -4/x$ or when $x \neq -12$. The system is redundant if $x = -12$ because then the second equation is precisely three times the first one and is thus redundant.   ∎

1.2   DETERMINANTS

We generalize the notion of a determinant with the following definition: A determinant of order n is written as

$$D_n = \begin{vmatrix} a_{11} & a_{12} & \cdots & a_{1n} \\ a_{21} & a_{22} & \cdots & a_{2n} \\ & & \cdot & \\ & & \cdot & \\ a_{n1} & a_{n2} & \cdots & a_{nn} \end{vmatrix} \tag{1.11}$$

with a typical element a_{ij} in row i and column j. The value of D_n is the algebraic sum of $n!$ possible terms, each term being the product of n elements in D_n, taking only one element from each row and column. The *algebraic sum* means that each such product has associated with it a sign, plus $(+)$ or minus $(-)$, according to the following rule: (1) Arrange each product in ascending order of the first subscript of the elements. For example, in D_3, a third-order determinant, there will be the product $a_{13}a_{22}a_{31}$, and it is already written in accordance with this rule. (2) Note the order of the second subscript and count as an *inversion* every time that a higher integer precedes a lower one. In our example the order of the second subscripts is 3, 2, 1 and there are three inversions: 3 precedes 2, 3 precedes 1, and 2 precedes 1. (3) Assign to the product a $(+)$ sign if the number of inversions is *even* or a $(-)$ sign if the number of inversions is *odd*.

Stated in other words, the determinant D_n has a value of

$$D_r = \sum \pm a_{1k}a_{2l}a_{3m} \cdots a_{nr} \tag{1.12}$$

where the summation is over all possible permutations, $n!$ in number, of the second subscripts $k, l, m, \ldots, r$.

Example 1.3   Evaluate

$$D_3 = \begin{vmatrix} a_{11} & a_{12} & a_{13} \\ a_{21} & a_{22} & a_{23} \\ a_{31} & a_{32} & a_{33} \end{vmatrix}$$

There will be $3! = 6$ terms in Equation 1.12, listed with their signs as follows:

Product	Number of Inversions	Sign
$a_{11}a_{22}a_{33}$	0	+
$a_{11}a_{23}a_{32}$	1	−
$a_{12}a_{21}a_{33}$	1	−
$a_{12}a_{23}a_{31}$	2	+
$a_{13}a_{21}a_{32}$	2	+
$a_{13}a_{22}a_{31}$	3	−

Hence

$$D_3 = a_{11}a_{22}a_{33} - a_{11}a_{23}a_{32} - a_{12}a_{21}a_{33} + a_{12}a_{23}a_{31} + a_{13}a_{21}a_{32} - a_{13}a_{22}a_{31} \qquad \blacksquare$$

Example 1.4   Evaluate

$$D_3 = \begin{vmatrix} -5 & 2 & 1 \\ -3 & -4 & 7 \\ -1 & 0 & 5 \end{vmatrix}$$

$$D_3 = a_{11}a_{22}a_{33} - a_{11}a_{23}a_{32} - a_{12}a_{21}a_{33} + a_{12}a_{23}a_{31} + a_{13}a_{21}a_{32} - a_{13}a_{22}a_{31}$$
$$= (-5)(-4)(5) - (-5)(7)(0) - (2)(-3)(5) + (2)(7)(-1) + (1)(-3)(0) - (1)(-4)(-1)$$
$$= 112 \qquad \blacksquare$$

The following properties of determinants of order n are important.

1. D_n = product of its main diagonal elements, if D_n is in a *triangular form* or a *diagonal form*. That is, $D_n = \prod_j a_{jj}$ if $a_{jk} = 0$, for $j < k$ or $j > k$ (triangular), or $a_{jk} = 0$ for $j \neq k$ (diagonal). The symbol $\prod$ indicates "product of . . . ."
2. $D_n = 0$ if any one row is full of zeros.
3. $D_n = 0$ if any one column is full of zeros.
4. D_n changes sign if two rows (or two columns) interchange their places.
5. If all the elements of a row (or a column) are multiplied by a scalar α, the value of D_n becomes αD_n.
6. $D_n = 0$ if any two rows (or columns) are proportional.
7. The value of D_n remains unchanged if the rows are written as columns (row 1 as column 1, row 2 as column 2, etc.).

For proofs of these properties, the student should consult one of the textbooks listed in the Bibliography at the end of this chapter.

1.3 MINORS, COFACTORS, AND LAPLACE'S EXPANSION OF D$_n$

When row i and column j are removed from D_n, the result is an $(n - 1)^{\text{th}}$-order determinant denoted by M_{ij} and called the *minor* of a_{ij}.

Example 1.5 In the second-order determinant

$$D_2 = \begin{vmatrix} 1 & -3 \\ 4 & 2 \end{vmatrix}$$

the minor of $a_{11} = 1$ is $M_{11} = 2$ and the minor of $a_{21} = 4$ is $M_{21} = -3$. $\qquad \blacksquare$

Example 1.6 In the third-order determinant

$$D_3 = \begin{vmatrix} 0 & -1 & 2 \\ 1 & -3 & 4 \\ 2 & -5 & 6 \end{vmatrix}$$

the minor of $a_{31} = 2$ is

$$M_{31} = \begin{vmatrix} -1 & 2 \\ -3 & 4 \end{vmatrix} = 2$$

The minor of $a_{22} = -3$ is

$$M_{22} = \begin{vmatrix} 0 & 2 \\ 2 & 6 \end{vmatrix} = -4 \qquad \blacksquare$$

The *signed* minor $(-1)^{i+j}M_{ij}$ is called the cofactor C_{ij} of a_{ij}.

$$C_{ij} = (-1)^{i+j}M_{ij} \tag{1.13}$$

Example 1.7 In Example 1.5, $C_{21} = (-1)^{2+1}(-3) = 3$, and in Example 1.6 the cofactor of a_{22} is $C_{22} = (-1)^{2+2}(-4) = -4$. ∎

In simple words, the cofactor has a $(+)$ sign if the sum of the subscripts is even and a $(-)$ sign if the sum is odd.

Laplace's expansion of D_n is based on cofactors and can be stated as follows: Multiply each element of any row (or column) by its cofactor, and then add these products. That is,

$$D_n = \sum_{j=1}^{n} a_{ij}C_{ij} \tag{1.14}$$

with $i = 1$, or 2, or 3, . . . or n, this being an expansion of D_n by row i; or

$$D_n = \sum_{i=1}^{n} a_{ij}C_{ij} \tag{1.15}$$

with $j = 1$, or 2, or 3, . . . or n, this being an expansion of D_n by column j.

Example 1.8 Expand D_3 by its first row, given

$$D_3 = \begin{vmatrix} 0 & -1 & 1 \\ 1 & 2 & 0 \\ 2 & 0 & 2 \end{vmatrix}$$

Using Equation (1.14) with $i = 1$ (the first row) we have

$$D_3 = 0 \cdot C_{11} + (-1) \cdot C_{12} + (1) \cdot C_{13} =$$
$$= (0) \cdot \begin{vmatrix} 2 & 0 \\ 0 & 2 \end{vmatrix} + (-1)(-1)\begin{vmatrix} 1 & 0 \\ 2 & 2 \end{vmatrix} + (1)\begin{vmatrix} 1 & 2 \\ 2 & 0 \end{vmatrix} =$$
$$= -2$$

∎

Some of the properties of determinants (listed in Section 1.2) can be used to good advantage in order to facilitate the evaluation of a determinant. Let us use D_3 as above and reduce it to triangular form by the following sequential operations: Subtract $(0.5) \times$ third row from first row; add first row to second row; subtract third column from first column. These operations do not change the value of D_3, as stated, and are shown in the following example.

Example 1.9

$$D_3 = \begin{vmatrix} 0 & -1 & 1 \\ 1 & 2 & 0 \\ 2 & 0 & 2 \end{vmatrix} = \begin{vmatrix} -1 & -1 & 0 \\ 1 & 2 & 0 \\ 2 & 0 & 2 \end{vmatrix} = \begin{vmatrix} -1 & -1 & 0 \\ 0 & 1 & 0 \\ 2 & 0 & 2 \end{vmatrix} = \begin{vmatrix} -1 & -1 & 0 \\ 0 & 1 & 0 \\ 0 & 0 & 2 \end{vmatrix} =$$

$$= (-1)(1)(2) = -2$$

as before. Note that we could have actually stopped after the first step and expanded D_3 by its third column containing only one nonzero term ($a_{33} = 2$) with its second-order cofactor, i.e.,

$$D_3 = 2 \cdot \begin{vmatrix} -1 & -1 \\ 0 & 1 \end{vmatrix} = (2)(-1) = -2 \qquad \blacksquare$$

1.4 PIVOTAL CONDENSATION

Clearly, as the order of D_n increases so do the difficulty and the computational length of evaluating it by cofactors. Several alternative, more convenient methods exist. Among these, pivotal condensation is one of the better methods, and is equally suited for ease in programming.

To explain the method, let us first consider a general third-order determinant:

$$D_3 = \begin{vmatrix} a_{11} & a_{12} & a_{13} \\ a_{21} & a_{22} & a_{23} \\ a_{31} & a_{32} & a_{33} \end{vmatrix} \qquad (1.16)$$

and, without loss of generality, assume that $a_{11} \neq 0$, and call it the *pivot*. (If $a_{11} = 0$, an interchange with a row or a column is needed, affecting only the sign of D_3.) We perform several of the previously mentioned operations, affecting the value of D_3 as indicated in each step.

Step 1: Multiply row 2 and row 3 by the pivot, yielding

$$a_{11}^2 D_3 = \begin{vmatrix} a_{11} & a_{12} & a_{13} \\ a_{11}a_{21} & a_{11}a_{22} & a_{11}a_{23} \\ a_{11}a_{31} & a_{11}a_{32} & a_{11}a_{33} \end{vmatrix} \qquad (1.17)$$

Step 2: In the new determinant, Equation 1.17, subtract $a_{21} \times$ (first row) from the second row, then $a_{31} \times$ (first row) from the third row. The result is still $a_{11}^2 D_3$:

$$a_{11}^2 D_3 = \begin{vmatrix} a_{11} & a_{12} & a_{13} \\ 0 & a_{11}a_{22} - a_{12}a_{21} & a_{11}a_{23} - a_{13}a_{21} \\ 0 & a_{11}a_{32} - a_{12}a_{31} & a_{11}a_{33} - a_{13}a_{31} \end{vmatrix} \qquad (1.18)$$

Two observations are made at this point. First, the elements below the pivot are made zero through this subtraction. Second, the other elements in rows 2 and 3 can be written as (2×2) determinants as follows:

$$a_{11}^2 D_3 = \begin{vmatrix} a_{11} & a_{12} & a_{13} \\ 0 & \begin{vmatrix} a_{11} & a_{12} \\ a_{21} & a_{22} \end{vmatrix} & \begin{vmatrix} a_{11} & a_{13} \\ a_{21} & a_{23} \end{vmatrix} \\ 0 & \begin{vmatrix} a_{11} & a_{12} \\ a_{31} & a_{32} \end{vmatrix} & \begin{vmatrix} a_{11} & a_{13} \\ a_{31} & a_{33} \end{vmatrix} \end{vmatrix} \qquad (1.19)$$

Step 3: Expand the determinant in Equation 1.19 by cofactors of the elements of the first column:

$$a_{11}^2 D_3 = a_{11} \begin{vmatrix} \begin{vmatrix} a_{11} & a_{12} \\ a_{21} & a_{22} \end{vmatrix} & \begin{vmatrix} a_{11} & a_{13} \\ a_{21} & a_{23} \end{vmatrix} \\ \begin{vmatrix} a_{11} & a_{12} \\ a_{31} & a_{32} \end{vmatrix} & \begin{vmatrix} a_{11} & a_{13} \\ a_{31} & a_{33} \end{vmatrix} \end{vmatrix} \qquad (1.20)$$

Step 4: Finally, since $a_{11} \neq 0$, divide by a_{11}^2 to get

$$D_3 = \frac{1}{a_{11}} \begin{vmatrix} \begin{vmatrix} a_{11} & a_{12} \\ a_{21} & a_{22} \end{vmatrix} & \begin{vmatrix} a_{11} & a_{13} \\ a_{21} & a_{23} \end{vmatrix} \\ \begin{vmatrix} a_{11} & a_{12} \\ a_{31} & a_{32} \end{vmatrix} & \begin{vmatrix} a_{11} & a_{13} \\ a_{31} & a_{33} \end{vmatrix} \end{vmatrix} \qquad (1.21)$$

We have thus reduced the evaluation of D_3 to calculating a (2×2) determinant in which each element in turn is a (2×2) determinant. The latter can be written by inspection.

The general pattern for D_n now becomes clear and can be summarized as follows:

1. Let $a_{11} \neq 0$ be the pivot. If $a_{11} = 0$ interchange two rows (or columns), if necessary, thus affecting at most the sign of D_n.
2. Form all possible (2×2) determinants found in D_n:

$$D_2 = \begin{vmatrix} a_{l1} & a_{lk} \\ a_{p1} & a_{pk} \end{vmatrix} \qquad (1.22)$$

3. The value of D_n is then given in terms of the reduced determinant as

$$D_n = \frac{1}{a_{11}^{n-2}} D_{n-1} \qquad (1.23)$$

where D_{n-1} is of the order $(n - 1) \times (n - 1)$ and its elements are the (2×2) determinants found in step 2. Specifically, D_2 of Equation 1.22 occupies the $(p - 1)$ row and $(k - 1)$ column in D_{n-1}.
4. To evaluate D_{n-1}, use these steps recursively (repeatedly), expressing its value in terms of D_{n-2}. Successive recursions will finally reduce the calculation to a single D_2, a (2×2) determinant.

Example 1.10 Evaluate the following D_4 by pivotal condensation.

$$D_4 = \begin{vmatrix} 1 & -1 & 2 & 4 \\ 3 & 2 & 0 & 1 \\ -2 & 1 & 1 & 3 \\ 2 & 4 & -1 & 1 \end{vmatrix}$$

Here $a_{11} = 1$, the pivot, and so we write

$$D_4 = \frac{1}{1^{4-2}} \begin{vmatrix} \begin{vmatrix} 1 & -1 \\ 3 & 2 \end{vmatrix} & \begin{vmatrix} 1 & 2 \\ 3 & 0 \end{vmatrix} & \begin{vmatrix} 1 & 4 \\ 3 & 1 \end{vmatrix} \\ \begin{vmatrix} 1 & -1 \\ -2 & 1 \end{vmatrix} & \begin{vmatrix} 1 & 2 \\ -2 & 1 \end{vmatrix} & \begin{vmatrix} 1 & 4 \\ -2 & 3 \end{vmatrix} \\ \begin{vmatrix} 1 & -1 \\ 2 & 4 \end{vmatrix} & \begin{vmatrix} 1 & 2 \\ 2 & -1 \end{vmatrix} & \begin{vmatrix} 1 & 4 \\ 2 & 1 \end{vmatrix} \end{vmatrix} = \begin{vmatrix} 5 & -6 & -11 \\ -1 & 5 & 11 \\ 6 & -5 & -7 \end{vmatrix}$$

The (3×3) determinant is again evaluated by pivotal condensation, with $a_{11} = 5$ as its pivot.

$$D_3 = \frac{1}{5^{3-2}} \begin{vmatrix} \begin{vmatrix} 5 & -6 \\ -1 & 4 \end{vmatrix} & \begin{vmatrix} 5 & -11 \\ -1 & 11 \end{vmatrix} \\ \begin{vmatrix} 5 & -6 \\ 6 & -5 \end{vmatrix} & \begin{vmatrix} 5 & -11 \\ 6 & -7 \end{vmatrix} \end{vmatrix} = \frac{1}{5} \begin{vmatrix} 19 & 44 \\ 11 & 31 \end{vmatrix} = \frac{1}{5}(105) = 21 \qquad \blacksquare$$

1.5   MATRICES

A matrix is a rectangular array of elements. These elements may be real or complex numbers, or may be some functions of a parameter. Square brackets are used to enclose the elements of the matrix. (Other common enclosures are double bars or parentheses.) The following are examples of matrices:

$$\begin{bmatrix} -1.6 & 4 \\ 0 & 1 \\ 2 & -2 \end{bmatrix} \qquad \begin{bmatrix} 6 + j5 & 0.7 - j0.5 \\ -j3 & -1 + j0 \end{bmatrix} \qquad \begin{bmatrix} \sin t & t^2 & 1/t & (t-4) \\ e^{-t} & 1/2t & t & t \\ \cos t & e^{-t} & t & t \end{bmatrix}$$

$$\text{(a)} \qquad\qquad\qquad \text{(b)} \qquad\qquad\qquad\qquad \text{(c)}$$

A general notation for a matrix is

$$\mathbf{A} = [a_{ij}] \qquad \begin{matrix} i = 1, 2, \ldots, m \\ j = 1, 2, \ldots, n \end{matrix} \qquad\qquad (1.24)$$

(Read: "Matrix $\mathbf{A}$ is made up of elements a_{ij}.")

The subscripts i, j designate, respectively, the row and column of element a_{ij}.

The *order* of a matrix is given by ($m \times n$), where m is the number of its rows and n the number of its columns. So, in matrices (a), (b), and (c) the orders of these matrices are (3×2), (2×2), and (3×4), respectively.

Certain special matrices are to be noted:

A *square matrix* has the same number of rows and columns, $m = n$.

A *row matrix* has one row, $m = 1$.

A *column matrix* has one column, $n = 1$.

If $m = n = 1$, the matrix reduces to a *scalar*.

The *null* (or *zero*) *matrix* has all its elements zero,

$$\mathbf{R} = \mathbf{0} \qquad \text{if } r_{ij} = 0 \qquad \begin{matrix} 1 \le i \le m \\ 1 \le j \le n \end{matrix} \qquad\qquad (1.25)$$

A *diagonal matrix* $\mathbf{D}$ is a square matrix with the elements off the main diagonal all zero; that is, $d_{ij} = 0$ for $i \ne j$.

The *unit matrix,* $\mathbf{I}$, is a diagonal matrix in which $i_{kk} = 1$.

The transpose of a matrix is obtained by rewriting every row as a column. Thus, the transpose of $\mathbf{A}$, denoted by $\mathbf{A}^T$, is

$$\mathbf{A}^T = [a_{ij}]^T = [a_{ji}] \qquad\qquad (1.26)$$

A *triangular matrix* is a square matrix in which all of the elements above or below the main diagonal are zero. The matrix then is *upper triangular* or *lower triangular*. The following are examples of a null, a diagonal, a unit, and a triangular matrix, respectively.

$$\begin{bmatrix} 0 & 0 & 0 \\ 0 & 0 & 0 \end{bmatrix} \qquad\qquad \begin{bmatrix} t^2 & 0 & 0 \\ 0 & (t-1) & 0 \\ 0 & 0 & 1/t \end{bmatrix}$$

A null matrix   A diagonal matrix

(a)   (b)

$$\begin{bmatrix} 1 & 0 & 0 & 0 \\ 0 & 1 & 0 & 0 \\ 0 & 0 & 1 & 0 \\ 0 & 0 & 0 & 1 \end{bmatrix} \qquad \begin{bmatrix} a & 0 & 0 & 0 \\ e & b & 0 & 0 \\ g & f & c & 0 \\ h & k & i & d \end{bmatrix}$$

A unit matrix   A triangular matrix

(c)   (d)

It is important to note that a matrix does not have a value; it is merely an arrangement of elements. The determinant of a square matrix, however, has a value. We return to this subject later.

1.6   ELEMENTARY MATRIX ALGEBRA

Equality of Matrices

Two matrices $\mathbf{R}$ and $\mathbf{Q}$ are equal if and only if they are equal element by element. That is, $\mathbf{R} = \mathbf{Q}$ if and only if

$$r_{ij} = q_{ij} \qquad 1 \leq i \leq m \qquad 1 \leq j \leq n \qquad (1.27)$$

In other words, $\mathbf{R}$ and $\mathbf{Q}$ must be of the same order and be equal element by element.

Example 1.11   Let

$$\mathbf{R} = \begin{bmatrix} x^2 + 3x + 2 \\ -y \\ z + 1 \end{bmatrix}, \quad \mathbf{Q} = \begin{bmatrix} 0 \\ 4 \\ -5 \end{bmatrix}$$

then $\mathbf{R} = \mathbf{Q}$ means that

$$\begin{array}{rcll} x^2 + 3x + 2 = & 0 & \text{or} & x = -1, -2 \\ -y = & 4 & \text{or} & y = -4 \\ z + 1 = & -5 & \text{or} & z = -6 \end{array}$$

■

Addition and Subtraction

Matrices may be added (subtracted) only if they are of the same order. Addition (subtraction) is then performed element by element:

$$\mathbf{P} \pm \mathbf{Q} = \mathbf{R} \quad \text{means} \quad r_{ij} = p_{ij} \pm q_{ij} \qquad (1.28)$$

The resulting matrix $\mathbf{R}$ is also of the order $(m \times n)$.

Example 1.12

$$\begin{bmatrix} 1.1 & -4.2 & 0 \\ 3 & 3 & 2 \end{bmatrix} + \begin{bmatrix} -1 & 6.8 & 1 \\ 5.3 & 2 & -2 \end{bmatrix} - \begin{bmatrix} 0 & -3 & 3 \\ 1 & 2.1 & -1 \end{bmatrix} = \begin{bmatrix} 0.1 & 5.6 & -2 \\ 7.3 & 2.9 & 1 \end{bmatrix}$$ ■

It is easily verified, using Equation 1.28, that the commutative and associative laws of addition hold for matrices, i.e.,

$$P + Q = Q + P \tag{1.29}$$

and

$$P + (Q + R) = (P + Q) + R \tag{1.30}$$

Also

$$P - P = 0 \tag{1.31}$$

the null matrix.

Example 1.13 Consider the matrices

$$P = \begin{bmatrix} -1 & 4 \\ 2 & 1 \\ 0 & 4 \end{bmatrix} \quad Q = \begin{bmatrix} 0 & -2 \\ 4 & 5 \\ 3 & -1 \end{bmatrix} \quad R = \begin{bmatrix} -1 & 2 & 0 & -1 \\ 4 & -1 & 1 & 4 \\ 3 & 2 & 1 & 7 \end{bmatrix}$$

Then

$$P + Q = \begin{bmatrix} -1 & 4 \\ 2 & 1 \\ 0 & 4 \end{bmatrix} + \begin{bmatrix} 0 & -2 \\ 4 & 5 \\ 3 & -1 \end{bmatrix} = \begin{bmatrix} -1 & 2 \\ 6 & 6 \\ 3 & 3 \end{bmatrix} = Q + P$$

$$P - Q = \begin{bmatrix} -1 & 4 \\ 2 & 1 \\ 0 & 4 \end{bmatrix} - \begin{bmatrix} 0 & -2 \\ 4 & 5 \\ 3 & -1 \end{bmatrix} = \begin{bmatrix} -1 & 6 \\ -2 & -4 \\ -3 & 5 \end{bmatrix}$$

$P \pm R$ and $Q \pm R$ are undefined since R is not of the same order as Q or P. ∎

Multiplication

Multiplication of matrices is restricted in the following manner: The product PQ is defined and exists only if the number of columns of P is equal to the number of rows of Q. In other words, P must be of the order $(m \times b)$ and Q of the order $(b \times n)$. Such matrices are said to be *compatible* (or *conformable*).

We notice immediately that, in general, the commutative law of multiplication does not hold:

$$PQ \neq QP \tag{1.32}$$

because the number of columns of P must be equal to the number of rows of Q for the product PQ to exist; but we have no assurance that the number of columns of Q is equal to the number of rows of P for the product QP to exist. Furthermore, even if it exists, the product QP may not necessarily equal the product PQ. For this reason, we must specify the way in which matrices are multiplied: We say that in the product PQ, matrix P is *postmultiplied* by matrix Q; alternatively, matrix Q is *premultiplied* by matrix P.

The actual multiplication is carried out as follows: Let P be of order $(m \times b)$ and Q of order $(b \times n)$. Then

$$PQ = R \tag{1.33a}$$

where R is a matrix of order $(m \times n)$ and

$$r_{ij} = \sum_{t=1}^{t=b} p_{it}q_{tj} \tag{1.33b}$$

Matrix **R**, then, "borrows" the number of its rows (m) from **P** and the number of its columns (n) from **Q**. Any element of **R** is formed according to Equation 1.33b.

Example 1.14

$$\mathbf{P} = \begin{bmatrix} 2 & -3 \\ 1 & 1 \\ 0 & -1 \end{bmatrix} \quad \mathbf{Q} = \begin{bmatrix} 5 & 0 & 4 & -2 \\ 2 & 1 & 3 & -1 \end{bmatrix}$$

The order of **P** is (3×2); the order of **Q** is (2×4). Hence the product **PQ** is defined: **P** and **Q** are compatible, and we have

$$\mathbf{PQ} = \begin{bmatrix} (2)(5)+(-3)(2) & (2)(0)+(-3)(1) & (2)(4)+(-3)(3) & (2)(-2)+(-3)(-1) \\ (1)(5)+(1)(2) & (1)(0)+(1)(1) & (1)(4)+(1)(3) & (1)(-2)+(1)(-1) \\ (0)(5)+(-1)(2) & (0)(0)+(-1)(1) & (0)(4)+(-1)(3) & (0)(-2)+(-1)(-1) \end{bmatrix}$$

$$= \begin{bmatrix} 4 & -3 & -1 & -1 \\ 7 & 1 & 7 & -3 \\ -2 & -1 & -3 & 1 \end{bmatrix} \qquad \blacksquare$$

Example 1.15   Consider the matrices

$$\mathbf{P} = \begin{bmatrix} -2 & 4 \\ 0 & 3 \end{bmatrix} \quad \mathbf{Q} = \begin{bmatrix} 3 & 0 \\ -1 & 2 \end{bmatrix}$$

Here both **PQ** and **QP** are defined. But

$$\mathbf{PQ} = \begin{bmatrix} -2 & 4 \\ 0 & 3 \end{bmatrix}\begin{bmatrix} 3 & 0 \\ -1 & 2 \end{bmatrix} = \begin{bmatrix} -10 & 8 \\ -3 & 6 \end{bmatrix}$$

while

$$\mathbf{QP} = \begin{bmatrix} 3 & 0 \\ -1 & 2 \end{bmatrix}\begin{bmatrix} -2 & 4 \\ 0 & 3 \end{bmatrix} = \begin{bmatrix} -6 & 12 \\ 2 & 2 \end{bmatrix}$$

and the two results are not equal. $\qquad \blacksquare$

The product of a matrix and a scalar is formed by multiplying every element of the matrix by the scalar. If α is a scalar, then

$$\alpha\mathbf{P} = \mathbf{R} \quad \text{means} \quad r_{ij} = \alpha p_{ij} \tag{1.34}$$

Example 1.16   Given

$$\mathbf{P} = \begin{bmatrix} -3 & 4 \\ -2 & t \end{bmatrix} \quad \mathbf{Q} = \begin{bmatrix} 2 & -1 \\ 7 & 3 \end{bmatrix}$$

it is required to compute $\mathbf{R} = 2\mathbf{P} + \mathbf{Q}$.

$$\mathbf{R} = \begin{bmatrix} -6 & 8 \\ -4 & 2t \end{bmatrix} + \begin{bmatrix} 2 & -1 \\ 7 & 3 \end{bmatrix} = \begin{bmatrix} -4 & 7 \\ 3 & 2t+3 \end{bmatrix} \qquad \blacksquare$$

Unlike the commutative law, which does not hold in general, the distributive and associative laws of multiplication hold:

$$\mathbf{P(Q \pm R) = PQ \pm PR} \tag{1.35}$$
$$\mathbf{(Q \pm R)P = QP \pm RP} \tag{1.36}$$
$$\mathbf{(PQ)R = P(QR)} \tag{1.37}$$

In all these cases, special care must be exercised to keep the order of multiplication (pre- or postmultiplication). The student is urged to prove the validity of Equations 1.35– 1.37.

The product of a matrix and the unit matrix is given by

$$\mathbf{IP = PI = P} \tag{1.38}$$

where $\mathbf{I}$, which can be of any order $(k \times k)$, is chosen to be compatible for either product.

Example 1.17   In Figure 1.3(a) we show a network with elements designated by $a, b, \ldots g$.

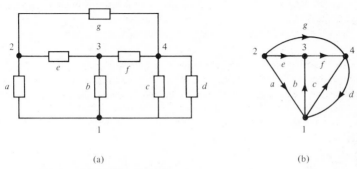

(a)   (b)

FIGURE 1.3   A network and its oriented graph.

The nodes are labeled 1, 2, 3, 4. In Figure 1.3(b) the same network is shown by its oriented graph: Each element is represented by a line segment (a *branch*), and a current reference is assigned to each branch, as shown by arrowheads.

Let us write Kirchhoff's current law at each node. Specifically, $\Sigma i = 0$ at each node, where a $(+)$ sign is assigned to a current leaving the node and a $(-)$ sign to a current entering.

At node 1: $-i_a + i_b + i_c - i_d = 0$
At node 2: $+i_a + i_e + i_g = 0$
At node 3: $-i_b - i_e + i_f = 0$
At node 4: $-i_e + i_d - i_f - i_g = 0$

In matrix form,

$$\begin{bmatrix} -1 & 1 & 1 & -1 & 0 & 0 & 0 \\ 1 & 0 & 0 & 0 & 1 & 0 & 1 \\ 0 & -1 & 0 & 0 & -1 & 1 & 0 \\ 0 & 0 & -1 & 1 & 0 & -1 & -1 \end{bmatrix} \begin{bmatrix} i_a \\ i_b \\ i_c \\ i_d \\ i_e \\ i_f \\ i_g \end{bmatrix} = \mathbf{0}$$

or

$$\mathbf{A_a i_b = 0} \tag{1.39}$$

where $\mathbf{A}_a$ is the *incidence matrix* of the oriented graph and $\mathbf{i}_b$ is the *branch current matrix*.

Note, in general, that $\mathbf{A}_a$ completely characterizes the oriented graph in the sense that it specifies which node and which branch are incident (connected) to each other, and the orientation (reference direction) of such a branch. Specifically, $\mathbf{A}_a = [a_{ij}]$ is of order $(n \times b)$ where n = number of nodes and b = number of branches. Each row corresponds to a node and each column to a branch. The elements a_{ij} are given by

$$a_{ij} = \begin{cases} +1 \text{ if branch } j \text{ is incident to node } i \text{ and oriented away from that node} \\ -1 \text{ if branch } j \text{ is incident to node } i \text{ and oriented toward that node} \\ 0 \text{ if branch } j \text{ is not incident to node } i \end{cases}$$

In our example,

$$\mathbf{A}_a = \begin{array}{c} \\ 1 \\ 2 \\ 3 \\ 4 \end{array} \begin{array}{c} \begin{array}{ccccccc} a & b & c & d & e & f & g \end{array} \\ \left[\begin{array}{ccccccc} -1 & 1 & 1 & -1 & 0 & 0 & 0 \\ 1 & 0 & 0 & 0 & 1 & 0 & 1 \\ 0 & -1 & 0 & 0 & -1 & 1 & 0 \\ 0 & 0 & -1 & 1 & 0 & -1 & -1 \end{array} \right] \end{array}$$

where the rows and columns carry the appropriate labeling (1, 2, 3, 4 for nodes and $a, b, \ldots$ g for columns). Kirchhoff's current law, in compact matrix form, is given in Equation 1.39 and the subscript a on $\mathbf{A}_a$ designates "at *all* the nodes."

Some properties of the matrix $\mathbf{A}_a$ are given in the problems at the end of the chapter. ■

Example 1.18   The second aspect of the network shown in Figure 1.3—namely, Kirchhoff's voltage law—can be explored as follows: Let the orientation (arrow) of each branch be the positive reference of the voltage drop across that branch. Then we can write Kirchhoff's voltage law around each closed loop as $\Sigma v = 0$, where a $(+)$ sign is assigned to a voltage drop and a $(-)$ sign to a voltage rise.

Specifically, for the loop 2-e-3-b-1-a-2

$$+v_e - v_b - v_a = 0$$

Similarly, for loop 3-f-4-c-1-b-3 we have

$$+v_f - v_c + v_b = 0$$

Around loop 2-g-4-c-1-a-2 we have

$$+v_g - v_c - v_a = 0$$

Around loop 4-d-1-c-4 we have

$$+v_d - v_c = 0$$

Around loop 1-c-4-f-3-e-2-a-1 we have

$$+v_c - v_f - v_e + v_a = 0$$

Around loop 1-d-4-g-2-a-1 we have

$$-v_d - v_g + v_a = 0$$

In the matrix form these equations read

$$\begin{bmatrix} -1 & -1 & 0 & 0 & 1 & 0 & 0 \\ 0 & 1 & -1 & 0 & 0 & 1 & 0 \\ -1 & 0 & -1 & 0 & 0 & 0 & 1 \\ 0 & 0 & -1 & 1 & 0 & 0 & 0 \\ 1 & 0 & 1 & 0 & -1 & -1 & 0 \\ 1 & 0 & 0 & -1 & 0 & 0 & -1 \end{bmatrix} \begin{bmatrix} v_a \\ v_b \\ v_c \\ v_d \\ v_e \\ v_f \\ v_g \end{bmatrix} = \mathbf{0}$$

or

$$\mathbf{B}_a \mathbf{v}_b = \mathbf{0} \qquad (1.40)$$

where $\mathbf{B}_a$ is the *loop matrix* and $\mathbf{v}_b$ is the *branch voltage matrix*. The matrix $\mathbf{B}_a$ characterizes the graph: Every row in $\mathbf{B}_a$ corresponds to a closed loop and every column corresponds to a branch. Specifically,

$$b_{ij} = \begin{cases} +1 \text{ if branch } j \text{ is in loop } i \text{ and their relative orientations are the same} \\ -1 \text{ if branch } j \text{ is in loop } i \text{ and their relative orientations are opposite} \\ 0 \text{ if branch } j \text{ is not in loop } i \end{cases}$$

As with $\mathbf{A}_a$, the subscript a in $\mathbf{B}_a$ denotes "*all* loops." In our example we have listed only six of these loops.

Some properties of the matrix $\mathbf{B}_a$ are given in the problems at the end of the chapter. ■

Inversion

Division of matrices is not defined; instead we resort to *inversion*. Prior to doing so, however, we introduce the concepts of singular matrices and elementary matrix transformations.

A square matrix is singular if its determinant is zero. If the determinant does not vanish, the matrix is nonsingular.

Example 1.19

$$\mathbf{P} = \begin{bmatrix} 3 & 2 & 1 \\ 1 & 0 & 1 \\ 0 & 2 & 1 \end{bmatrix}$$

is nonsingular because

$$\det \mathbf{P} = \begin{vmatrix} 3 & 2 & 1 \\ 1 & 0 & 1 \\ 0 & 2 & 1 \end{vmatrix} \neq 0$$

■

Example 1.20

$$\mathbf{Q} = \begin{bmatrix} 4 & 0 & 2 \\ -1 & 1 & 6 \\ 2 & 0 & 1 \end{bmatrix}$$

is singular because

$$\det \mathbf{Q} = \begin{vmatrix} 4 & 0 & 2 \\ -1 & 1 & 6 \\ 2 & 0 & 1 \end{vmatrix} = 0$$

■

Consider now the following set of linear equations:

$$\begin{aligned} a_{11}x_1 + a_{12}x_2 + \cdots + a_{1n}x_n &= b_1 \\ a_{21}x_1 + a_{22}x_2 + \cdots + a_{2n}x_n &= b_2 \\ &\cdots\cdots\cdots\cdots\cdots\cdots\cdots \\ a_{n1}x_1 + a_{n2}x_2 + \cdots + a_{nn}x_n &= b_n \end{aligned} \qquad (1.41)$$

In matrix notation, we can write these as follows:

$$\mathbf{Ax} = \mathbf{B} \tag{1.42a}$$

where

$$\mathbf{A} = \begin{bmatrix} a_{11} & \cdots & a_{1n} \\ a_{21} & \cdots & a_{2n} \\ \cdots & \cdots & \cdots \\ a_{n1} & \cdots & a_{nn} \end{bmatrix} \qquad \mathbf{x} = \begin{bmatrix} x_1 \\ x_2 \\ \cdot \\ \cdot \\ x_n \end{bmatrix} \qquad \mathbf{B} = \begin{bmatrix} b_1 \\ b_2 \\ \cdot \\ \cdot \\ b_n \end{bmatrix} \tag{1.42a}$$

From our knowledge of the solution of simultaneous algebraic equations, we know that a unique solution exists for the x's provided

$$\det \mathbf{A} \neq 0 \tag{1.43}$$

Then the solution of these equations, by Cramer's rule, is

$$x_1 = \frac{\Delta_{11}}{\Delta} b_1 + \frac{\Delta_{21}}{\Delta} b_2 + \cdots + \frac{\Delta_{n1}}{\Delta} b_n$$

$$x_2 = \frac{\Delta_{12}}{\Delta} b_1 + \frac{\Delta_{22}}{\Delta} b_2 + \cdots + \frac{\Delta_{n2}}{\Delta} b_n$$

$$\vdots \tag{1.44}$$

$$x_n = \frac{\Delta_{1n}}{\Delta} b_1 + \frac{\Delta_{2n}}{\Delta} b_2 + \cdots + \frac{\Delta_{nn}}{\Delta} b_n$$

where $\Delta = \det \mathbf{A}$ and Δ_{ij} is the cofactor of the (i, j) element in Δ.

In matrix notation, Equation 1.44 can be written as

$$\mathbf{x} = \mathbf{CB} \tag{1.45}$$

where

$$\mathbf{C} = \frac{1}{\Delta} \begin{bmatrix} \Delta_{11} & \Delta_{21} & \cdots & \Delta_{n1} \\ \Delta_{12} & \Delta_{22} & \cdots & \Delta_{n2} \\ \vdots & & & \\ \Delta_{1n} & \Delta_{n} & \cdots & \Delta_{nn} \end{bmatrix} \tag{1.46}$$

Example 1.21 Given

$$\begin{bmatrix} 2 & -3 \\ -2 & 7 \end{bmatrix} \begin{bmatrix} x_1 \\ x_2 \end{bmatrix} = \begin{bmatrix} 1 \\ 4 \end{bmatrix}$$

we solve for x_1 and x_2 as in Equation 1.44

$$x_1 = \frac{7}{\begin{vmatrix} 2 & -3 \\ -2 & 7 \end{vmatrix}} \cdot 1 + \frac{-(-3)}{\begin{vmatrix} 2 & -3 \\ -2 & 7 \end{vmatrix}} \cdot 4 = \frac{7}{8} \cdot 1 + \frac{3}{8} \cdot 4$$

and

$$x_2 = \frac{-(-2)}{\begin{vmatrix} 2 & -3 \\ -2 & 7 \end{vmatrix}} \cdot 1 + \frac{2}{\begin{vmatrix} 2 & -3 \\ -2 & 7 \end{vmatrix}} \cdot 4 = \frac{2}{8} \cdot 1 + \frac{2}{8} \cdot 4$$

or, in the form of Equation 1.45,

$$\begin{bmatrix} x_1 \\ x_2 \end{bmatrix} = \frac{1}{8} \begin{bmatrix} 7 & 3 \\ 2 & 2 \end{bmatrix} \begin{bmatrix} 1 \\ 4 \end{bmatrix}$$

that is,

$$\mathbf{x} = \mathbf{CB} \qquad \blacksquare$$

Let us consider Equations 1.42 and 1.45, repeated here for convenience:

$$\mathbf{Ax} = \mathbf{B} \qquad (1.42)$$
$$\mathbf{CB} = \mathbf{x} \qquad (1.45)$$

Immediately we ask ourselves: By what matrix operation can we get Equation 1.45 from Equation 1.42? The answer is: We must find a matrix that, when premultiplying Equation 1.42, will yield Equation 1.45. This matrix is called *the inverse* of **A**, symbolized by $\mathbf{A}^{-1}$. So,

$$\mathbf{C} = \mathbf{A}^{-1} \qquad (1.47)$$

and the product (pre- or postmultiplication) of **A** and $\mathbf{A}^{-1}$ is the unit matrix **I**. (By way of comparison, we recall in scalar algebra that $a \cdot a^{-1} = a^{-1} \cdot a = 1$, for any $a \neq 0$.)

Let us then premultiply Equation 1.42 by $\mathbf{A}^{-1}$:

$$\mathbf{A}^{-1}(\mathbf{Ax}) = \mathbf{A}^{-1}(\mathbf{B}) \qquad (1.48)$$

Therefore,

$$(\mathbf{A}^{-1}\mathbf{A})\mathbf{x} = \mathbf{A}^{-1}\mathbf{B} \qquad (1.49)$$
$$\mathbf{Ix} = \mathbf{A}^{-1}\mathbf{B} \qquad (1.50)$$

and so

$$\mathbf{x} = \mathbf{A}^{-1}\mathbf{B} \qquad (1.51)$$

We note that Equation 1.51 is precisely the same as Equation 1.45, with $\mathbf{C} = \mathbf{A}^{-1}$.

In summary: The inverse of a nonsingular square matrix **A** is a square matrix $\mathbf{A}^{-1}$ such that

$$\mathbf{A}^{-1}\mathbf{A} = \mathbf{I} = \mathbf{AA}^{-1} \qquad (1.52)$$

and the elements of $\mathbf{A}^{-1}$ are found according to Equation 1.46:

$$\mathbf{A}^{-1} = [a_{ij}]^{-1} = \frac{1}{\Delta}[\Delta_{ji}] \qquad (1.53a)$$

Note: The matrix of the transposed cofactors in Equation 1.53a is called the *adjoint* of **A**, and so

$$\mathbf{A}^{-1} = \frac{1}{\Delta} \cdot \text{Adj } \mathbf{A} \qquad (1.53b)$$

Example 1.22   Find the inverse of **P**, where

$$\mathbf{P} = \begin{bmatrix} 3 & 2 & 1 \\ 1 & 0 & 1 \\ 0 & 2 & 1 \end{bmatrix}$$

Here

$$\Delta = \det \mathbf{P} = \begin{vmatrix} 3 & 2 & 1 \\ 1 & 0 & 1 \\ 0 & 2 & 1 \end{vmatrix} = -6$$

Therefore $\mathbf{P}$ is nonsingular and has an inverse.

Now

$$\begin{array}{lll} \Delta_{11} = -2 & \Delta_{21} = 0 & \Delta_{31} = 2 \\ \Delta_{12} = -1 & \Delta_{22} = 3 & \Delta_{32} = -2 \\ \Delta_{13} = 2 & \Delta_{23} = -6 & \Delta_{33} = -2 \end{array}$$

So

$$\mathbf{P}^{-1} = \frac{1}{\Delta} \operatorname{Adj} \mathbf{P}$$

or

$$\mathbf{P}^{-1} = \frac{1}{-6} \begin{bmatrix} -2 & 0 & 2 \\ -1 & 3 & -2 \\ 2 & -6 & -2 \end{bmatrix} = \begin{bmatrix} \frac{1}{3} & 0 & -\frac{1}{3} \\ \frac{1}{6} & -\frac{1}{2} & \frac{1}{3} \\ -\frac{1}{3} & 1 & \frac{1}{3} \end{bmatrix}$$

(As an exercise, the student can verify that $\mathbf{P}^{-1}\mathbf{P} = \mathbf{P}\mathbf{P}^{-1} = \mathbf{I}$.) ■

Example 1.23 In the circuit shown in Figure 1.4, find the node voltages v_a, v_b, v_c by matrix inversion. Element values are in ohms.

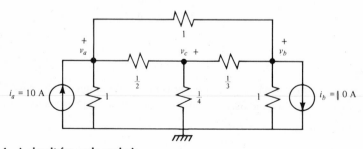

FIGURE 1.4 A circuit for node analysis.

The node equations, in matrix form, read

$$\begin{bmatrix} 4 & -1 & -2 \\ -1 & 5 & -3 \\ -2 & -3 & 9 \end{bmatrix} \begin{bmatrix} v_a \\ v_b \\ v_c \end{bmatrix} = \begin{bmatrix} 10 \\ -10 \\ 0 \end{bmatrix}$$

or $\mathbf{Yv} = \mathbf{J}$, where $\mathbf{Y}$ is the *node admittance matrix*, $\mathbf{v}$ is the *node voltage matrix*, and $\mathbf{J}$ is the *node sources matrix*.

Here, $\det \mathbf{Y} = 103$ and $\mathbf{Y}^{-1}$ is given by

$$\mathbf{Y}^{-1} = \frac{1}{103} \begin{bmatrix} 36 & 15 & 13 \\ 15 & 32 & 14 \\ 13 & 14 & 19 \end{bmatrix}$$

and so

$$\mathbf{v} = \mathbf{Y}^{-1}\mathbf{J} = \begin{bmatrix} 2.03 \\ -1.65 \\ -0.097 \end{bmatrix}$$

i.e., $v_a = 2.03$ volts, $v_b = -1.65$ volts, $v_c = -0.097$ volt. ■

A second method for inverting a matrix is based on its defining property

$$\mathbf{AA}^{-1} = \mathbf{I} \qquad (1.54)$$

First, however, we introduce the idea of *elementary row operations* on a given matrix. An elementary row operation is one of the following operations:

1. Interchanging the place of two rows.
2. Multiplying the elements of a row by a nonzero number.
3. Adding a row obtained from operation 2 to another row in the matrix.*

The following example illustrates these operations, with the matrices separated by a tilde ($\sim$).

Example 1.24

$$\begin{bmatrix} 1 & 0 & -3 & 2 \\ 4 & 1 & -1 & 1 \\ 2 & 0 & -2 & 1 \end{bmatrix} \sim \begin{bmatrix} 1 & 0 & -3 & 2 \\ 0 & 1 & 3 & -1 \\ 2 & 0 & -2 & 1 \end{bmatrix} \sim \begin{bmatrix} 2 & 0 & -4 & 2.5 \\ 0 & 1 & 3 & -1 \\ 2 & 0 & -2 & 1 \end{bmatrix}$$

Given matrix   Twice row 3   Half row 3 added
subtracted   to row 1
from row 2   ■

We use elementary row operations on Equation 1.54. Compare this equation with Equation 1.42, repeated here for convenience.

$$\mathbf{Ax} = \mathbf{B} \qquad (1.42)$$

The formal solution of the latter is

$$\mathbf{x} = \mathbf{A}^{-1}\mathbf{B} \qquad (1.55)$$

and can be obtained from Equation 1.42 by elementary row operations—specifically, by a sequence of these operations that will transform matrix $\mathbf{A}$ in Equation 1.42 to the unit matrix $\mathbf{I}$. The same operations must, of course, be done on matrix $\mathbf{B}$. Symbolically, we write it as

$$\mathbf{Ax} = \mathbf{B} \sim \mathbf{Ix} = \mathbf{A}^{-1}\mathbf{B} \qquad (1.56)$$

where the tilde ($\sim$) indicates, as before, matrices obtained by elementary row operations.

By comparison, in Equation 1.54 $\mathbf{A}^{-1}$ is the unknown matrix (corresponding to $\mathbf{X}$) and $\mathbf{I}$ is the known matrix (corresponding to $\mathbf{B}$). Therefore, a sequence of elementary

---

*Elementary *column operations* can be defined similarly.

row operations must be done on $\mathbf{AA}^{-1} = \mathbf{I}$ to transform matrix $\mathbf{A}$ into the unit matrix $\mathbf{I}$. The same operations on the right-hand side will yield $\mathbf{A}^{-1}$. Symbolically,

$$\mathbf{AA}^{-1} = \mathbf{I} \sim \mathbf{IA}^{-1} = \mathbf{A}^{-1} \tag{1.57}$$

In practice, these row operations are done on the *augmented* matrix $\mathbf{A}$, obtained by writing to the right of matrix $\mathbf{A}$ the unit matrix $\mathbf{I}$. The appropriate row operations are then applied until matrix $\mathbf{A}$ is transformed in $\mathbf{I}$. In brief,

$$[\mathbf{A} : \mathbf{I}] \sim [\mathbf{I} : \mathbf{A}^{-1}] \tag{1.58}$$

What are the specific row operations that will reduce matrix $\mathbf{A}$ to the unit matrix $\mathbf{I}$?

1. Multiply row k ($k = 1, 2, \ldots n$ successively) by $1/a_{kk}$ in order to get "1" on the main diagonal. If, for a particular row, $a_{kk} = 0$, then interchange that row with another one so that the new $a_{kk} \neq 0$.
2. Use proper multiples of the result in step 1 to add, in succession, to every row above it and below it, so as to produce zeros in column k.

These steps, repeated for every row, will yield the desired result.

Example 1.25 Find $\mathbf{P}^{-1}$ of Example 1.22 using elementary row operations. The successive steps are shown below, with appropriate comments.

$$\begin{bmatrix} 3 & 2 & 1 & \vdots & 1 & 0 & 0 \\ 1 & 0 & 1 & \vdots & 0 & 1 & 0 \\ 0 & 2 & 1 & \vdots & 0 & 0 & 1 \end{bmatrix}$$

This is the original $[\mathbf{P} \vdots \mathbf{I}]$. Multiply row 1 by $\frac{1}{3}$, then subtract it from row 2.

$$\begin{bmatrix} 1 & \frac{2}{3} & \frac{1}{3} & \vdots & \frac{1}{3} & 0 & 0 \\ 0 & -\frac{2}{3} & \frac{2}{3} & \vdots & -\frac{1}{3} & 1 & 0 \\ 0 & 2 & 1 & \vdots & 0 & 0 & 1 \end{bmatrix}$$

Multiply row 2 by $-\frac{3}{2}$. Add $-\frac{2}{3}$ times the result to row 1. Next, add -2 times the result to row 3.

$$\begin{bmatrix} 1 & 0 & 1 & \vdots & 0 & 1 & 0 \\ 0 & 1 & -1 & \vdots & \frac{1}{2} & -\frac{3}{2} & 0 \\ 0 & 0 & 3 & \vdots & -1 & 3 & 1 \end{bmatrix}$$

Multiply row 3 by $\frac{1}{3}$. Add -1 times the result to row 1. Next, add the result to row 2.

$$\begin{bmatrix} 1 & 0 & 0 & \vdots & \frac{1}{3} & 0 & -\frac{1}{3} \\ 0 & 1 & 0 & \vdots & \frac{1}{6} & -\frac{1}{2} & \frac{1}{3} \\ 0 & 0 & 1 & \vdots & -\frac{1}{3} & 1 & \frac{1}{3} \end{bmatrix}$$

This is the final result $[\mathbf{I} \vdots \mathbf{P}^{-1}]$.

The inverse matrix $\mathbf{P}^{-1}$ is readily seen to agree with the result of Example 1.22. ∎

Some properties of the inversion are to be noted:

1.
$$(\mathbf{P}^{-1})^{-1} = \mathbf{P} \tag{1.59}$$

Proof

$$(\mathbf{P}^{-1})^{-1} = \mathbf{I}(\mathbf{P}^{-1})^{-1} = (\mathbf{P}\,\mathbf{P}^{-1})(\mathbf{P}^{-1})^{-1} = \mathbf{P}(\mathbf{P}^{-1})(\mathbf{P}^{-1})^{-1} = \mathbf{PI} = \mathbf{P}$$

i.e., the inverse of an inverse matrix yields the original matrix.

2.
$$(\mathbf{PQ})^{-1} = \mathbf{Q}^{-1}\mathbf{P}^{-1} \tag{1.60}$$

Proof

$$(PQ)Q^{-1}P^{-1} = P(QQ^{-1})P^{-1} = PIP^{-1} = PP^{-1} = I$$

A similar proof holds for a product of more than two matrices. In words: The inverse of a product of matrices is the product of their inverses taken in the opposite order of multiplication, provided, of course, each of the inverses exists. See also Problem 1-23.

Matrix Partitioning

In some cases involving matrix multiplication, we *partition* the matrices in a convenient way. For example, in Equation 1.42, repeated here,

$$Ax = B \tag{1.42}$$

we may wish to partition the matrices as follows:

$$\begin{bmatrix} a_{11} & a_{12} \dots a_{1p} & & \dots & a_{1n} \\ & & & & \\ & & & & \\ a_{p1} & a_{p2} \dots a_{pp} & & \dots & a_{pn} \\ & & & & \\ a_{n1} & a_{n2} & & & a_{nn} \end{bmatrix} \begin{bmatrix} x_1 \\ x_2 \\ \vdots \\ x_p \\ x_{p+1} \\ \vdots \\ x_n \end{bmatrix} = \begin{bmatrix} b_1 \\ b_2 \\ \vdots \\ b_p \\ b_{p+1} \\ \vdots \\ b_n \end{bmatrix} \tag{1.61}$$

where the dotted lines show the partitioning. The result is an equivalent matrix equation with submatrices as follows:

$$\begin{bmatrix} A_{11} & A_{12} \\ A_{21} & A_{22} \end{bmatrix} \begin{bmatrix} x_{11} \\ x_{21} \end{bmatrix} = \begin{bmatrix} B_{11} \\ B_{21} \end{bmatrix} \tag{1.62}$$

We recall that a matrix is merely an array of elements. In Equation 1.61 all of the elements a_{ij} are in a single array, the matrix A. Conveniently, and equally valid, these elements can be in four submatrices, A_{11}, A_{12}, A_{21}, and A_{22}, as shown in Equation 1.62. Similarly, the single-column matrix x has been partitioned into two submatrices, x_{11} and x_{21}. The same can be said of matrix B.

Such a partitioning is not unique. It can be done in more than one way, with only one provision: In the partitioned form the submatrices must be compatible for the indicated multiplications. In our case the products $A_{11}x_{11}$, $A_{12}x_{21}$, $A_{21}x_{11}$, and $A_{22}x_{21}$ must be compatible, i.e., the number of columns in A_{11} must equal the number of rows in x_{11}, etc. Then Equation 1.62 is equivalent to the two matrix equations

$$A_{11}x_{11} + A_{12}x_{21} = B_{11} \tag{1.63a}$$

and

$$A_{21}x_{11} + A_{22}x_{21} = B_{21} \tag{1.63b}$$

The following examples illustrate two applications of matrix partitioning.

Example 1.26[7]   In the network of Figure 1.5, what is the equivalent resistance (the so-called "driving-point resistance") at terminals $a-b$? Element values are in ohms.

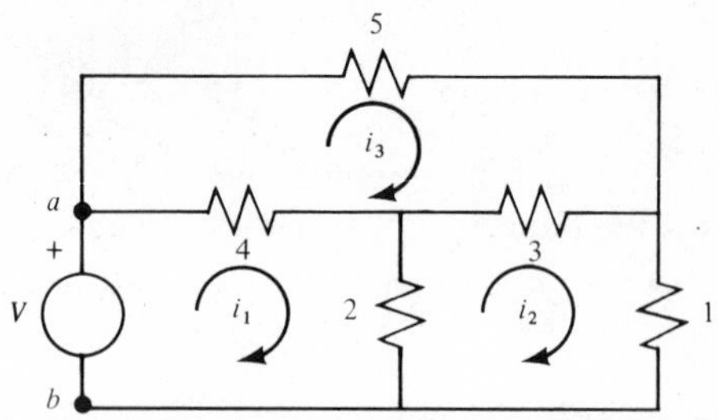

FIGURE 1.5 Calculation of a driving-point resistance.

Let us write loop equations, choosing i_1 for the loop of the source, the other loop currents being assigned as shown. The resulting matrix equation is

$$\begin{bmatrix} 6 & -2 & -4 \\ -2 & 6 & -3 \\ -4 & -3 & 12 \end{bmatrix} \begin{bmatrix} i_1 \\ i_2 \\ i_3 \end{bmatrix} = \begin{bmatrix} V \\ 0 \\ 0 \end{bmatrix}$$

To answer the original question, let us first rephrase it as follows: Find a one-loop network in which i_1 will be the same as in the given network. If we find such a network, then obviously the required resistance will be $R_{eq} = V/i_1$. Thus, to find the one-loop equivalent network, the equations are partitioned as follows:

$$\left[\begin{array}{c|cc} 6 & -2 & -4 \\ \hline -2 & 6 & -3 \\ -4 & -3 & 12 \end{array}\right] \begin{bmatrix} i_1 \\ i_2 \\ i_3 \end{bmatrix} = \begin{bmatrix} V \\ 0 \\ 0 \end{bmatrix}$$

or

$$\left[\begin{array}{c|c} \mathbf{R}_{11} & \mathbf{R}_{12} \\ \hline \mathbf{R}_{21} & \mathbf{R}_{22} \end{array}\right] \left[\begin{array}{c} \mathbf{I}_{11} \\ \mathbf{I}_{21} \end{array}\right] = \left[\begin{array}{c} \mathbf{V}_{11} \\ \hline \mathbf{0} \end{array}\right]$$

with $\mathbf{R}_{11} = [6]$, $\mathbf{R}_{12} = [-2 \quad -4]$, etc.
$\mathbf{I}_{11} = [i_1]$, $\mathbf{V}_{11} = [V]$

The two matrix equations are

$$\mathbf{R}_{11}\mathbf{I}_{11} + \mathbf{R}_{12}\mathbf{I}_{21} = \mathbf{V}_{11}$$
$$\mathbf{R}_{21}\mathbf{I}_{11} + \mathbf{R}_{22}\mathbf{I}_{21} = \mathbf{0}$$

From the second equation we have

$$\mathbf{I}_{21} = -\mathbf{R}_{22}^{-1}\mathbf{R}_{21}\mathbf{I}_{11}$$

(recall that these are matrices) and substitution into the first equation yields

$$\mathbf{R}_{11}\mathbf{I}_{11} + \mathbf{R}_{12}(-\mathbf{R}_{22}^{-1}\mathbf{R}_{21}\mathbf{I}_{11}) = \mathbf{V}_{11}$$

that is,

$$6 \cdot i_1 - [-2 \quad -4] \begin{bmatrix} 6 & -3 \\ -3 & 12 \end{bmatrix}^{-1} \begin{bmatrix} -2 \\ -4 \end{bmatrix} i_1 = V$$

And, finally,

$$6i_1 - \frac{64}{21} i_1 = V$$

or

$$\frac{62}{21} i_1 = V$$

and the equivalent resistance is 62/21 ohms.   ∎

Example 1.27   For the three-node network shown in Figure 1.6(a) find a two-node equivalent network in the sense that v_1 and v_2 will be preserved in both.

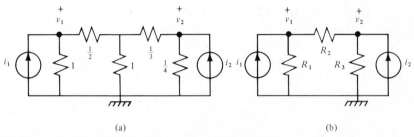

(a)   (b)

FIGURE 1.6   Equivalent networks (element values in ohms).

For the network in Figure 1.6(a) the node equations are, in partitioned form:

$$\left[\begin{array}{cc:c} 3 & 0 & -2 \\ 0 & 7 & -3 \\ \hdashline -2 & -3 & 6 \end{array}\right]\left[\begin{array}{c} v_1 \\ v_2 \\ \hdashline v_3 \end{array}\right] = \left[\begin{array}{c} i_1 \\ i_2 \\ \hdashline 0 \end{array}\right]$$

or

$$\left[\begin{array}{c:c} \mathbf{G}_{11} & \mathbf{G}_{12} \\ \hdashline \mathbf{G}_{21} & \mathbf{G}_{22} \end{array}\right]\left[\begin{array}{c} \mathbf{V}_{11} \\ \hdashline \mathbf{V}_{21} \end{array}\right] = \left[\begin{array}{c} \mathbf{I}_{11} \\ \hdashline \mathbf{0} \end{array}\right]$$

Explicitly, then,

$$\mathbf{G}_{11}\mathbf{V}_{11} + \mathbf{G}_{12}\mathbf{V}_{21} = \mathbf{I}_{11}$$
$$\mathbf{G}_{21}\mathbf{V}_{11} + \mathbf{G}_{22}\mathbf{V}_{21} = \mathbf{0}$$

and we wish to preserve submatrix $\mathbf{V}_{11}$ (and $\mathbf{I}_{11}$), while $\mathbf{V}_{21} = [v_3]$ is to be eliminated. Therefore,

$$\mathbf{V}_{21} = -\mathbf{G}_{22}^{-1}\mathbf{G}_{21}\mathbf{V}_{11}$$

and

$$\mathbf{G}_{11}\mathbf{V}_{11} + \mathbf{G}_{12}(-\mathbf{G}_{22}^{-1}\mathbf{G}_{21})\mathbf{V}_{11} = \mathbf{I}_{11}$$

or

$$(\mathbf{G}_{11} - \mathbf{G}_{12}\mathbf{G}_{22}^{-1}\mathbf{G}_{21})\mathbf{V}_{11} = \mathbf{I}_{11}$$

$$\therefore \left[\begin{array}{cc} 3 & 0 \\ 0 & 7 \end{array}\right] - \left[\begin{array}{c} -2 \\ -3 \end{array}\right]\left[6\right]^{-1}\left[\begin{array}{cc} -2 & -3 \end{array}\right]\left[\begin{array}{c} v_1 \\ v_2 \end{array}\right] = \left[\begin{array}{c} i_1 \\ i_2 \end{array}\right]$$

$$\therefore \left[\begin{array}{cc} 7/3 & -1 \\ -1 & 11/2 \end{array}\right]\left[\begin{array}{c} v_1 \\ v_2 \end{array}\right] = \left[\begin{array}{c} i_1 \\ i_2 \end{array}\right]$$

Consequently, we must have

$$-\frac{1}{R_2} = -1 \qquad \therefore R_2 = 1 \; ohm$$

$$\frac{1}{R_1} + \frac{1}{R_2} = \frac{7}{3} \qquad \therefore R_1 = \frac{3}{4} \; ohm$$

$$\frac{1}{R_2} + \frac{1}{R_3} = \frac{11}{2} \qquad \therefore R_3 = \frac{2}{9} \; ohm \qquad \blacksquare$$

1.7   THE SYSTEM OF LINEAR EQUATIONS Ax = B

In general, any system of m simultaneous linear equations in n unknowns can be written, similar to Equation 1.42, as follows:

$$\begin{aligned}
a_{11}x_1 + a_{12}x_2 + \cdots + a_{1n}x_n &= b_1 \\
a_{21}x_1 + a_{22}x_2 + \cdots + a_{2n}x_n &= b_2 \\
&\vdots \\
a_{m1}x_1 + a_{m2}x_2 + \cdots + a_{mn}x_n &= b_m
\end{aligned} \tag{1.64}$$

Its equivalent matrix equation is

$$\begin{bmatrix}
a_{11} & a_{12} & \cdots & a_{1n} \\
a_{21} & a_{22} & \cdots & a_{2n} \\
\vdots & \vdots & & \vdots \\
a_{m1} & a_{m2} & \cdots & a_{mn}
\end{bmatrix}
\begin{bmatrix}
x_1 \\ x_2 \\ \vdots \\ x_n
\end{bmatrix}
=
\begin{bmatrix}
b_1 \\ b_2 \\ \vdots \\ b_m
\end{bmatrix} \tag{1.65}$$

that is,

$$\mathbf{Ax = B} \tag{1.66}$$

Let us develop a method for solving this equation in a systematic way, suitable for either longhand or computer use. Two closely related methods are presented here.

The Gauss Method of Elimination

Consider the m simultaneous equations in m unknowns:

$$a_{11}x_1 + a_{12}x_2 + \cdots + a_{1m}x_m = b_1 \tag{1.67a}$$
$$a_{21}x_1 + a_{22}x_2 + \cdots + a_{2m}x_m = b_2 \tag{1.67b}$$
$$\vdots$$
$$a_{m1}x_1 + a_{m2}x_2 + \cdots + a_{mm}x_m = b_m \tag{1.69m}$$

We carry out the following successive cycles.

1. First cycle:
    (a) Assume $a_{11} \neq 0$. (If $a_{11} = 0$ we choose another equation whose x_1 coefficient is nonzero and make it the first equation.) This $a_{11} \neq 0$ is called the *pivot*.

(b) Divide the first equation by the pivot to get

$$x_1 + a'_{12}x_2 + a'_{13}x_3 + \cdots + a'_{1m}x_m = b'_1 \qquad (1.67a')$$

where $a'_{12} = a_{12}/a_{11}$, etc. Equation 1.67a' is called the "slave equation." (Although not a standard term, it describes well the role of this equation!)

(c) Use appropriate multiples of the slave equation to add to succeeding equations in order to eliminate x_1 from them. For example, if we multiply the slave equation by $(-a_{21})$ and add it to Equation 1.67b, x_1 is eliminated and we obtain

$$a'_{22}x_2 + a'_{23}x_3 + \cdots + a'_{2m}x_m = b'_2 \qquad (1.67b')$$

as the new second equation.

(d) Similarly, eliminate x_1 from the 3rd, 4th, ... m^{th} equation. The new system of equations is then

$$x_1 + a'_{12}x_2 + a'_{13}x_3 + \cdots + a'_{1m}x_m = b'_1 \qquad (1.67a')$$
$$a'_{22}x_2 + a'_{23}x_3 + \cdots + a'_{2m}x_m = b'_2 \qquad (1.67b')$$
$$a'_{32}x_2 + a'_{33}x_3 + \cdots + a'_{3m}x_m = b'_3 \qquad (1.67c')$$
$$\vdots \qquad \vdots \qquad \qquad \vdots \qquad \vdots$$
$$a'_{m2}x_2 + a'_{m3}x_3 + \cdots + a'_{mm}x_m = b'_m \qquad (1.67m')$$

2. Second cycle:

   (a) Let $a'_{22} \neq 0$. (If $a'_{22} = 0$, we choose, again, any succeeding equation whose x_2 coefficient is nonzero.)

   (b) Divide Equation 1.67b' by a'_{22}, the second pivot, to obtain the slave equation for this cycle:

$$x_2 + a''_{23}x_3 + \cdots + a''_{2m}x_m = b''_1 \qquad (1.67b'')$$

   (c) Use multiples of the slave equation to eliminate the variable x_2 from all equations except the first two. At this stage the system of equations looks like this:

$$x_1 + a'_{12}x_2 + a'_{13}x_3 + \cdots + a'_{1m}x_m = b'_1 \qquad (1.67a')$$
$$x_2 + a''_{23}x_3 + \cdots + a''_{2m}x_m = b''_2 \qquad (1.67b'')$$
$$a''_{33}x_3 + \cdots + a''_{3m}x_m = b''_3 \qquad (1.67c'')$$
$$\vdots \qquad \qquad \vdots \qquad \vdots$$
$$a''_{m3}x_3 + \cdots + a''_{mm}x_m = b''_m \qquad (1.67m'')$$

After m cycles the system has the following form:

$$x_1 + a'_{12}x_2 + a'_{13}x_3 + \cdots + a'_{1m}x_m = b'_1 \qquad (1.67a')$$
$$x_2 + a''_{23}x_3 + \cdots + a''_{2m}x_m = b''_2 \qquad (1.67b'')$$
$$x_3 + \cdots + a'''_{3m}x_m = b'''_3 \qquad (1.67c''')$$
$$\vdots \qquad \qquad \vdots \qquad \vdots$$
$$x_m = b_m^{(m)} \qquad (1.67m)$$

In matrix notation this set is written as

$$\begin{bmatrix} 1 & a'_{12} & a'_{13} & \cdots & a'_{1m} \\ 0 & 1 & a''_{23} & \cdots & a''_{2m} \\ 0 & 0 & 1 & \cdots & a'''_{3m} \\ & & \vdots & & \\ 0 & 0 & 0 & \cdots & 1 \end{bmatrix} \mathbf{x} = \begin{bmatrix} b'_1 \\ b''_2 \\ \vdots \\ b_m^{(m)} \end{bmatrix} \tag{1.68}$$

showing the new coefficient matrix of **x** as an *upper triangular* matrix with 1's on its diagonal.

The last equation immediately yields the value of x_m. We then substitute the value of x_m into the $(m-1)^{\text{th}}$ equation and find the value of x_{m-1}. Continue with this *back substitution* in order to find $x_{m-2}, \ldots x_3, x_2$, and x_1.

Example 1.28   Consider the system of linear equations

$$\begin{aligned} 2x_1 - x_2 + x_3 - 2x_4 &= 1 \\ -x_1 \quad\quad + x_3 - x_4 &= -1 \\ x_1 + 2x_2 - x_3 \quad\quad &= 2 \\ 2x_1 + x_2 - 2x_3 + x_4 &= 3 \end{aligned}$$

or, in matrix notation,

$$\begin{bmatrix} 2 & -1 & 1 & -2 \\ -1 & 0 & 1 & -1 \\ 1 & 2 & -1 & 0 \\ 2 & 1 & -2 & 1 \end{bmatrix} \begin{bmatrix} x_1 \\ x_2 \\ x_3 \\ x_4 \end{bmatrix} = \begin{bmatrix} 1 \\ -1 \\ 2 \\ 3 \end{bmatrix}$$

The first cycle: We divide the first equation by the pivot $a_{11} = 2$ to get

$$x_1 - (\tfrac{1}{2})x_2 + (\tfrac{1}{2})x_3 - x_4 = \tfrac{1}{2}$$

Add this equation to eliminate x_1 from the second one and get

$$-(\tfrac{1}{2})x_2 + (\tfrac{3}{2})x_3 - 2x_4 = -\tfrac{1}{2}$$

Multiply the slave equation by -1 and add to the third equation to get

$$(\tfrac{5}{2})x_2 - (\tfrac{3}{2})x_3 + x_4 = \tfrac{3}{2}$$

Multiply the slave equation by -2 and add to the fourth equation to get

$$2x_2 - 3x_3 + 3x_4 = 2$$

The second cycle: The second equation of the first cycle is divided by its pivot, $-\tfrac{1}{2}$, to get

$$x_2 - 3x_3 + 4x_4 = 1$$

Use multiples of this slave equation to eliminate x_2 from the third and fourth equations. The results are

$$\begin{aligned} 6x_3 - 9x_4 &= -1 \\ 3x_3 - 5x_4 &= 0 \end{aligned}$$

The third cycle: The third equation in the second cycle is divided by its pivot, 6, to get

$$x_3 - (\tfrac{3}{2})x_4 = -\tfrac{1}{6}$$

Use a multiple of this equation to eliminate x_3 from the fourth one. The result is

$$-\tfrac{1}{2}x_4 = \tfrac{1}{2}$$

The final form of the system is then

$$
\begin{aligned}
x_1 - (\tfrac{1}{2})x_2 + (\tfrac{1}{2})x_3 - \quad x_4 &= \tfrac{1}{2} \\
x_2 - \quad 3x_3 + \quad 4x_4 &= 1 \\
+ \quad x_3 - (\tfrac{3}{2})x_4 &= -\tfrac{1}{6} \\
- (\tfrac{1}{2})x_4 &= \tfrac{1}{2}
\end{aligned}
$$

The solution of the system is, then, by back substitution:

$$x_4 = -1; \quad x_3 = -\tfrac{1}{15}; \quad x_2 = \tfrac{24}{5}; \quad x_1 = \tfrac{58}{30} \qquad \blacksquare$$

Several remarks about this procedure are in order. First, we observe that, in each cycle, we generate a new set of equations from the original ones by performing certain operations. And two systems of equations are *equivalent* if every solution of one system is also a solution of the other. It is not too difficult to recognize that the three operations involved in the Gauss method—namely, (1) interchanging the position of an equation, (2) multiplying an equation by a nonzero constant, and (3) adding multiples of one equation to another—generate equivalent systems of equations.

When a system of simultaneous equations is written in matrix form, the coefficients of the kth equation become the elements of the kth row of matrix **A**. When the Gauss elimination is performed on the matrix equation, the three operations done above are the familiar elementary row operations introduced earlier in this chapter. Thus elementary row operations produce an equivalent system of equations whose solution is identical with that of the original system.

Another comment can be made at this point. We do not necessarily have to divide by the pivot in every cycle. The slave equation for x_k can retain its pivot ($\neq 1$) without any loss of generality. The resulting coefficient matrix in Equation 1.68 will be, then, upper triangular with its diagonal terms not necessarily 1's.

Two additional questions remain. First, will this Gauss method perform successfully for any $m \times m$ system? Second, what about a *non-square* system of m equations with n unknowns? These are discussed in a later section.

The Gauss-Jordan Method of Elimination

This method is a slight modification of the Gauss method. Here we perform the same cycles as before, except that in each cycle the slave equation is used to eliminate the unknown of that cycle from *all* the equations, both above *and* below the slave equation. The final form of the equivalent system of equations will, then, take the form

$$
\begin{bmatrix}
1 & 0 & 0 & 0 & \cdots & 0 \\
0 & 1 & 0 & 0 & \cdots & 0 \\
\vdots & & & & & \\
0 & 0 & 0 & 0 & \cdots & 1
\end{bmatrix}
\mathbf{x} =
\begin{bmatrix}
b_1' \\
b_2'' \\
\vdots \\
b_m^{(m)}
\end{bmatrix}
\tag{1.69}
$$

showing the unit matrix as the coefficient matrix. Recall that, in comparison, the Gauss method yields an upper triangular matrix, as in Equation 1.68.

Example 1.29   Consider the system of linear equations

$$
\begin{aligned}
x_1 - x_2 - 2x_3 - x_4 &= -1 \\
2x_1 - 3x_2 - 4x_3 + 2x_4 &= -1 \\
-x_1 + 2x_2 + x_3 - 2x_4 &= 3 \\
x_1 + x_2 + x_3 + x_4 &= 1
\end{aligned}
$$

Cycle 1:   Use multiples of the first equation to eliminate x_1 from the second, third, and fourth equations. The result is

$$
\begin{aligned}
x_1 - x_2 - 2x_3 - x_4 &= -1 \\
- x_2 \qquad\quad + 4x_4 &= 1 \\
x_2 - x_3 - 3x_4 &= 2 \\
2x_2 + 3x_3 + 2x_4 &= 2
\end{aligned}
$$

Cycle 2:   Use multiples of the second equation of the new system to eliminate x_2 from the first, third, and fourth equations. The result is

$$
\begin{aligned}
x_1 - 2x_3 - 5x_4 &= -2 \\
- x_2 + 4x_4 &= 1 \\
-x_3 + x_4 &= 3 \\
3x_3 + 10x_4 &= 4
\end{aligned}
$$

Cycle 3:   Use multiples of the third equation of the new system to eliminate x_3 from the first, second, and fourth equations. The result is

$$
\begin{aligned}
x_1 - 7x_4 &= -8 \\
- x_2 + 4x_4 &= 1 \\
- x_3 + x_4 &= 3 \\
13x_4 &= 13
\end{aligned}
$$

Cycle 4:   Divide the fourth equation of the new system by 13 and use multiples of this equation to eliminate x_4 from the first, second, and third equations. The result is

$$
\begin{aligned}
x_1 \qquad\qquad\qquad &= -1 \\
x_2 \qquad\qquad &= 3 \\
x_3 \qquad &= -2 \\
x_4 &= 1
\end{aligned}
$$

■

We note here that the final coefficient matrix is the unit matrix $\mathbf{I}$, yielding the x's directly without the need for back substitution. As in the Gauss method, slave equations here need not be divided by their pivots; in that case the final coefficient matrix will be diagonal, with elements not necessarily 1's.

1.8   LINEAR INDEPENDENCE AND THE RANK OF A MATRIX

Let the rows of a given matrix $\mathbf{P}$ be $\mathbf{r}_1, \mathbf{r}_2, \ldots \mathbf{r}_m$, each being a row submatrix, or a *row vector,* in $\mathbf{P}$:

$$
\mathbf{r}_i = [p_{i1} \quad p_{i2} \quad \cdots \quad p_{in}], \quad i = 1, 2, \ldots m \tag{1.70}
$$

This set of vectors is *linearly dependent* if we can find constant scalars $k_1, k_2, \ldots k_m$, not all zero, such that

$$k_1\mathbf{r}_1 + k_2\mathbf{r}_2 + \cdots + k_m\mathbf{r}_m = \mathbf{0} \tag{1.71}$$

If Equation 1.71 is satisfied only for $k_1 = k_2 = \cdots = k_m = 0$, the vectors are *linearly independent*.

Stated differently, let us assume that we found $k_i \neq 0$ in Equation 1.71. Then we can write

$$\mathbf{r}_i = -\frac{1}{k_i}[k_1\mathbf{r}_1 + k_2\mathbf{r}_2 + \cdots + k_{i-1}\mathbf{r}_{i-1} + k_{i+1}\mathbf{r}_{i+1} + \cdots] \tag{1.72}$$

i.e., vector $\mathbf{r}_i$ is linearly dependent on the other vectors, being a linear combination of them. If no such relation exists, $\mathbf{r}_i$ is not expressible in such a form and is linearly independent of the others.

Example 1.30   Let

$$\mathbf{P} = \begin{bmatrix} 1 & 0 & -1 \\ 2 & 1 & 1 \end{bmatrix} = \begin{bmatrix} \mathbf{r}_1 \\ \hline \mathbf{r}_2 \end{bmatrix}$$

We are looking for nonzero scalars k_1 and k_2 that will satisfy

$$k_1\mathbf{r}_1 + k_2\mathbf{r}_2 = \mathbf{0}$$

that is,

$$[k_1 \quad 0 \quad -k_1] + [2k_2 \quad k_2 \quad k_2] = \mathbf{0}$$

or

$$\begin{aligned} k_1 + 2k_2 &= 0 \\ k_2 &= 0 \\ -k_1 + k_2 &= 0 \end{aligned}$$

It is easily seen that only $k_1 = 0$, $k_2 = 0$ satisfy these requirements. In other words, $\mathbf{r}_1$ and $\mathbf{r}_2$ are linearly independent.   ∎

Example 1.31   Let

$$\mathbf{Q} = \begin{bmatrix} 1 & -1 & 2 \\ 0 & 2 & -3 \\ 2 & -4 & 7 \end{bmatrix} = \begin{bmatrix} \mathbf{r}_1 \\ \hline \mathbf{r}_2 \\ \hline \mathbf{r}_3 \end{bmatrix}$$

Trying to find scalars k_1, k_2, k_3 such that

$$k_1\mathbf{r}_1 + k_2\mathbf{r}_2 + k_3\mathbf{r}_3 = \mathbf{0}$$

yields the following equations for them:

$$\begin{aligned} k_1 + 2k_3 &= 0 \\ -k_1 + 2k_2 - 4k_3 &= 0 \\ 2k_1 - 3k_2 + 7k_3 &= 0 \end{aligned}$$

that is,

$$
\begin{bmatrix} 1 & 0 & 2 \\ -1 & 2 & -4 \\ 2 & -3 & 7 \end{bmatrix} \begin{bmatrix} k_1 \\ k_2 \\ k_3 \end{bmatrix} = \mathbf{0}
$$

or

$$\mathbf{Q}^T \mathbf{k} = \mathbf{0}$$

Note that this matrix equation for the unknowns k_1, k_2, k_3 has the transpose of our original matrix as the coefficient matrix.

Applying the Gauss method (elementary row operations) to $\mathbf{Q}^T$, we obtain

$$
\begin{bmatrix} 1 & 0 & 2 \\ 0 & 1 & -1 \\ 0 & 0 & 0 \end{bmatrix} \begin{bmatrix} k_1 \\ k_2 \\ k_3 \end{bmatrix} = \mathbf{0}
$$

that is,

$$
\begin{aligned}
k_1 + 2k_3 &= 0 \\
k_2 - k_3 &= 0
\end{aligned}
$$

two equations with three unknowns. We can choose, therefore, an arbitrary value for k_3, say, $k_3 = 1$, and then $k_2 = 1$, $k_1 = -2$. Consequently,

$$-2\mathbf{r}_1 + \mathbf{r}_2 + \mathbf{r}_3 = \mathbf{0}$$

and the rows are linearly dependent.   ■

A similar definition and discussion apply to the linear dependence (or independence) of column vectors in a given matrix. A most useful theorem is based on the concepts of row rank and column rank of a matrix, defined as follows:

The row rank of a matrix $\mathbf{P}$ is the maximum number of linearly independent rows in $\mathbf{P}$. In Example 1.30 the row rank is 2, and the same happens to be true in Example 1.31 (where only two of the three rows are independent). Similarly, the column rank is defined as the maximum number of linearly independent columns. The theorem states that the row rank of $\mathbf{P}$ is equal to the column rank of $\mathbf{P}$. Therefore, we speak simply of *the rank* of a matrix $\mathbf{P}$, and denote it by r.

$$r = \text{rank of } \mathbf{P} = \text{column rank of } \mathbf{P} = \text{row rank of } \mathbf{P} \qquad (1.73)$$

The rank r is also equal to the order of the largest nonsingular submatrix in $\mathbf{P}$. In Example 1.30 the submatrix made up of the first two columns, for example, is nonsingular. It is the largest 2×2 nonsingular matrix. Hence $r = 2$. However, in Example 1.31 $\mathbf{Q}$ itself is singular, as verified through the Gauss method. The 2×2 submatrix found in the upper left corner after the application of the Gauss method is nonsingular. In fact, it is the unit submatrix. Hence the rank of $\mathbf{Q}$ is 2.

The previous example also outlines a general method for finding the rank r of a matrix. Let $\mathbf{P}$ be, in general, of order ($m \times n$). Then we perform elementary row and column operations until we get an equivalent matrix with an upper triangular, nonsingular ($r \times r$) submatrix in the upper left corner.

Example 1.32 Find the rank of **P**.

$$P = \begin{bmatrix} 1 & 2 & -1 & 3 & 4 \\ 2 & -1 & 1 & 1 & -1 \\ -1 & 8 & -5 & 7 & 14 \end{bmatrix}$$

By elementary row operations (Gauss elimination) we obtain the equivalent matrices

$$P \sim \begin{bmatrix} 1 & 2 & -1 & 3 & 4 \\ 0 & -5 & 3 & -5 & -9 \\ 0 & 10 & -6 & 10 & 18 \end{bmatrix} \sim \begin{bmatrix} 1 & 2 & -1 & 3 & 4 \\ 0 & -5 & 3 & -5 & -9 \\ 0 & 0 & 0 & 0 & 0 \end{bmatrix}$$

The last matrix contains the nonsingular (2×2) upper triangular submatrix shown in dotted lines. Hence the rank of **P** is 2. ∎

Example 1.33 Find the rank of **Q**.

Again, equivalent matrices are generated by row operations.

$$Q = \begin{bmatrix} 2 & -2 & -2 & 2 & 6 \\ -1 & 2 & 3 & -4 & -9 \\ 2 & -1 & -1 & 1 & 4 \\ -1 & 2 & 0 & 1 & 0 \\ 1 & 3 & -1 & -1 & 6 \end{bmatrix} \sim \begin{bmatrix} 1 & -1 & -1 & 1 & 3 \\ 0 & 1 & 2 & -3 & -6 \\ 0 & 1 & 1 & -1 & -2 \\ 0 & 1 & -1 & 2 & 3 \\ 0 & 4 & 0 & -3 & 3 \end{bmatrix} \sim$$

$$\sim \begin{bmatrix} 1 & 0 & 1 & -2 & -3 \\ 0 & 1 & 2 & -3 & -6 \\ 0 & 0 & -1 & 2 & 4 \\ 0 & 0 & -3 & 5 & 9 \\ 0 & 0 & -8 & 9 & 25 \end{bmatrix} \sim \begin{bmatrix} 1 & 0 & 0 & 0 & 1 \\ 0 & 1 & 0 & 1 & 2 \\ 0 & 0 & -1 & 2 & 4 \\ 0 & 0 & 0 & -1 & -3 \\ 0 & 0 & 0 & -7 & -7 \end{bmatrix}$$

wrong

$$\sim \begin{bmatrix} 1 & 0 & 0 & 0 & 1 \\ 0 & 1 & 0 & 0 & -1 \\ 0 & 0 & 1 & 0 & 2 \\ 0 & 0 & 0 & 1 & 3 \\ 0 & 0 & 0 & 0 & 14 \end{bmatrix}$$

The upper left corner submatrix shown in dotted lines is the largest nonsingular one. Therefore the rank of **Q** is 4. ∎

1.9 Ax = B REVISITED

In Sections 1.6 and 1.7 we discussed the solution of the set of linear equations

$$Ax = B \tag{1.74}$$

with **A**, the coefficient matrix, being square $(n \times n)$. By matrix inversion, we obtained the solution

$$x = A^{-1}B \tag{1.77}$$

when **A** was nonsingular.

Here we extend the discussion to the general case where **A** may be non-square, of order $(m \times n)$, and where **B** is or is not the null matrix. As we will see, the ideas of the Gauss (or Gauss-Jordan) method, the rank, the solutions, and their nature will all merge naturally.

Recall that in performing row operations on the system of equations $\mathbf{Ax} = \mathbf{B}$, we do so on an entire row, including the term on the right-hand side. It is, therefore, natural to deal with the *augmented matrix* $[\mathbf{A} \mid \mathbf{B}]$, where the column matrix $\mathbf{B}$ is simply appended to matrix $\mathbf{A}$. Row operations, when applied to this augmented matrix, will yield all the necessary information. It is important also to realize that elementary row (and column) operations do not change the rank of a matrix. This fact is based on the properties of determinants studied earlier in this chapter. Consequently, if the largest nonsingular submatrix in the original matrix was of order $(r \times r)$, then the largest nonsingular submatrix in the equivalent system is still of order $(r \times r)$—an upper triangular submatrix in the Gauss method, or a unit submatrix in the Gauss-Jordan method. The rank of the matrix remains r. A preliminary example is given in the following.

Example 1.34   Consider the non-homogeneous system

$$\begin{bmatrix} 1 & 2 & -1 & 3 \\ 2 & -1 & 1 & -1 \\ -1 & 8 & -5 & 7 \end{bmatrix} \begin{bmatrix} x_1 \\ x_2 \\ x_3 \\ x_4 \end{bmatrix} = \begin{bmatrix} 4 \\ -1 \\ 14 \end{bmatrix}$$

Using the augmented matrix $[\mathbf{A} \mid \mathbf{B}]$, we apply the Gauss-Jordan elimination method, and obtain the result as in Example 1.32, i.e.,

$$[\mathbf{A} \mid \mathbf{B}] \sim \begin{bmatrix} 1 & 2 & -1 & 3 & \mid & 4 \\ 0 & -5 & 3 & -5 & \mid & -9 \\ 0 & 0 & 0 & 0 & \mid & 0 \end{bmatrix} \sim \begin{bmatrix} 1 & 0 & 0.2 & 1 & \mid & 0.4 \\ 0 & 1 & -0.6 & 1 & \mid & 1.8 \\ 0 & 0 & 0 & 0 & \mid & 0 \end{bmatrix}$$

From this, we establish all of the following observations:

(a)   The rank of $\mathbf{A} = 2$.
(b)   The rank of $[\mathbf{A} \mid \mathbf{B}]$ also $= 2$.
(c)   The last equation is redundant, since it states that

$$0 \cdot x_1 + 0 \cdot x_2 + 0 \cdot x_3 + 0 \cdot x_4 = 0$$

(d)   Since the rank is 2, we use the unit submatrix in the upper left corner and write these two equations as

$$\begin{bmatrix} 1 & 0 \\ 0 & 1 \end{bmatrix} \begin{bmatrix} x_1 \\ x_2 \end{bmatrix} = \begin{bmatrix} 0.4 \\ 1.8 \end{bmatrix} + \begin{bmatrix} -0.2 & -1 \\ 0.6 & -1 \end{bmatrix} \begin{bmatrix} x_3 \\ x_4 \end{bmatrix}$$

i.e., x_3 and x_4 can be assigned arbitrary (but real) values, say, $x_3 = \alpha$ and $x_4 = \beta$. Then the complete solution is

$$\mathbf{x} = \begin{bmatrix} x_1 \\ x_2 \\ x_3 \\ x_4 \end{bmatrix} = \begin{bmatrix} 0.4 \\ 1.8 \\ 0 \\ 0 \end{bmatrix} + \alpha \begin{bmatrix} -0.2 \\ 0.6 \\ 1 \\ 0 \end{bmatrix} + \beta \begin{bmatrix} -1 \\ -1 \\ 0 \\ 1 \end{bmatrix}$$

(e)   If the original system were homogeneous, i.e., $\mathbf{B} = \mathbf{0}$, the equivalent augmented matrix would retain the zero column as its last column. Then observations (a), (b), and (c) are still valid.

(f)   Any homogeneous system is satisfied by the *trivial* solution **x** = **0**. Here the homogeneous system has, in addition, the *nontrivial* solution

$$\mathbf{x}_h = \alpha \begin{bmatrix} -0.2 \\ 0.6 \\ 1 \\ 0 \end{bmatrix} + \beta \begin{bmatrix} -1 \\ -1 \\ 0 \\ 1 \end{bmatrix}$$

(g)   The original non-homogeneous system has, then, a complete solution that is the sum of the homogeneous solution and a particular solution, the latter being

$$\mathbf{x}_p = \begin{bmatrix} 0.4 \\ 1.8 \\ 0 \\ 0 \end{bmatrix}$$

∎

We are ready now to consider the general case of Equation 1.74, *m* equations with *n* unknowns. The augmented matrix [**A** ⋮ **B**], after undergoing the Gauss-Jordan elimination, becomes

$$[\mathbf{A} \quad \mathbf{B}] \sim \left[\begin{array}{ccccccc|c} & & & \mathbf{I}_{(r \times r)} & & & & \begin{array}{c} b'_1 \\ b''_2 \\ \vdots \\ b_r^{(r)} \end{array} \\ 0 & 0 & 0 & \cdots & 0 & \cdots & 0 & b_{r+1}^{(r+1)} \\ & & \cdots & & & \cdots & & \vdots \\ 0 & 0 & 0 & \cdots & 0 & \cdots & & b_m^{(m)} \end{array} \right] \qquad (1.76)$$

The unit submatrix of order $(r \times r)$, in the upper left corner, having rows of zeros below it, shows that the rank of **A** is r. If one or more of the constants

$$b_{r+1}^{(r+1)}, \ b_{r+2}^{(r+2)}, \ \ldots , \ b_m^{(m)}$$

is different from zero, then two observations are made:

1.   The system is *inconsistent,* i.e., it has no solution, because then the equations corresponding to that nonzero term will read

$$0 \cdot x_1 + 0 \cdot x_2 + \cdots + 0 \cdot x_n \neq 0$$

an obvious inconsistency.

2.   The rank of [**A** ⋮ **B**] is greater than the rank of **A** because in [**A** ⋮ **B**] there is a nonsingular submatrix of order higher than $(r \times r)$.

A necessary and sufficient condition for the *consistency* of the system **Ax** = **B** (existence of a solution) is

$$\text{rank } \mathbf{A} = \text{rank } [\mathbf{A} \vdots \mathbf{B}] \qquad (1.77)$$

If

$$b_{r+1}^{(r+1)} = b_{r+2}^{(r+2)} = \cdots = b_m^{(m)} = 0$$

then the following observations are made:

3. The system is *consistent*. The $(r + 1)^{st}$, $(r + 2)^{nd}$, . . . , m^{th} equations are *redundant*, of the form

$$0 \cdot x_1 + 0 \cdot x_2 + \cdots = 0$$

4. The first r equations whose coefficient matrix is the unit matrix $\mathbf{I}_{(r \times r)}$ are linearly independent. The remaining $(m - r)$ equations are linearly dependent on the r equations. The unknowns $x_{r+1}, x_{r+2}, \ldots, x_n$ are arbitrary (but real, if $\mathbf{A}$ and $\mathbf{B}$ are real). The first r unknowns $x_1, x_2, \ldots, x_r$ can then be expressed in terms of these arbitrary values.

5. If the number of unknowns n equals the rank r

$$n = r \tag{1.78}$$

then their solution is unique, without any arbitrary constants.

For the homogeneous case, $\mathbf{B} = \mathbf{0}$, the following observations are made:

6. The system is always consistent since, obviously,

$$\text{rank } \mathbf{A} = \text{rank } [\mathbf{A} \mid \mathbf{0}]$$

and the *trivial* solution $\mathbf{x} = \mathbf{0}$ is equally obvious.

7. If $n = r$, as in item 5, the trivial solution is the *only* solution. Otherwise, as in item 4, many nontrivial solutions exist in terms of $(n - r)$ arbitrary constants.

Finally, we recognize the principle of *superposition* in the solution of the linear system of equations: The solution of a non-homogeneous system consists of the sum of the homogeneous solution and a particular solution

$$\mathbf{x} = \mathbf{x}_h + \mathbf{x}_p \tag{1.79}$$

Example 1.35   Consider matrix $\mathbf{Q}$, in Example 1.33. Let it be the augmented matrix of a system $\mathbf{Ax} = \mathbf{B}$. The equivalent augmented matrix shows immediately that the system is inconsistent, without a solution.   ∎

Example 1.36   Consider the system

$$\begin{bmatrix} 2 & -1 \\ 1 & 1 \\ 3 & 2 \end{bmatrix} \begin{bmatrix} x_1 \\ x_2 \end{bmatrix} = \begin{bmatrix} 4 \\ -1 \\ -1 \end{bmatrix}$$

Using the augmented matrix $[\mathbf{A} \mid \mathbf{B}]$ we apply the Gauss-Jordan elimination method and obtain

$$[\mathbf{A} \mid \mathbf{B}] = \begin{bmatrix} 2 & -1 & \vdots & 4 \\ 1 & 1 & \vdots & -1 \\ 3 & 2 & \vdots & -1 \end{bmatrix} \sim \begin{bmatrix} 1 & 0 & \vdots & 1 \\ 0 & 1 & \vdots & -2 \\ 0 & 0 & \vdots & 0 \end{bmatrix}$$

The system is consistent. The third equation is redundant of the form $0 \cdot x_1 + 0 \cdot x_2 = 0$. The solution is

$$\begin{aligned} x_1 &= 1 \\ x_2 &= -2 \end{aligned}$$

∎

Example 1.37   Consider the system **Ax = B** with

$$[\mathbf{A} \mid \mathbf{B}] = \begin{bmatrix} 2 & -1 & 3 & \mid & -4 \\ -1 & 2 & -1 & \mid & -1 \\ 1 & 1 & -2 & \mid & 7 \\ 3 & -2 & 1 & \mid & 5 \\ 1 & -1 & 1 & \mid & 0 \end{bmatrix}$$

Apply the Gauss-Jordan elimination method and obtain

$$[\mathbf{A} \mid \mathbf{B}] \sim \begin{bmatrix} 2 & -1 & 3 & \mid & -4 \\ -1 & 2 & -1 & \mid & -1 \\ 1 & 1 & -2 & \mid & 7 \\ 3 & -2 & 1 & \mid & 5 \\ 1 & -1 & 1 & \mid & 0 \end{bmatrix} \sim \begin{bmatrix} 1 & 0 & 10/6 & \mid & -3 \\ 0 & 1 & 1/3 & \mid & -2 \\ 0 & 0 & -4 & \mid & 12 \\ 0 & 0 & -10/3 & \mid & 10 \\ 0 & 0 & -1/3 & \mid & 1 \end{bmatrix} \sim \begin{bmatrix} 1 & 0 & 0 & \mid & 2 \\ 0 & 1 & 0 & \mid & -1 \\ 0 & 0 & 1 & \mid & -3 \\ 0 & 0 & 0 & \mid & 0 \\ 0 & 0 & 0 & \mid & 0 \end{bmatrix}$$

and therefore $x_1 = 2$, $x_2 = -1$, $x_3 = -3$. If the original system were homogeneous (**B = 0**), the equivalent augmented matrix would be

$$[\mathbf{A} \mid \mathbf{B}] \sim \begin{bmatrix} 1 & 0 & 0 & \mid & 0 \\ 0 & 1 & 0 & \mid & 0 \\ 0 & 0 & 1 & \mid & 0 \\ 0 & 0 & 0 & \mid & 0 \\ 0 & 0 & 0 & \mid & 0 \end{bmatrix}$$

and the only solution here is the trivial solution $x_1 = x_2 = x_3 = 0$.   ∎

1.10   LINEAR VECTOR SPACES

Earlier we used the conventional names for a row matrix and a column matrix, a *row vector* and a *column vector*, respectively. In two-dimensional and three-dimensional spaces we can easily visualize the meaning of vectors. The elements of a vector are its components along the rectangular coordinate system, as shown in Figure 1.7(a) and 1.7(b).

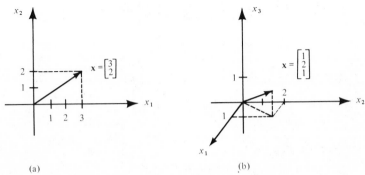

(a)   (b)

FIGURE 1.7   A vector in (a) a plane and (b) a three-dimensional space.

For multidimensional spaces ($n > 3$) we use the same terminology and ideas.

Example 1.38 In a four-dimensional space, the vectors

$$\mathbf{i}_1 = \begin{bmatrix} 1 \\ 0 \\ 0 \\ 0 \end{bmatrix} \quad \mathbf{i}_2 = \begin{bmatrix} 0 \\ 1 \\ 0 \\ 0 \end{bmatrix} \quad \mathbf{i}_3 = \begin{bmatrix} 0 \\ 0 \\ 1 \\ 0 \end{bmatrix} \quad \mathbf{i}_4 = \begin{bmatrix} 0 \\ 0 \\ 0 \\ 1 \end{bmatrix}$$

can be considered as the unit vectors along the four mutually orthogonal axes x_1, x_2, x_3, and x_4. ∎

Scalar Product of Two Vectors

Let $\mathbf{u}$ and $\mathbf{v}$ be ($n \times 1$) column vectors with real components. Then the scalar product of $\mathbf{u}$ and $\mathbf{v}$ is defined as

$$\langle \mathbf{u}, \mathbf{v} \rangle = \mathbf{u}^T \mathbf{v} = \sum_{i=1}^{n} u_i v_i \tag{1.80}$$

and is a scalar. It is recognized also as the *dot product* $\mathbf{u} \cdot \mathbf{v}$ in vector calculus. For the more general case when the vectors may be complex, their scalar product is

$$\langle \mathbf{u}, \mathbf{v} \rangle = \mathbf{u}^{*T} \mathbf{v} = \sum_{i=1}^{n} u_i^* v_i \tag{1.81}$$

Example 1.39 In the network shown, each element (a, b, c, d) has a current reference assigned. For the two resistors, this is also the reference for the voltage drop. It is easy to calculate all of the individual currents, given by the vector

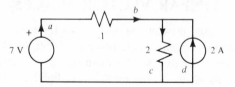

FIGURE 1.8 Example 1.39.

$$\mathbf{i} = \begin{bmatrix} i_a \\ i_b \\ i_c \\ i_d \end{bmatrix} = \begin{bmatrix} 1 \\ 1 \\ 3 \\ 2 \end{bmatrix}$$

and the voltage vector

$$\mathbf{v} = \begin{bmatrix} v_a \\ v_b \\ v_c \\ v_d \end{bmatrix} = \begin{bmatrix} -7 \\ 1 \\ 6 \\ -6 \end{bmatrix}$$

Now the scalar product of $\mathbf{v}$ and $\mathbf{i}$ is

$$\langle \mathbf{v}, \mathbf{i} \rangle = \mathbf{v}^T \mathbf{i} = \begin{bmatrix} -7 & 1 & 6 & -6 \end{bmatrix} \begin{bmatrix} 1 \\ 1 \\ 3 \\ 2 \end{bmatrix} = 0$$

as it should be, since $\mathbf{v}^T\mathbf{i} = v_a i_a + v_b i_b + v_c i_c + v_d i_d = -7 + 1 + 18 - 12$ represents the algebraic sum of the instantaneous power $p(t)$ in all the elements. The first (-7) and the last (-12) are the powers *delivered* by the sources, whereas the second $(+1)$ and the third $(+18)$ are *absorbed* by the resistors. We have here an illustration of the principle of conservation of energy, namely,

$$\langle \mathbf{v}, \mathbf{i} \rangle = p(t) = 0 \qquad \blacksquare$$

Example 1.40 Under sinusoidal steady state, the network shown (impedances of elements are given) has the phasor currents and phasor voltages calculated as

$$\bar{I} = \begin{bmatrix} \bar{I}_a \\ \bar{I}_b \\ \bar{I}_c \\ \bar{I}_d \end{bmatrix} = \begin{bmatrix} -0.423 + j1.115 \\ -0.423 + j1.115 \\ 1.577 + j1.115 \\ 2.0 \quad + j0 \end{bmatrix} \qquad \bar{V} = \begin{bmatrix} \bar{V}_a \\ \bar{V}_b \\ \bar{V}_c \\ \bar{V}_d \end{bmatrix} = \begin{bmatrix} -7 \quad + j0 \\ -2.653 + j0.289 \\ 9.653 - j0.271 \\ -9.653 + j0.271 \end{bmatrix}$$

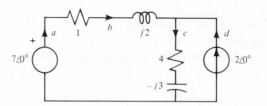

FIGURE 1.9 Example 1.40.

The average power P and the reactive power Q are given by

$$P + jQ = \bar{V}^{*T}\bar{I} =$$

$$= [-7 - j0 \mid -2.653 - j0.289 \mid 9.653 + j0.271 \mid -9.653 - j0.271] \times$$

$$\times \begin{bmatrix} -0.423 + j1.115 \\ -0.423 + j1.115 \\ 1.577 + j1.115 \\ 2 \quad + j0 \end{bmatrix} = 0, \text{ as expected.} \qquad \blacksquare$$

The two vectors $\mathbf{u}$ and $\mathbf{v}$ are *orthogonal* if their scalar product vanishes, i.e.,

$$\langle \mathbf{u}, \mathbf{v} \rangle = 0 \tag{1.82}$$

Example 1.41 The unit vectors in Example 1.38 are mutually orthogonal since $\langle \mathbf{i}_1, \mathbf{i}_2 \rangle = \langle \mathbf{i}_2, \mathbf{i}_3 \rangle = \langle \mathbf{i}_3, \mathbf{i}_4 \rangle = \langle \mathbf{i}_4, \mathbf{i}_1 \rangle = 0$. $\qquad \blacksquare$

The *length* (or *norm*) of a vector $\mathbf{v}$ is $\|\mathbf{v}\|$ and given by

$$\|\mathbf{v}\| = \langle \mathbf{v}, \mathbf{v} \rangle^{1/2} \tag{1.83}$$

It is the familiar length of a vector in two- and three-dimensional Euclidean geometry, and Equation 1.83 extends this concept to $n > 3$. If the length of a vector is a unit, the vector is called a unit vector. We can scale a given vector $\mathbf{u}$ by its norm in order to obtain the corresponding unit vector.

Example 1.42 Given

$$\mathbf{u} = \begin{bmatrix} 1 \\ 0 \\ -1 \end{bmatrix} \quad \mathbf{v} = \begin{bmatrix} 1 + j \\ 2 - 3j \end{bmatrix}$$

we find $\|\mathbf{u}\| = \sqrt{2}$ and $\|\mathbf{v}\| = \sqrt{15}$. Therefore the unit vectors are

$$\hat{\mathbf{u}} = \begin{bmatrix} 1/\sqrt{2} \\ 0 \\ -1/\sqrt{2} \end{bmatrix} \quad \hat{\mathbf{v}} = \begin{bmatrix} (1 + j)/\sqrt{15} \\ (2 - 3j)/\sqrt{15} \end{bmatrix} \qquad \blacksquare$$

The ideas of linear independence (or dependence) of rows, or of columns, in a matrix were explored in a previous section. To review, a set of vectors $\mathbf{r}_1, \mathbf{r}_2, \ldots, \mathbf{r}_m$ is linearly independent if

$$\sum_{i=1}^{m} k_i \mathbf{r}_i = \mathbf{0} \tag{1.84}$$

is satisfied only by the scalars $k_1 = k_2 = \cdots = 0$. If the vectors are dependent, then there are some scalars $k_i \neq 0$.

An alternate test for dependence may be formulated as follows: In Equation 1.84 let us form the scalar product with $\mathbf{r}_1$ first, then with $\mathbf{r}_2, \ldots, \mathbf{r}_m$. We get

$$\begin{aligned}
k_1\langle\mathbf{r}_1, \mathbf{r}_1\rangle + k_2\langle\mathbf{r}_1, \mathbf{r}_2\rangle + \cdots + k_m\langle\mathbf{r}_1, \mathbf{r}_m\rangle &= 0 \\
k_1\langle\mathbf{r}_2, \mathbf{r}_1\rangle + k_2\langle\mathbf{r}_2, \mathbf{r}_2\rangle + \cdots + k_m\langle\mathbf{r}_2, \mathbf{r}_m\rangle &= 0 \\
&\vdots \\
k_1\langle\mathbf{r}_m, \mathbf{r}_1\rangle + k_2\langle\mathbf{r}_m, \mathbf{r}_2\rangle + \cdots + k_m\langle\mathbf{r}_m, \mathbf{r}_m\rangle &= 0
\end{aligned} \tag{1.85}$$

This is a homogeneous set of equations for the unknowns $k_1, k_2, \ldots k_m$. We know that a nontrivial solution exists if, and only if, the determinant of the coefficients vanishes, i.e.,

$$G = \begin{vmatrix} \langle\mathbf{r}_1, \mathbf{r}_1\rangle & \langle\mathbf{r}_1, \mathbf{r}_2\rangle & \cdots & \langle\mathbf{r}_1, \mathbf{r}_m\rangle \\ \vdots & & & \\ \langle\mathbf{r}_m, \mathbf{r}_1\rangle & \langle\mathbf{r}_m, \mathbf{r}_2\rangle & \cdots & \langle\mathbf{r}_m, \mathbf{r}_m\rangle \end{vmatrix} = 0 \tag{1.86}$$

This determinant is called the *Gram determinant* (or, briefly, the *Gramian*). Therefore, we say that the necessary and sufficient condition for the independence of a set of vectors is that their Gramian be nonzero.

Example 1.43 Consider the set of vectors

$$\mathbf{r}_1 = \begin{bmatrix} 2 \\ 1 \\ 0 \end{bmatrix} \quad \mathbf{r}_2 = \begin{bmatrix} 3 \\ -1 \\ 1 \end{bmatrix} \quad \mathbf{r}_3 = \begin{bmatrix} 0 \\ 2 \\ -2 \end{bmatrix}$$

The Gram determinant is given by

$$G = \begin{vmatrix} 5 & 5 & 2 \\ 5 & 11 & -4 \\ 2 & -4 & 8 \end{vmatrix} = 36$$

Therefore the vectors are linearly independent. An alternate check would be on the rank of the matrix formed by these three column vectors.   ∎

Example 1.44   Consider the set of complex vectors

$$\mathbf{r}_1 = \begin{bmatrix} 1 \\ -j \\ 2 + j \end{bmatrix} \qquad \mathbf{r}_2 = \begin{bmatrix} j \\ -1 - j \\ 3 \end{bmatrix}$$

The Gram determinant is

$$G = \begin{vmatrix} 7 & 7 - 3j \\ 7 + 3j & 12 \end{vmatrix} = 26$$

These vectors are, therefore, linearly independent.   ∎

Example 1.45   Consider the three vectors

$$\mathbf{r}_1 = \begin{bmatrix} 1 \\ 0 \\ -1 \\ 2 \end{bmatrix} \qquad \mathbf{r}_2 = \begin{bmatrix} -1 \\ 1 \\ 2 \\ 1 \end{bmatrix} \qquad \mathbf{r}_3 = \begin{bmatrix} 3 \\ -1 \\ -4 \\ 3 \end{bmatrix}$$

We can check the rank of the matrix of these three columns. Alternately, use the Gramian, which is given by

$$G = \begin{vmatrix} 6 & -1 & 13 \\ -1 & 7 & -9 \\ 13 & -9 & 35 \end{vmatrix} = 0$$

and, consequently, the three vectors are linearly dependent: In fact, $2\mathbf{r}_1 - \mathbf{r}_2 - \mathbf{r}_3 = \mathbf{0}$.   ∎

A *linear vector space* is the set of vectors satisfying the following conditions:

1. If $\mathbf{u}_1$ and $\mathbf{u}_2$ are in the set, so is their sum, $\mathbf{u}_1 + \mathbf{u}_2$.
2. If $\mathbf{u}_1$ is in the set, so is $\alpha\mathbf{u}_1$ where α is a scalar.
3. $1\mathbf{u} = \mathbf{u}$.
4. $\alpha_1(\alpha_2\mathbf{u}) = \alpha_1\alpha_2\mathbf{u}$ for any scalars α_1, α_2 and for any $\mathbf{u}$ in the space.
5. $(\alpha_1 + \alpha_2)\mathbf{u} = \alpha_1\mathbf{u} + \alpha_2\mathbf{u}$ for any scalars α_1, α_2 and for any $\mathbf{u}$ in the space.
6. Addition of vectors is commutative, $\mathbf{u}_1 + \mathbf{u}_2 = \mathbf{u}_2 + \mathbf{u}_1$.
7. $\alpha(\mathbf{u}_1 + \mathbf{u}_2) = \alpha\mathbf{u}_1 + \alpha\mathbf{u}_2$ for any scalar α and for any $\mathbf{u}_1$, $\mathbf{u}_2$ in the space.
8. Addition of vectors is distributive, $(\mathbf{u}_1 + \mathbf{u}_2) + \mathbf{u}_3 = \mathbf{u}_1 + (\mathbf{u}_2 + \mathbf{u}_3)$.
9. A zero (null) vector exists in the space, satisfying $\mathbf{u} + \mathbf{0} = \mathbf{u}$ for any $\mathbf{u}$ in the space.
10. A negative vector exists in the space, satisfying $\mathbf{u} + (-\mathbf{u}) = \mathbf{0}$ for any $\mathbf{u}$ in the space.

The set of all vectors $\mathbf{v}$ that are linear combinations of $\mathbf{u}_1, \mathbf{u}_2, \ldots \mathbf{u}_m$

$$\mathbf{v} = k_1\mathbf{u}_1 + k_2\mathbf{u}_2 + \cdots + k_m\mathbf{u}_m \tag{1.87}$$

is a vector space generated by the $\mathbf{u}$'s. The maximum number r of linearly independent vectors in the space is the *dimension* of the space. If $r < m$, then obviously Equation 1.87 will contain only r terms in the sum

$$\mathbf{v} = k_1\mathbf{u}_1 + k_2\mathbf{u}_2 + \cdots + k_r\mathbf{u}_r \tag{1.88}$$

where $\mathbf{u}_1, \ldots, \mathbf{u}_r$ are the linearly independent vectors. The remaining vectors $\mathbf{u}_{r+1}, \ldots, \mathbf{u}_m$ are dependent on $\mathbf{u}_1, \ldots, \mathbf{u}_r$ and, as such, are linear combinations of them.

Example 1.46 Let

$$\mathbf{u}_1 = \begin{bmatrix} -1 \\ 1 \\ 1 \end{bmatrix} \qquad \mathbf{u}_2 = \begin{bmatrix} 0 \\ -1 \\ -1 \end{bmatrix} \qquad \mathbf{u}_3 = \begin{bmatrix} -2 \\ 1 \\ 3 \end{bmatrix}$$

Here $\mathbf{u}_3 = 2\mathbf{u}_1 - \mathbf{u}_2$, so only two of these vectors are independent; the rank of the three vectors $[\mathbf{u}_1 \vdots \mathbf{u}_2 \vdots \mathbf{u}_3]$ is $r = 2$. Consequently, the dimension of the space is 2, and any vector in that space can be written as

$$\mathbf{v} = k_1\mathbf{u}_1 + k_2\mathbf{u}_2 + k_3\mathbf{u}_3 = (k_1 + 2k_2)\mathbf{u}_1 + (k_2 - k_3)\mathbf{u}_2 \qquad \blacksquare$$

When there are n independent vectors in an n-dimensional space, we speak of them as *spanning* that space. These vectors can form a *basis*, so that any other vector is a unique linear combination of the basis vectors.

Example 1.47 In a two-dimensional space, the two unit vectors

$$\mathbf{u}_1 = \begin{bmatrix} 1 \\ 0 \end{bmatrix} \qquad \mathbf{u}_2 = \begin{bmatrix} 0 \\ 1 \end{bmatrix}$$

form an orthogonal basis. In terms of these, any vector in this space can be written as $\mathbf{v} = k_1\mathbf{u}_1 + k_2\mathbf{u}_2$. For example,

$$\mathbf{v} = \begin{bmatrix} 4 \\ -1 \end{bmatrix} = 4\mathbf{u}_1 - \mathbf{u}_2 \qquad \blacksquare$$

Example 1.48 In the same two-dimensional space, the two vectors

$$\mathbf{w}_1 = \begin{bmatrix} 2 \\ -1 \end{bmatrix} \qquad \mathbf{w}_2 = \begin{bmatrix} 1 \\ 1 \end{bmatrix}$$

(each specified in terms of $\mathbf{u}_1$ and $\mathbf{u}_2$ of the previous example) are linearly independent, and thus also span that space. By using $\mathbf{w}_1$ and $\mathbf{w}_2$ as a basis, we can express $\mathbf{v}$ of the previous example as

$$\mathbf{v} = k_1\mathbf{w}_1 + k_2\mathbf{w}_2$$

To find k_1 and k_2, we form the scalar product of $\mathbf{v}$ with $\mathbf{w}_1$, then with $\mathbf{w}_2$:

$$9 = 5k_1 + k_2$$
$$3 = k_1 + 2k_2$$

The coefficient matrix for the k's is guaranteed to be nonsingular (since it is the Gramian), and therefore we can find a unique solution. Here, $k_1 = 15/9$ and $k_2 = 2/3$. Consequently, on the basis of $\mathbf{w}_1$ and $\mathbf{w}_2$,

$$\mathbf{v} = \frac{15}{9}\,\mathbf{w}_1 + \frac{2}{3}\,\mathbf{w}_2 \qquad\qquad \blacksquare$$

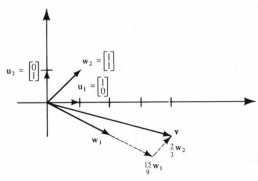

FIGURE 1.10   Geometry of Example 1.48.

1.11   CHARACTERISTIC VALUES AND VECTORS

An important topic in linear system analysis is that of characteristic values and characteristic vectors (also called *eigenvalues* and *eigenvectors*, respectively). We encounter these in a later chapter; here we give a brief introduction.

A relationship such as

$$\mathbf{Ax} = \mathbf{B} \qquad\qquad (1.89)$$

which we discussed previously in detail, can be interpreted as follows: A vector $\mathbf{x}$ is transformed by matrix $\mathbf{A}$ and yields another vector $\mathbf{B}$. In general, the vector $\mathbf{x}$ is not parallel to $\mathbf{B}$. But in some cases it is.

Example 1.49   Consider the transformation $\mathbf{Ax} = \mathbf{B}$ for two cases:
(a)

$$\mathbf{A} = \begin{bmatrix} -2 & -1 \\ 2 & -5 \end{bmatrix} \qquad \mathbf{x}_a = \begin{bmatrix} 0 \\ 1 \end{bmatrix}$$

Here

$$\mathbf{Ax}_a = \begin{bmatrix} -1 \\ -5 \end{bmatrix}$$

a vector $\mathbf{B}_a$ not parallel to $\mathbf{x}_a$.
(b)   With the same $\mathbf{A}$, consider

$$\mathbf{x}_b = \begin{bmatrix} -1 \\ -1 \end{bmatrix}$$

Then

$$\mathbf{Ax}_b = \begin{bmatrix} 3 \\ 3 \end{bmatrix} = -3\mathbf{x}_b .$$

Here the transformation of $\mathbf{x}_b$ by $\mathbf{A}$ produced a vector $\mathbf{B}_b$ parallel to $\mathbf{x}_b$. See Figure 1.11. ∎

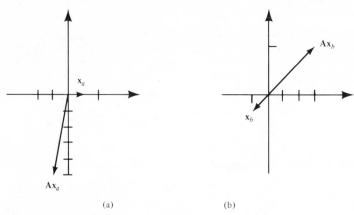

(a)   (b)

FIGURE 1.11 Two transformations of a vector x.

The general problem is to find $\mathbf{x}$ such that, when transformed by a square matrix $\mathbf{A}$, its direction is unchanged and it remains parallel to itself. Stated briefly, we are seeking the solution to

$$\mathbf{Ax} = \lambda \mathbf{x} \qquad (1.90)$$

where λ is a scalar. This problem is called the characteristic value problem. The scalars λ and the corresponding vectors $\mathbf{x}$ are called, respectively, the characteristic values and characteristic vectors of the matrix $\mathbf{A}$. In the previous example we showed one characteristic value $\lambda = -3$ and one characteristic vector $\mathbf{x}_b$.

The motivation and origin of the characteristic value problem can be best illustrated by considering the scalar case first. In the differential equation

$$\dot{x} = ax \qquad (1.91)$$

we classically assume a solution

$$x = Ke^{\lambda t} \qquad (1.92)$$

and substitute it into Equation 1.91. The result is

$$\lambda Ke^{\lambda t} = aKe^{\lambda t} \qquad (1.93)$$

that is,

$$\lambda x = ax \qquad (1.94)$$

the characteristic value problem, Equation 1.90, for the scalar case. Similarly, given the *matrix* first-order differential equation

$$\dot{\mathbf{x}} = \mathbf{Ax} \qquad (1.95)$$

we assume a solution

$$\mathbf{x} = \mathbf{K}e^{\lambda t} \tag{1.96}$$

and substitute. The result is

$$\lambda \mathbf{K}e^{\lambda t} = \mathbf{A}\mathbf{K}e^{\lambda t} \tag{1.97}$$

or, as before,

$$\lambda \mathbf{x} = \mathbf{A}\mathbf{x} \tag{1.90}$$

i.e., the characteristic value problem.

We encounter a matrix first-order differential equation like Equation 1.95 in practically all problems of dynamic systems analysis. Here we illustrate it with a state-variable analysis of an electrical network.

Example 1.50 In the network shown, let us choose $v_C(t)$ and $i_L(t)$ as the unknowns. They are called the *state variables,* and

$$\mathbf{x}(t) = \begin{bmatrix} v_C(t) \\ i_L(t) \end{bmatrix}$$

is the *state vector.* The initial state vector $\mathbf{x}(0)$ specifies the initial conditions that must be given.

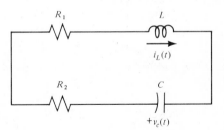

FIGURE 1.12 State-variable analysis.

We have here

$$i_C(t) = C\frac{dv_C}{dt} = -i_L(t)$$

and

$$v_C(t) - L\frac{di_L}{dt} - (R_1 + R_2)i_L = 0$$

or

$$\frac{dv_C}{dt} = -\frac{1}{C}i_L(t)$$

$$\frac{di_L}{dt} = \frac{1}{L}v_C(t) - \frac{R_1 + R_2}{L}i_L(t)$$

and, in matrix form,

$$\frac{d}{dt}\begin{bmatrix} v_C(t) \\ i_L(t) \end{bmatrix} = \begin{bmatrix} 0 & -\dfrac{1}{C} \\ \dfrac{1}{L} & \dfrac{-(R_1 + R_2)}{L} \end{bmatrix}\begin{bmatrix} v_C(t) \\ i_L(t) \end{bmatrix}$$

i.e., $\dot{\mathbf{x}} = \mathbf{A}\mathbf{x}$. We deal with these equations, and their solutions, later in this text.   ■

Let us return to Equation 1.90. When written fully, it reads

$$\begin{aligned}
\lambda x_1 &= a_{11}x_1 + a_{12}x_2 + \cdots + a_{1n}x_n \\
\lambda x_2 &= a_{21}x_1 + a_{22}x_2 + \cdots + a_{2n}x_n \\
&\quad\vdots \\
\lambda x_n &= a_{n1}x_1 + a_{n2}x_2 + \cdots + a_{nn}x_n
\end{aligned} \tag{1.98}$$

or

$$\begin{aligned}
(\lambda - a_{11})x_1 - a_{12}x_2 - \cdots - a_{1n}x_n &= 0 \\
-a_{21}x_1 + (\lambda - a_{22})x_2 - \cdots - a_{2n}x_n &= 0 \\
&\quad\vdots \\
-a_{n1}x_1 - a_{n2}x_2 - \cdots + (\lambda - a_{nn})x_n &= 0
\end{aligned} \tag{1.99}$$

that is,

$$(\lambda \mathbf{I} - \mathbf{A})\mathbf{x} = \mathbf{0} \tag{1.100}$$

where $\mathbf{I}$ is the $n \times n$ unit matrix.

As we recall, Equation 1.100 has a nontrivial solution ($\mathbf{x} \neq \mathbf{0}$) provided that

$$\det (\lambda \mathbf{I} - \mathbf{A}) = 0 \tag{1.101}$$

This equation, called the characteristic equation of $\mathbf{A}$, will be of degree n

$$\lambda^n + \beta_1\lambda^{n-1} + \beta_2\lambda^{n-2} + \cdots + \beta_n = 0 \tag{1.102}$$

and will yield n roots, the n characteristic values of $\mathbf{A}$.

Example 1.51   Find the characteristic values of $\mathbf{A}$ in Example 1.49. We have

$$\det (\lambda \mathbf{I} - \mathbf{A}) = \begin{vmatrix} \lambda + 2 & 1 \\ -2 & \lambda + 5 \end{vmatrix} = 0$$

or

$$\lambda^2 + 7\lambda + 12 = 0$$

that is,

$$\lambda_1 = -3, \qquad \lambda_2 = -4 \qquad\qquad ■$$

In general, roots of the characteristic equation are either distinct ($\lambda_1 \neq \lambda_2 \neq \cdots$) or repeated, of multiplicity p ($\lambda_1 = \lambda_2 = \cdots = \lambda_p \neq \lambda_{p+1} \cdots$), and complex roots occur in conjugate pairs if $\mathbf{A}$ is real. Some other properties of the roots, related to the coefficients β_i in Equation 1.102, are explored in the problems at the end of this chapter.

Corresponding to each characteristic value λ_p we can find a characteristic vector $\mathbf{x}_p$ satisfying Equation 1.90. That is,

$$(\lambda_p \mathbf{I} - \mathbf{A})\mathbf{x}_p = \mathbf{0} \tag{1.103}$$

can be solved for $\mathbf{x}_p$. Note, however, that $k\mathbf{x}_p$, a scalar multiple of $\mathbf{x}_p$, also satisfies Equation 1.103. Thus we conclude that characteristic vectors are determined only to within a scalar multiplier.

Example 1.52 Find the characteristic vectors of $\mathbf{A}$ in Example 1.51. We found $\lambda_1 = -3$ and $\lambda_2 = -4$. Therefore, corresponding to λ_1, we have

$$\begin{bmatrix} -2 & -1 \\ 2 & -5 \end{bmatrix} \mathbf{x}_1 = -3\mathbf{x}_1$$

or, as in Equation 1.103,

$$\begin{bmatrix} -1 & 1 \\ -2 & 2 \end{bmatrix} \mathbf{x}_1 = \mathbf{0}$$

The rank of this system is 1, hence we find

$$\mathbf{x}_1 = \begin{bmatrix} 1 \\ 1 \end{bmatrix}$$

or a scalar multiple of it, $k\mathbf{x}_1$, where k is any scalar. Similarly, for λ_2 we have

$$\begin{bmatrix} -2 & -1 \\ 2 & -5 \end{bmatrix} \mathbf{x}_2 = -4\mathbf{x}_2$$

or

$$\begin{bmatrix} -2 & 1 \\ -2 & 1 \end{bmatrix} \mathbf{x}_2 = \mathbf{0}$$

Again, the solution is within a multiple scalar of $\mathbf{x}_2$, where

$$\mathbf{x}_2 = \begin{bmatrix} 1 \\ 2 \end{bmatrix} \qquad \blacksquare$$

A special case of interest in circuits is when $\mathbf{A}$ is real and symmetric. Then the following results hold (see also Problems 1-50, 1-51, and 1-52).

1. The characteristic values are real.
2. The characteristic vectors form an orthogonal set.
3. If the n characteristic values are distinct (simple), their corresponding vectors can be an orthogonal basis in the n-dimensional space spanned by them.
4. A multiple characteristic value, of multiplicity p, has associated with it p characteristic vectors which are linearly independent.

As a final illustration of the first-order matrix differential equation $\dot{\mathbf{x}} = \mathbf{A}\mathbf{x}$, consider a system described by a scalar n^{th}-order homogeneous differential equation

$$a_n \frac{d^n y}{dt^n} + a_{n-1} \frac{d^{n-1} y}{dt^{n-1}} + \cdots + a_1 \frac{dy}{dt} + a_0 y = 0 \tag{1.104}$$

Define a vector $\mathbf{x}(t)$, often called a *state vector*, by its components, as follows:

$$x_1(t) = y(t), \; x_2(t) = \frac{dy}{dt}, \; \ldots, \; x_n(t) = \frac{d^{n-1}y}{dt^{n-1}} \qquad (1.105)$$

Then we have, together with Equation 1.105,

$$\begin{aligned}
x_1 &= y \\
\dot{x}_1 &= x_2 = \dot{y} \\
\dot{x}_2 &= x_3 = \ddot{y} \\
&\;\;\vdots
\end{aligned} \qquad (1.106)$$

$$\dot{x}_n = \frac{d^n y}{dt^n} = \frac{1}{a_n}\,(-a_0 x_1 - \cdots - a_{n-1}x_n)$$

In matrix form these equations read

$$\dot{\mathbf{x}} = \begin{bmatrix} 0 & 1 & 0 & 0 & \cdots & 0 \\ 0 & 0 & 1 & 0 & \cdots & 0 \\ & \cdots & & & \cdots & \\ -\dfrac{a_0}{a_n} & -\dfrac{a_1}{a_n} & & & & -\dfrac{a_{n-1}}{a_n} \end{bmatrix} \mathbf{x} \qquad (1.107)$$

that is, $\dot{\mathbf{x}} = \mathbf{Ax}$.

The non-homogeneous case of Equation 1.104, when the right-hand side is non-zero, and related topics are considered in the chapter on Laplace transforms, and all of Chapter 6 is devoted to a study of matrix state equations.

PROBLEMS

1-1 In each of the following D_2, find x which will make $D_2 = 0$.

(a) $\begin{vmatrix} 2 & -x \\ x+1 & -4 \end{vmatrix}$; (b) $\begin{vmatrix} x & -x \\ 2 & -4 \end{vmatrix}$; (c) $\begin{vmatrix} 2x & -2 \\ -3x & x \end{vmatrix}$; (d) $\begin{vmatrix} x & 3 \\ 5 & 2x+1 \end{vmatrix}$

1-2 Write two loop equations, as shown, and use Cramer's rule to solve for i_1 and i_2; hence find $v(t)$. Element values are in ohms.

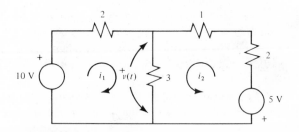

FIGURE 1.13 Problem 1-2.

1-3 Repeat Problem 1-2 for the network shown. Notice: $i_1 = 3$ amperes and is therefore known. Element values are in ohms.

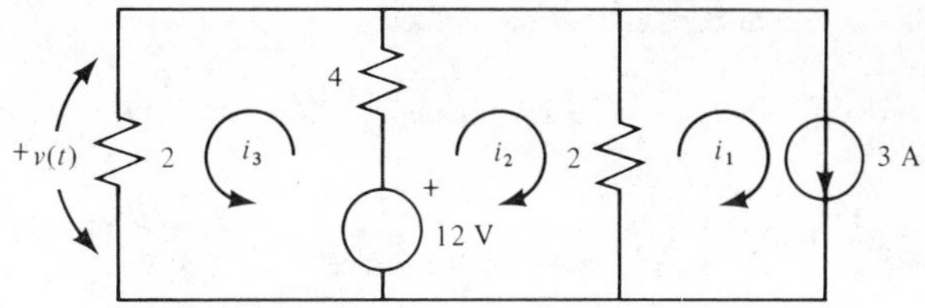

FIGURE 1.14   Problem 1-3.

1-4   In the system

$$x_1 + 2x_2 = b_1$$
$$-4x_1 - 8x_2 = b_2$$

find the relationship between b_1 and b_2 if the system is to be consistent.

1-5   Prove the properties of D_n, as listed in Section 1.2.

1-6   If we know that

$$D_3 = \begin{vmatrix} g & h & i \\ a & b & c \\ d & e & f \end{vmatrix} = -2$$

what is, by inspection, the value of each of the following?

(a) $\begin{vmatrix} a & b & c \\ d & e & f \\ g & h & i \end{vmatrix}$;   (b) $\begin{vmatrix} g & h & i \\ a & b & c \\ 3d & 3e & 3f \end{vmatrix}$;   (c) $\begin{vmatrix} a & b & c \\ g & h & i \\ d & e & f \end{vmatrix}$

(d) $\begin{vmatrix} a & d & g \\ b & e & h \\ c & f & i \end{vmatrix}$;   (e) $\begin{vmatrix} i & h & g \\ c & b & a \\ f & e & d \end{vmatrix}$;   (f) $\begin{vmatrix} i & c & f \\ h & b & e \\ g & a & d \end{vmatrix}$

1-7   By inspection, evaluate each determinant given:

(a) $\begin{vmatrix} -2 & -4 & 7 \\ 0 & 1 & 5 \\ 0 & 0 & -2 \end{vmatrix}$;   (b) $\begin{vmatrix} -1 & 0 & 0 & 0 \\ 7 & -1 & 0 & 0 \\ 4 & 9 & -2 & 0 \\ 16 & 2 & 4 & 6 \end{vmatrix}$;   (c) $\begin{vmatrix} 1 & -2 & 4 \\ 2 & 6 & 0 \\ -4 & 8 & -16 \end{vmatrix}$

1-8   Repeat Problem 1-7 for

(a) $\begin{vmatrix} 8 & 4 & 9 \\ -2 & -1 & 6 \\ 6 & 3 & -5 \end{vmatrix}$;   (b) $\begin{vmatrix} -5 & 14 & 3 \\ 0 & 0 & 2 \\ 0 & 0 & 6 \end{vmatrix}$;   (c) $\begin{vmatrix} 2 & -4 & 0 & 1 \\ 4 & 3 & 0 & -1 \\ -1 & -2 & 0 & 2 \\ 0 & 5 & 0 & 7 \end{vmatrix}$

1-9   In

$$D_3 = \begin{vmatrix} -2 & 3 & -4 \\ -1 & 6 & 2 \\ 1 & -1 & 3 \end{vmatrix}$$

list all the minors and all the cofactors.

1-10 Evaluate each D_3 by expansion about a row or a column of your choice.

(a) $\begin{vmatrix} 4 & 7 & -2 \\ 1 & -5 & 0 \\ 3 & 0 & -2 \end{vmatrix}$; (b) $\begin{vmatrix} 1 & -1 & 0 \\ 2 & 3 & 1 \\ 7 & 10 & -2 \end{vmatrix}$; (c) $\begin{vmatrix} 7 & 5 & -2 & 0 \\ 11 & 0 & 1 & 1 \\ 12 & -1 & 3 & -1 \\ 10 & 0 & 1 & 1 \end{vmatrix}$;

(d) $\begin{vmatrix} 1 & 1 & 2 & 1 & 4 \\ -1 & -1 & 3 & 2 & 0 \\ 2 & 0 & 1 & 1 & 0 \\ 2 & 0 & -1 & -1 & 0 \\ 1 & 1 & 0 & 1 & -1 \end{vmatrix}$

1-11 Reduce each determinant to its diagonal form.

(a) $\begin{vmatrix} 1 & 2 & 2 \\ -1 & 0 & 1 \\ 1 & -1 & 2 \end{vmatrix}$; (b) $\begin{vmatrix} 6 & -3 & 2 \\ 1 & -2 & 1 \\ 3 & -1 & -1 \end{vmatrix}$; (c) $\begin{vmatrix} 2 & -1 & 0 \\ 1 & -2 & 1 \\ 0 & 1 & -3 \end{vmatrix}$

1-12 Use pivotal condensation in Problem 1-10.

1-13 Write a computer program for pivotal condensation. Use Problems 1-10 and 1-11 as numerical verifications.

1-14 Let

$$\mathbf{P} = \begin{bmatrix} 2 & -1 \\ 4 & 7 \end{bmatrix} \qquad \mathbf{Q} = \begin{bmatrix} -1 & 0 \\ 4 & 5 \end{bmatrix}$$

Show that $\mathbf{PQ} \neq \mathbf{QP}$, even though each product exists.

1-15 Prove that a square matrix is singular if any row (or column) is full of zeros.

1-16 Prove that a square matrix is singular if any row (or column) is the sum of two or more rows (or columns).

1-17 Give an example of two (2×2) singular matrices whose sum is not singular.

1-18 Give an example of two (3×3) nonsingular matrices whose sum is singular.

1-19 Let

$$\mathbf{P} = \begin{bmatrix} a & b \\ c & d \end{bmatrix} \qquad \mathbf{Q} = \begin{bmatrix} -b & a \\ -d & c \end{bmatrix}$$

what are the conditions on a, b, c, and d if $\mathbf{PQ} = \mathbf{QP}$?

1-20 In the network shown, write the node equations in matrix form; then, by matrix inversion, solve for the node voltages v_1, v_2, v_3. Do the inversion by (a) the adjoint method, and (b) elementary row operations. Element values are in ohms.

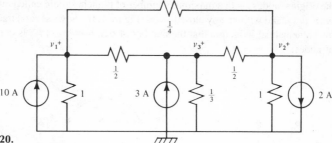

FIGURE 1.15 Problem 1-20.

1-21 Invert each given matrix by (a) the adjoint method, and (b) elementary row operations.

$$A = \begin{bmatrix} 1 & -1 & 0 \\ -1 & 1 & 1 \\ 1 & -1 & 1 \end{bmatrix} \quad B = \begin{bmatrix} 4 & -1 & 2 \\ 0 & 3 & -2 \\ 1 & 6 & 1 \end{bmatrix} \quad C = \begin{bmatrix} 1 & 0 & 1 & 0 \\ -1 & 1 & 0 & 1 \\ 1 & 0 & 1 & 1 \\ -1 & -1 & 1 & 0 \end{bmatrix}$$

1-22 Given that $\mathbf{PQ} = \mathbf{PR}$ and $\mathbf{P}$ is nonsingular, prove that $\mathbf{Q} = \mathbf{R}$. What, if anything, can be stated when $\mathbf{P}$ is singular? Give examples for both cases.

1-23 Give an example where $\mathbf{Q}^{-1}$ and $\mathbf{P}^{-1}$ do not exist individually, yet $(\mathbf{PQ})^{-1}$ exists. See Equation 1.60.

1-24 Prove that $(\mathbf{P}^T)^T = \mathbf{P}$.

1-25 Prove that $(\mathbf{P} + \mathbf{Q})^T = \mathbf{P}^T + \mathbf{Q}^T$.

1-26 Prove that $(\mathbf{PQ})^T = \mathbf{Q}^T\mathbf{P}^T$.

1-27 A *symmetric matrix* is one satisfying the equality $\mathbf{P} = \mathbf{P}^T$. State two basic properties of such a matrix—one related to its size, and the other to its off-diagonal elements.

1-28 A *skew-symmetric matrix* satisfies $\mathbf{P} = -\mathbf{P}^T$. State two basic properties of such a matrix—one related to its size, and the other to its main diagonal elements.

1-29 If $\mathbf{P}$ is a square matrix, prove that (a) $\mathbf{P} + \mathbf{P}^T$ is symmetric, (b) $\mathbf{P} - \mathbf{P}^T$ is skew-symmetric, and (c) $\mathbf{PP}^T$ is symmetric.

1-30 Let $\mathbf{P}$ and $\mathbf{Q}$ be both symmetric matrices. Show that $\mathbf{PQ}$ is symmetric if, and only if, $\mathbf{PQ} = \mathbf{QP}$.

1-31 (a) Prove that every column of the incidence matrix $\mathbf{A}_a$, Equation 1.39, contains exactly one $+1$ and one -1, and the rest of the elements are zeros.
(b) Prove that any row in $\mathbf{A}_a$ is equal to the negative of the sum of the remaining $(n - 1)$ rows. Give a physical (electrical) interpretation.
(c) Since such a row is redundant, we omit it from $\mathbf{A}_a$. The remaining matrix, $\mathbf{A}$, is called the *reduced incidence matrix* and $\mathbf{Ai}_b = \mathbf{0}$ is Kirchhoff's current law at $(n - 1)$ nodes.
(d) What does a row full of zeros mean in $\mathbf{A}_a$? Why is it reasonable to exclude such a case?

1-32 In a graph of a network [such as Figure 1.3(b)] we define a *tree* as a subgraph with all the original nodes, with a maximum number of branches (here called, appropriately enough, *tree branches*), and without any closed loops. Figure 1.16 shows several trees in Figure 1.3(b). Prove by mathematical induction that the number of *tree branches*, b_t, is one less than n, the number of nodes, $b_t = n - 1$.

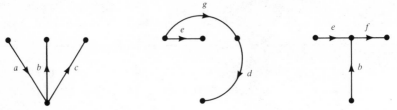

FIGURE 1.16   Problem 1-32: trees of a graph.

1-33   Prove[8] that any $(n - 1) \times (n - 1)$ nonsingular submatrix in **A** corresponds to a tree. (**A** is the reduced incidence matrix, see Problem 1-31.) This property provides a useful way of searching for all the trees in a graph.

1-34   In Example 1.17 let us add the equations for nodes 1 and 2. The result is

$$i_b + i_c - i_d + i_e + i_g = 0$$

which certainly looks like Kirchhoff's current law. It is valid not at a node, but rather for the set of branches (b, c, d, e, g). This set is shown in Figure 1.17. This set, when "cut," will separate

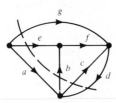

FIGURE 1.17   Problem 1-34.

the graph into two parts. One of these parts can be an isolated node. Such a set is called a *cut-set*, and Kirchhoff's current law holds for every cut-set. Another way to look at it is to recognize that the sum of the currents entering the "cutting plane" (the heavy dotted line) is necessarily equal to the sum of the currents leaving that plane.

(a) List and show other cut-sets for this graph.

(b) Verify that if one of the two parts is an isolated node, the cut-set current equation is the familiar Kirchhoff's current law at that node.

1-35   An alternate way of formulating Kirchhoff's current law (KCL), similar to Equation 1.39, is via the *fundamental cut-sets*. The latter are found as follows:

1. Pick a tree (see Problem 1-32) and identify the tree branches. Identify those branches that do not belong in the tree, called *links*. As an example, let the tree branches be d, e, g, and therefore the links are a, b, c, f, as shown in Figure 1.18(a).

2. "Cut" *one* tree branch and some links to form the first fundamental cut-set. For example, tree branch d and links a, b, c form the first fundamental cut-set. The direction of the tree branch that forms this cut-set is taken to be the positive reference for the currents of the cut-set.

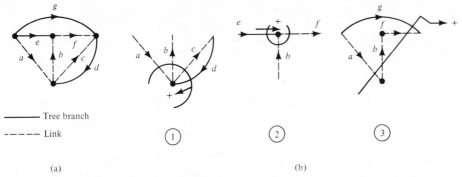

——— Tree branch

– – – – Link

(1)   (2)   (3)

(a)   (b)

FIGURE 1.18   Problem 1-35: (a) tree branches and links and (b) fundamental cut-sets 1, 2, 3.

3. Repeat, with the second tree branch e forming a fundamental cut-set with links b, f.

4. Repeat, with tree branch g forming the last fundamental cut-set with links a, b, f. The fundamental cut-sets are shown in Figure 1.18(b).

(a) Verify that there are $(n - 1)$ fundamental cut-sets.

(b) Write Kirchhoff's current law (KCL) in a matrix form similar to Equation 1.39. More specifically, $\mathbf{Q}_f \mathbf{i}_b = \mathbf{0}$, where $\mathbf{Q}_f$ is the *fundamental cut-set* matrix.

(c) Arrange the matrix $\mathbf{Q}_f$ in partitioned form, as

$$\mathbf{Q}_f = [\mathbf{Q}_{f_{11}} \mid \mathbf{Q}_{f_{12}}]$$

where $\mathbf{Q}_{f_{11}}$ corresponds to the links and $\mathbf{Q}_{f_{12}}$ corresponds to the tree branches. The branch current matrix $\mathbf{i}_b$ must be listed and partitioned accordingly. The ordered columns of $\mathbf{Q}_{f_{12}}$ should correspond to the first tree branch, the second tree branch, etc. Then submatrix $\mathbf{Q}_{f_{12}}$ is a special, simple matrix. Identify it.

(d) Use the relation $\mathbf{Q}_f \mathbf{i}_b = \mathbf{0}$, written in this partitioned form, to express the tree branch currents in terms of the link currents.

(e) Prove that the rank of $\mathbf{Q}_f$ is $(n - 1)$. Hence the $(n - 1)$ fundamental cut-set KCL equations are independent.

1-36   A systematic way to formulate Kirchhoff's voltage law (KVL), similar to Equation 1.40, is via the *fundamental loops*. These are formulated as follows:

1. Pick a tree (see Problem 1-35).

2. Add one link to the tree, thus forming the first fundamental loop consisting of that link and some tree branches. For example, link a forms a fundamental loop with tree branches g and d. The direction of the loop is assigned the same direction as the link that forms it.

3. Repeat, with the second link b forming the second fundamental loop together with tree branches e, g, d. Continue with link c, and, finally, with link f, as shown.

(a) Verify that there are $l = b - n + 1$ links, and hence l fundamental loops.

FIGURE 1.19   Problem 1-36: fundamental loops 1, 2, 3, 4.

(b) Write Kirchhoff's voltage law (KVL) in a matrix form similar to Equation 1.40. More specifically, $\mathbf{B}_f \mathbf{v}_b = \mathbf{0}$, where $\mathbf{B}_f$ is the *fundamental loop matrix*. Verify that $\mathbf{B}_f \subset \mathbf{B}_a$, i.e., $\mathbf{B}_f$ is a submatrix of the loop matrix $\mathbf{B}_a$.

(c) Arrange the matrix $\mathbf{B}_f$ in partitioned form as

$$\mathbf{B}_f = [\mathbf{B}_{f_{11}} \mid \mathbf{B}_{f_{12}}]$$

where $\mathbf{B}_{f_{11}}$ corresponds to the links and $\mathbf{B}_{f_{12}}$ corresponds to the tree branches. Of course, the branch voltage matrix $\mathbf{v}_b$ must be listed and partitioned accordingly. The ordered columns in $\mathbf{B}_{f_{11}}$ should correspond to the first link, second link, etc. Then submatrix $\mathbf{B}_{f_{11}}$ is a special, simple matrix. Identify it.

(d) Use the relation $\mathbf{B}_f \mathbf{v}_b = \mathbf{0}$, written in this partitioned form, to express the link voltages in terms of the tree branch voltages.

(e) Prove that the rank of $\mathbf{B}_f$ is $l = b - n + 1$. Hence, the l fundamental loops of KVL are independent.

1-37   Using matrix partitioning techniques, derive the familiar "wye-delta" (or "star-mesh") transformations as shown (Figure 1.20).

From delta to wye: $R_1' = R_1 R_2/\Sigma$; $R_2' = R_2 R_3/\Sigma$; $R_3' = R_1 R_3/\Sigma$ where
$$\Sigma = R_1 + R_2 + R_3$$

From wye to delta: $R_1 = \Sigma'/R_2'$; $R_2 = \Sigma'/R_3'$; $R_3 = \Sigma'/R_1'$ where
$$\Sigma' = R_1' R_2' + R_2' R_3' + R_3' R_1'$$

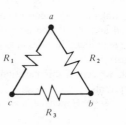
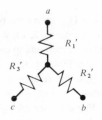

FIGURE 1.20   Problem 1-37.   Delta (Δ)   Wye (Y)

1-38   Consider the system of equations $\mathbf{Ax} = \mathbf{B}$.

(a) Show that it is equivalent to the homogeneous system

$$[\mathbf{A} \mid \mathbf{B}]\begin{bmatrix} \mathbf{x} \\ \hline x_{n+1} \end{bmatrix} = \mathbf{0}$$

where the additional unknown x_{n+1} is restricted to have the value of -1.

(b) Discuss in detail the solution of this homogeneous system. Your conclusions should agree with those in Section 1.9.

1-39   Give a geometrical interpretation, similar to Figure 1.2, for each of the following systems.

(a) $\begin{bmatrix} 1 & 2 \\ -1 & 1 \\ 4 & -3 \end{bmatrix}\begin{bmatrix} x_1 \\ x_2 \end{bmatrix} = \begin{bmatrix} 3 \\ 0 \\ 1 \end{bmatrix}$;   (b) $\begin{bmatrix} 1 & 2 \\ -1 & 1 \\ 4 & -3 \end{bmatrix}\begin{bmatrix} x_1 \\ x_2 \end{bmatrix} = \begin{bmatrix} 3 \\ 0 \\ 2 \end{bmatrix}$

1-40   The Gauss-Siedel method, one of the many iterative methods for solving $\mathbf{Ax} = \mathbf{B}$, is outlined in the following steps.

(a) Rearrange the equations and relabel the unknowns so that the main diagonal of **A** contains the largest terms, i.e.,

$$|a_{ii}| > |a_{ik}| \qquad k = 1, 2, \ldots$$

(b) Guess an initial arbitrary solution, say, $x_1^{(0)}, x_2^{(0)}, \ldots, x_n^{(0)}$.

(c) Use the first equation to iterate for the next value of x_1, $x_1^{(1)}$, i.e., solve for $x_1^{(1)}$ from

$$a_{11}x_1^{(1)} + a_{12}x_2^{(0)} + a_{13}x_3^{(0)} + \cdots = b_1$$

(d) Use $x_1^{(1)}$ and $x_3^{(0)}, x_4^{(0)}, \ldots$, in the second equation to iterate for $x_2^{(1)}$.

(e) Use $x_1^{(1)}, x_2^{(1)}, x_4^{(0)}, \ldots$, in the third equation to iterate for $x_3^{(1)}$.

(f) Continue, thus obtaining the first approximate solution $\mathbf{x}^{(1)}$.

(g) Repeat steps (c), (d), (e), and (f) to obtain the next approximation $\mathbf{x}^{(2)}$, etc. The sequence $\mathbf{x}^{(k)}$ converges to the exact solution if

$$\max_{k} \sum_{\substack{k=1 \\ i \neq k}}^{n} \left| \frac{a_{ik}}{a_{ii}} \right| < 1$$

for all i. Try this method on

$$
\begin{array}{rcl}
3x_1 + x_2 - x_3 &=& 5 \\
x_1 + 4x_2 + 2x_3 &=& 3 \\
2x_1 + x_2 - 3x_3 &=& 2
\end{array}
$$

and compare with the exact solution.

1-41   The method of *finite differences* provides a numerical approximate solution to an ordinary or a partial differential equation. That equation is replaced by a set of algebraic equations **Ax = B**, which, when solved, yields the approximate solution at a discrete number of points in the region. Consider, for example, a two-dimensional potential distribution inside a rectangular enclosure, as shown in Figure 1.21. Three sides are at zero potential, while the fourth one is at

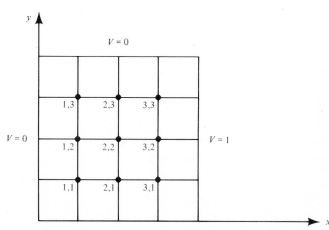

FIGURE 1.21   Problem 1-41.

$V \neq 0$ (say, $V = 1$ here). At every point inside the rectangle, the potential obeys Laplace's equation,

$$\frac{\partial^2 V}{\partial x^2} + \frac{\partial^2 V}{\partial y^2} = 0$$

We divide the interior into a grid of points (nine interior points in our example), conveniently labeled by their index (i,j). Then we write the potential $V_{i,j}$ as the average of its four surrounding potentials, for example,

$$V_{3,2} = \tfrac{1}{4}(1 + V_{3,3} + V_{2,2} + V_{3,1})$$

Obtain the remaining eight equations. Solve the resulting system of equations.

1-42   The result $\langle \mathbf{v}, \mathbf{i} \rangle = 0$, obtained in Examples 1.39 and 1.40, can be generalized in the following way. Let N and $\hat{N}$ be two networks with the same graphs. Let $\mathbf{v}$ be the column vector of branch voltages in network N, unrestricted except by Kirchhoff's voltage law. Let $\mathbf{i}$ be the column vector of branch currents in N, unrestricted except by Kirchhoff's current law. Let $\hat{\mathbf{v}}$ and $\hat{\mathbf{i}}$ be, similarly, in network $\hat{N}$. Then

$$\langle \mathbf{v}, \hat{\mathbf{i}} \rangle = \langle \hat{\mathbf{v}}, \mathbf{i} \rangle$$

This result is known as *Tellegen's theorem*. Verify it for the two networks whose graph is shown (Figure 1.22), with branches identified as follows:

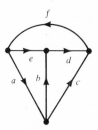

FIGURE 1.22   Problem 1-42.

Network N: Branch a is a voltage source $v_a(t) = 10$ volts; all other branches are 1-ohm resistors.

Network $\hat{N}$: Branch a is a sinusoidal voltage source, $\bar{V}_a = 10\angle 0°$. The other branches have the following sinusoidal impedances:

$$\bar{Z}_b = 1 + j1; \quad \bar{Z}_c = 1 - j1; \quad \bar{Z}_d = 1 + j0; \quad \bar{Z}_e = \bar{Z}_c; \quad \bar{Z}_f = \bar{Z}_b$$

1-43   Using the definitions of length of a vector and the scalar product, prove
(a) $\|\mathbf{u} + \mathbf{v}\| \leq \|\mathbf{u}\| + \|\mathbf{v}\|$
(b) $|\langle \mathbf{u}, \mathbf{v} \rangle| \leq \|\mathbf{u}\| \cdot \|\mathbf{v}\|$
and illustrate geometrically in a two-dimensional space.

1-44   Show the geometry of the scalar product of two real vectors $\langle \mathbf{u}, \mathbf{v} \rangle$ in a two-dimensional space. Also prove that the angle θ between these two vectors is given by

$$\cos \theta = \frac{\langle \mathbf{u}, \mathbf{v} \rangle}{\|\mathbf{u}\| \cdot \|\mathbf{v}\|}$$

1-45   Given a set of r linearly independent vectors, $\mathbf{u}_1, \ldots, \mathbf{u}_r$, we wish to find an *orthogonal* set of vectors $\mathbf{v}_1, \ldots, \mathbf{v}_r$ in the same space, in terms of the $\mathbf{u}$'s. Specifically, consider a three-dimensional space: Without loss of generality, we can choose $\mathbf{v}_1 = \mathbf{u}_1$. Next, let $\mathbf{v}_2 = \mathbf{u}_2 - \alpha_1 \mathbf{v}_1$ and we choose α_1 so that $\mathbf{v}_2$ is orthogonal to $\mathbf{v}_1$, namely,

$$\langle \mathbf{v}_2, \mathbf{v}_1 \rangle = \langle (\mathbf{u}_2 - \alpha_1 \mathbf{v}_1), \mathbf{v}_1 \rangle = 0$$

This equation yields the desired value for α_1 and, with it, we have $\mathbf{v}_2$. Next, let $\mathbf{v}_3 = \mathbf{u}_3 - \alpha_2 \mathbf{v}_2 - \alpha_3 \mathbf{v}_1$ where α_2 and α_3 are chosen so that $\mathbf{v}_3$ is orthogonal to $\mathbf{v}_1$ and to $\mathbf{v}_2$, so that we have

$$\langle \mathbf{v}_3, \mathbf{v}_1 \rangle = \langle (\mathbf{u}_3 - \alpha_2 \mathbf{v}_2 - \alpha_3 \mathbf{v}_1), \mathbf{v}_1 \rangle = 0$$

$$\langle \mathbf{v}_3, \mathbf{v}_2 \rangle = \langle (\mathbf{u}_3 - \alpha_2 \mathbf{v}_2 - \alpha_3 \mathbf{v}_1), \mathbf{v}_2 \rangle = 0$$

These two equations yield the values for α_2 and α_3, and consequently we have $\mathbf{v}_3$.
(a) Illustrate this method for

$$\mathbf{u}_1 = \begin{bmatrix} 1 \\ 1 \\ 1 \end{bmatrix} \qquad \mathbf{u}_2 = \begin{bmatrix} 2 \\ 0 \\ -1 \end{bmatrix} \qquad \mathbf{u}_3 = \begin{bmatrix} 0 \\ 2 \\ 0 \end{bmatrix}$$

and sketch the set $\mathbf{u}$ and the orthogonal set $\mathbf{v}$. Normalize the set $\mathbf{v}$ by dividing each vector by its norm.
(b) Generalize this procedure for a set of n vectors ($n > 3$).

1-46 Find the characteristic equation and the characteristic values of

(a) $\mathbf{A} = \begin{bmatrix} 2 & 1 & 1 \\ -2 & 1 & 3 \\ 3 & 1 & -1 \end{bmatrix}$ (b) $\mathbf{A} = \begin{bmatrix} 6 & -2 & 2 \\ 4 & 0 & 2 \\ 2 & -2 & 4 \end{bmatrix}$ (c) $\mathbf{A} = \begin{bmatrix} -1 & 1 \\ 1 & -2 \end{bmatrix}$

1-47 Prove that β_1 in the characteristic equation of $\mathbf{A}$, Equation 1.102, is equal to the sum of the characteristic values

$$\beta_1 = \sum_{i=1}^{n} \lambda_i$$

and also $\beta_1 = -\text{Tr}(\mathbf{A})$, where $\text{Tr}(\mathbf{A})$ is the *trace* of $\mathbf{A}$, given by the sum of the main diagonal

$$\text{Tr}(\mathbf{A}) = \Sigma a_{jj}$$

1-48 Prove that β_n in the characteristic equation of $\mathbf{A}$, Equation 1.102, is related to the characteristic values and to $\mathbf{A}$ as follows:

$$(-1)^n \beta_n = \lambda_1 \lambda_2 \ldots \lambda_n = \det \mathbf{A}$$

1-49 Consider a homogeneous system of n equations with n unknowns

$$\mathbf{Ax} = \mathbf{0}$$

If it is known that rank $\mathbf{A} = n - 1$, prove that every unknown x_p is proportional to the cofactor of its coefficients in any row of $\mathbf{A}$, that is,

$$x_p = k A_{mp} \qquad \begin{aligned} p &= 1,2, \ldots, n \\ m &= 1,2, \ldots, n \end{aligned}$$

where A_{mp} is the cofactor. As an illustration, use the results of Example 1.52.

1-50 Let $\mathbf{A}$ be real and symmetric ($a_{ij} = a_{ji}$). Prove that if λ_1 and λ_2 are two distinct characteristic values ($\lambda_1 \neq \lambda_2$), then the corresponding characteristic vectors are orthogonal, i.e., $\langle \mathbf{x}_1, \mathbf{x}_2 \rangle = 0$.

Hint   Set up the two defining equations for x_1 and x_2, then manipulate each equation to have $\lambda_1 x_1^T x_2$ and $\lambda_2 x_1^T x_2$, respectively, on each side. Subtract the equations.

1-51   Prove that if **A** is real and symmetric, its characteristic values are real.
Hint   Prove by contradiction.

1-52   A matrix is *Hermitian* if $\mathbf{A} = \mathbf{A}^{*T}$. Prove that the characteristic values of a Hermitian matrix are real, and that the characteristic vectors are orthogonal.

1-53   Having found the n distinct characteristic values and characteristic vectors of **A**, we know that $\mathbf{A}\mathbf{x}_1 = \lambda_1 \mathbf{x}_1$, $\mathbf{A}\mathbf{x}_2 = \lambda_2 \mathbf{x}_2$, . . . , $\mathbf{A}\mathbf{x}_n = \lambda_n \mathbf{x}_n$. These can be written compactly as

$$\mathbf{AM} = \mathbf{M\Lambda}$$

where **M** is the *modal matrix*, with $\mathbf{x}_1, \mathbf{x}_2, \ldots \mathbf{x}_n$ as its columns. The matrix $\mathbf{\Lambda}$ is diagonal, with the λ's on its diagonal. Since **M** is nonsingular (why?), we can write

$$\mathbf{\Lambda} = \mathbf{M}^{-1} \mathbf{AM}$$

This process, known as a *similarity transformation* of **A**, diagonalizes this matrix. Illustrate with

$$\mathbf{A} = \begin{bmatrix} -2 & -1 \\ 2 & -5 \end{bmatrix}$$

1-54   An iterative method for the solution of the matrix differential equation $\dot{\mathbf{x}} = \mathbf{Ax}$ is illustrated by considering the scalar case:

$$dx/dt = ax, \qquad a = \text{constant}$$

with the initial condition $x(t_0)$ given. Integrate this equation between t_0 and t:

$$x(t) = x(t_0) + a \int_{t_0}^{t} x(\sigma) d\sigma$$

Then substitute for the integrand the entire expression for x as given by this equation. Continue, with the resulting "nested" integrations carried out. Show that the result converges to the closed-form solution $x(t) = e^{at} x(t_0)$.

SELECTED BIBLIOGRAPHY

1.   J. Agnew and R. C. Knapp, *Linear Algebra with Applications*. Monterey, Calif.: Brooks/Cole Publishing Co., 1978.

2.   B. Carnahan, H. A. Luther, and J. O. Wilkes, *Applied Numerical Methods*. New York: John Wiley & Sons, Inc., 1969.

3.   S. P. Chan, *Introductory Topological Analysis of Electrical Networks*. New York: Holt, Rinehart & Winston, Inc., 1969.

4.   J. de Pillis, *Linear Algebra*. New York: Holt, Rinehart & Winston, Inc., 1969.

5.   G. E. Forsythe and C. B. Moler, *Computer Solution of Linear Algebraic Systems*. Englewood Cliffs, N.J.: Prentice-Hall, Inc., 1967.

6. A. Graham, *Matrix Theory and Applications for Engineers and Mathematicians*. New York: Halsted Press (John Wiley & Sons), 1979.

7. S. Karni, *Network Theory: Analysis and Synthesis*. Boston: Allyn & Bacon, Inc., 1966.

8. S. Seshu and M. B. Reed, *Linear Graphs and Electrical Networks*. Reading, Mass.: Addison-Wesley Publishing Co., Inc., 1961.

CHAPTER 2

Complex

Variables

and

Contour

Integration

2.1 INTRODUCTION

In studying the properties of real variables x, y, z there is no real quantity x such that $x^2 < 0$; similarly, there is no circle of radius ρ such that $x^2 + y^2 = \rho^2 < 0$; finally, there is no sphere of radius r such that $x^2 + y^2 + z^2 = r^2 < 0$. In short, when studying real variables we define the square of a real variable as a positive quantity.

The extension to the case where there exists a quantity

$$j^2 = -1 \tag{2.1}$$

requires the definition of the imaginary unit $j \equiv \sqrt{-1}$ so that $(\pm j)^2 = -1$. The imaginary quantity $j = \sqrt{-1}$ then satisfies the series of identities: $j^2 = -1, j^3 = -j,$ $j^4 = +1$, etc. In general,

$$\begin{aligned} j^{2n} &= (-1)^n \\ j^{2n+1} &= (-1)^n j \end{aligned} \tag{2.2}$$

for n an integer ≥ 0.

2.2 ARITHMETIC OPERATIONS

With $j = \sqrt{-1}$, a complex variable z is defined as

$$z = x + jy \tag{2.3}$$

where x, y are real. Equation 2.3 is the *rectangular form* of z. Note that $z = 0$ if, and only if, $x = y = 0$.

Frequently we write $\text{Re}(z) = x$ (read "the real part of z is equal to x") and $\text{Im}(z) = y$ (read "the imaginary part of z is equal to y"). By writing

$$x = r \cos \theta$$

and   (2.4)

$$y = r \sin \theta$$

Equation 2.3 becomes

$$z = r(\cos \theta + j \sin \theta) \tag{2.5}$$

By virtue of Euler's formula, $e^{j\theta} = \cos \theta + j \sin \theta$, Equation 2.5 is written as

$$z = re^{j\theta} \tag{2.6a}$$

or, in notation common in engineering,

$$z = r\underline{/\theta} \tag{2.6b}$$

The expression in Equation 2.6a is known as the *exponential form* of z, while that of Equation 2.6b is the *polar form*. According to Equation 2.4 we have $x^2 + y^2 = r^2$ and $\tan \theta = y/x$. The quantity r is the *modulus* (or *magnitude*) of z and θ is its *argument*.

Figure 2.1 shows the relationships among the variables x,y on the one hand and r,θ on the other.

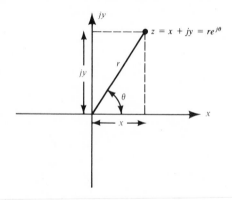

FIGURE 2.1   Rectangular and polar representation of the quantity $z = x + jy = re^{j\theta}$.

Example 2.1   If $r = 1$, so that $z = e^{j\theta}$, some interesting identities result. For $\theta = \pi/2$, we get

$$e^{j\pi/2} = \cos \frac{\pi}{2} + j \sin \frac{\pi}{2}$$

which reduces to

$$e^{j\pi/2} \equiv j$$

while for $\theta = \pi$,

$$e^{j\pi} \equiv -1$$

For $\theta = 2n\pi$ and n any integer,

$$e^{2n\pi j} \equiv 1 \qquad \blacksquare$$

For a fixed x_1,y_1, the quantity $z_1 = x_1 + jy_1$ is a point in the complex plane; in such a case, $z_1 = x_1 + jy_1$ is called a complex number. If $z_1 = z_2 = x_2 + jy_2$, then $x_1 = x_2$ and $y_1 = y_2$.

The arithmetic operations of addition, subtraction, multiplication, and division are now discussed. For two complex numbers z_1, z_2 the sum or difference of z_1 and z_2 is given by

$$z_1 \pm z_2 = x_1 \pm x_2 + j(y_1 \pm y_2) \tag{2.7}$$

Thus the sum or difference of two complex numbers is itself a complex number.

In rectangular representation, the product of two complex numbers z_1, z_2 is given by

$$z_1 z_2 = (x_1 + jy_1)(x_2 + jy_2)$$

which becomes

$$z_1 z_2 = x_1 x_2 - y_1 y_2 + j(y_1 x_2 + y_2 x_1)$$

Thus the product of two complex numbers is complex.

Example 2.2   Let $z_1 = 4 + j3$, $z_2 = 1 - j$. Here,

$$\mathrm{Re}(z_1) = 4, \quad \mathrm{Im}(z_1) = 3$$
$$\mathrm{Re}(z_2) = 1, \quad \mathrm{Im}(z_2) = -1$$

In polar form we have

$$z_1 = \sqrt{4^2 + 3^2}\, e^{j\theta_1}$$

where

$$\sqrt{4^2 + 3^2} = r_1$$

and $\theta_1 = \tan^{-1}(3/4)$. Hence $z_1 = 5e^{j\theta_1}$. Similarly,

$$r_2 = \sqrt{1^2 + (-1)^2} = \sqrt{2}, \quad \theta_2 = \tan^{-1}(-1/1) = -\pi/4$$

and

$$z_2 = \sqrt{2}\, e^{-j\pi/4}$$

If z_3 represents the sum of z_1 and z_2, then $z_3 = (4 + 1) + j(3 - 1) = 5 + j2$. The product of z_1 and z_2 is $z_4 = (4 + j3)(1 - j) = 7 - j$.   ∎

Before we proceed to a discussion of the quotient of two complex numbers, a few definitions are given. The *complex conjugate* of the quantity $z = x + jy$ is given by

$$z^* = x - jy \tag{2.9}$$

Then, by the rule for multiplication, we get

$$zz^* = (x + jy)(x - jy) = x^2 + y^2 \tag{2.10}$$

But $x^2 + y^2 = r^2$, so that

$$zz^* = r^2 \tag{2.11a}$$

The *absolute value* of the complex variable z, denoted by $|z|$, is defined as

$$|z| = +\sqrt{zz^*} = r \qquad (2.11b)$$

It is now possible to discuss the quotient of two complex numbers $z_1 = x_1 + jy_1$ and $z_2 = x_2 + jy_2$. Letting the quotient be denoted by z_3, we have, for $z_2 \neq 0$,

$$z_3 = \frac{z_1}{z_2} = \frac{x_1 + jy_1}{x_2 + jy_2} \qquad (2.12)$$

Multiplying numerator and denominator by z_2^* produces a real number in the denominator, and then

$$z_3 = \frac{x_1 x_2 + y_1 y_2 + j(y_1 x_2 - y_2 x_1)}{x_2^2 + y_2^2} \qquad (2.13)$$

Again, it is seen that the quotient z_3 is complex in general.

In many applications use of the exponential or polar representations of complex variables is preferable because of the ease of calculation. Consider multiplication first and let $z_1 = r_1 e^{j\theta_1}$ and $z_2 = r_2 e^{j\theta_2}$. Then

$$z_1 z_2 = r_1 r_2 e^{j(\theta_1 + \theta_2)} \qquad (2.14)$$

In general, the product of the n complex numbers $z_1, z_2, \ldots, z_n$ is given by

$$z_1 z_2 \cdots z_n = r_1 r_2 \cdots r_n e^{j\psi} \qquad (2.15)$$

where $\psi = \theta_1 + \theta_2 + \cdots + \theta_n$. It is seen that the product of complex numbers $z_1, z_2,$ $\ldots z_n$ is identically zero if any one of the r_i ($i = 1, \ldots, n$) is zero, i.e., if $x_i^2 + y_i^2 \equiv 0$. Since x_i, y_i are real, the product is zero if, and only if, one of the $z_i \equiv 0$.

The quotient of two complex numbers, in the same representation, is, for $z_2 = r_2 e^{j\theta_2} = r_2 \underline{/\theta_2} \neq 0$,

$$z_3 = \frac{z_1}{z_2} = \frac{r_1}{r_2} e^{j(\theta_1 - \theta_2)} = r_3 \underline{/\theta_1 - \theta_2} \qquad (2.16)$$

The polar representation is of particular use in finding the value of a quantity such as z^n. We have

$$z^n = r^n e^{jn\theta} \qquad (2.17)$$

From this we get

$$\mathrm{Re}(z^n) = r^n \cos n\theta$$

and $\qquad\qquad\qquad\qquad\qquad\qquad\qquad\qquad\qquad\qquad\qquad\qquad (2.18)$

$$\mathrm{Im}(z^n) = r^n \sin n\theta$$

Calculations in the rectangular form leading to equations analogous to Equation 2.18 are tedious for n large. The use of a polar representation is then preferable.

Example 2.3 In the op-amp circuit show in Figure 2.2, find the sinusoidal gain

$$G = E_{\mathrm{out}}(j\omega)/E_{\mathrm{in}}(j\omega)$$

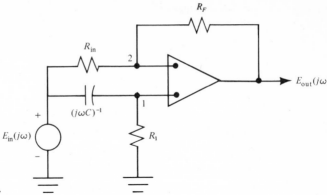

FIGURE 2.2 Example 2.3.

As a result of a voltage divider, we have

$$V_1 = \left[\frac{E_{in}(j\omega)}{\dfrac{1}{j\omega C} + R_1} \right] R_1$$

Also, Kirchoff's current law at node 2 is, with $V_2 = V_1$,

$$\frac{V_1 - E_{in}}{R_{in}} + \frac{V_1 - E_{out}}{R_F} = 0$$

By combining these two equations we get

$$G = \frac{-R_F + j\omega C R_1 R_{in}}{R_{in} + j\omega C R_1 R_{in}}$$

If we let $R = R_1 = R_{in} = R_F$, then

$$G = \frac{-1 + j\omega RC}{1 + j\omega RC} = \frac{\sqrt{1 + \omega^2 R^2 C^2}\, e^{j\,\tan^{-1}/(-\omega RC)}}{\sqrt{1 + \omega^2 R^2 C^2}\, e^{j\,\tan^{-1}/(\omega RC)}} = e^{-2j\,\tan^{-1}/(\omega RC)}$$

or

$$G = 1 \; \underline{/-2\,\tan^{-1}(\omega RC)}$$

i.e., in magnitude $E_{out} = E_{in}$ but there is a phase shift between the two voltages,

$$E_{out}(j\omega) = E_{in}(j\omega) \underline{/-2\,\tan^{-1}/(\omega RC)} \qquad\blacksquare$$

For finding fractional powers of z, such as $z^{1/n}$, with n an integer, the polar representation is useful. Let, once again,

$$z = re^{j\theta} \tag{2.19a}$$

Noting that $e^{2\pi jp} \equiv 1$ for any integer p, we also have, then,

$$z = re^{j\theta}e^{2\pi jp} \tag{2.19b}$$

Therefore, $z^{1/n}$ is readily formed as

$$z^{1/n} = r^{1/n}e^{j(\theta + 2\pi p)/n} \tag{2.20}$$

Example 2.4   Find the cube roots of j.
   Solution: Since

$$j = e^{j\pi/2}e^{2\pi jp} \quad (p \text{ an integer})$$
$$j^{1/3} = e^{j\pi/6}e^{2\pi jp/3}$$

For $p = 0$ the first root is

$$j_1 = e^{j\pi/6}$$

For $p = 1,2$ the two additional roots are

$$j_2 = e^{j\pi/6}e^{2\pi j/3} = e^{5j\pi/6}$$

and

$$j_3 = e^{j\pi/6}e^{4\pi j/3} = e^{3\pi j/2}$$

The roots are shown in Figure 2.3.

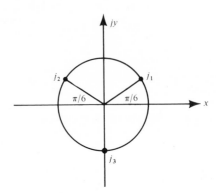

FIGURE 2.3   The three cube roots of j.

Note that if we try to use the next integer value for p, $p = 3$, we get back to j_1. In other words, there are only three solutions here. ∎

Example 2.5   Find the square roots of $z = (3 + j4)$. Here we write

$$z^{1/2} = (3 + j4)^{1/2} = 5^{1/2}e^{j\theta/2}e^{p\pi j}$$

with

$$\theta = \tan^{-1}\frac{4}{3} \approx 53.1°$$

For $p = 0$ the first square root is

$$(3 + j4)_1^{1/2} = 5^{1/2}e^{j\theta/2}$$

For $p = 1$ the second square root is

$$(3 + j4)_2^{1/2} = 5^{1/2}e^{j(\theta/2 + \pi)}$$

Here the roots are separated by π radians or 180 degrees, as shown in Figure 2.4. ∎

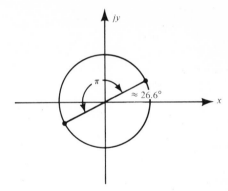

FIGURE 2.4 The square roots of $z = 3 + j4$.

2.3 FUNCTIONS OF A COMPLEX VARIABLE

A function $f(z)$ of the complex variable $z = x + jy$ is given, generally, as the sum

$$f(z) = f(x + jy) = u(x,y) + jv(x,y) \tag{2.21}$$

where both $u(x,y)$ and $v(x,y)$ are real. Conditions that make $f(z)$ continuous* at some point $z = z_0 = x_0 + jy_0$ are that *both* $u(x_0,y_0)$ and $v(x_0,y_0)$ be continuous at the point (x_0,y_0).

Example 2.6   Find $u(x,y)$, $v(x,y)$ if $f(z) = e^{\pm z}$. We write

$$e^{\pm z} = e^{\pm (x+jy)} = e^{\pm x}(\cos y \pm j \sin y)$$

Thus,

$$u(x,y) = e^{\pm x} \cos y$$

and

$$v(x,y) = \pm e^{\pm x} \sin y \qquad\blacksquare$$

Example 2.7   Find $u(x,y)$, $v(x,y)$ if $f(z) = \sin z$. Since $\sin z = \sin (x + jy)$, we have, from the trigonometric identity for the sine of the sum of two angles,

$$\sin (x + jy) = \sin x \cos (jy) + \cos x \sin (jy)$$

But $\cos jy = \cosh y$ and $\sin (jy) = j \sinh y$, so that

$$\sin z = \sin x \cosh y + j \cos x \sinh y$$

Consequently,

$$u(x,y) = \sin x \cosh y$$

---

* It is assumed that the reader knows the definition of continuity at a point for functions of one (or more) *real* variables.

and

$$v(x,y) = \cos x \sinh y$$ ∎

Example 2.8 Find $u(x,y)$ and $v(x,y)$ if $f(z) = \ln z$, where "ln" is the natural logarithm. In this case, it is preferable to write $z = re^{j\theta}$. Then

$$\ln z = \ln (re^{j\theta}) = \ln r + j\theta$$

Thus, since $r = \sqrt{x^2 + y^2}$ and $\theta = \tan^{-1}(y/x)$,

$$u(x,y) = \tfrac{1}{2} \ln (x^2 + y^2)$$

and

$$v(x,y) = \tan^{-1}\left(\frac{y}{x}\right)$$

Note: Since $2n\pi$ $(n = \pm 1, \pm 2, \ldots)$ can be added to θ without affecting z, then

$$\ln z = \ln r + j(\theta \pm 2n\pi)$$

and $\ln z$ is a *multiple-valued* function. Such functions will be discussed later. ∎

2.4 DERIVATIVES OF A COMPLEX FUNCTION

With $f(z) = u(x,y) + jv(x,y)$, let us consider the derivative of $f(z)$ at some point z_0 in the complex plane. The first derivative of $f(z)$ at $z = z_0$ is defined by

$$\frac{df}{dz} = \lim_{\Delta z \to 0} \frac{f(z_0 + \Delta z) - f(z_0)}{\Delta z} \tag{2.22}$$

The problem of the uniqueness of this derivative is in determining the manner in which $\Delta z = \Delta x + j\Delta y$ approaches zero. Geometrically, it is clear that there is an infinite number of paths in the complex plane by means of which Δz may approach zero. See Figure 2.5. Regardless of any path chosen, we want the expression df/dz to be unique.

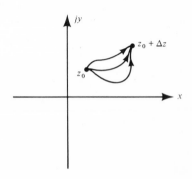

FIGURE 2.5 Paths of Δz.

Now, since $f(z) = u(x,y) + jv(x,y)$, we have

$$\lim_{\Delta z \to 0} \frac{f(z_0 + \Delta z) - f(z_0)}{\Delta z} =$$

$$= \lim_{\substack{\Delta x \to 0 \\ \Delta y \to 0}} \frac{u(x_0 + \Delta x, y_0 + \Delta y) + jv(x_0 + \Delta x, y_0 + \Delta y) - u(x_0, y_0) - jv(x_0, y_0)}{\Delta x + j\Delta y} \tag{2.23}$$

In general, there will be some slope at which $\Delta z \to 0$, for which we can write $\Delta y = m\Delta x$, with m the slope of the line. Thus, in order to find conditions under which df/dz is unique, it is sufficient to consider two cases: first, when $\Delta y \equiv 0$, and then when $\Delta x \equiv 0$. In the first case,

$$\frac{df}{dz} = \lim_{\Delta x \to 0} \frac{u(x_0 + \Delta x, y_0) + jv(x_0 + \Delta x, y_0) - u(x_0, y_0) - jv(x_0, y_0)}{\Delta x} \tag{2.24}$$

Expanding $u(x_0 + \Delta x, y_0)$ in a Taylor series about x_0, we get

$$u(x_0 + \Delta x, y_0) = u(x_0, y_0) + \frac{\partial u}{\partial x} \Delta x + \cdots$$

while the expression for $v(x_0 + \Delta x, y_0)$ is

$$v(x_0 + \Delta x, y_0) = v(x_0, y_0) + \frac{\partial v}{\partial x} \Delta x + \cdots$$

Then

$$\frac{df}{dz} = \lim_{\Delta x \to 0} \frac{\dfrac{\partial u}{\partial x} \Delta x + j\dfrac{\partial v}{\partial x} \Delta x}{\Delta x}$$

becomes

$$\frac{df}{dx} = \frac{\partial u}{\partial x} + j\frac{\partial v}{\partial x} \tag{2.25}$$

In the second case, with $\Delta x \equiv 0$, $\Delta z = j\Delta y$ and

$$\frac{df}{dz} = \lim_{\Delta y \to 0} \frac{u(x_0, y_0 + \Delta y) + jv(x_0, y_0 + \Delta y) - u(x_0 y_0) - jv(x_0, y_0)}{j\Delta y}$$

becomes, in a similar way,

$$\frac{df}{dz} = \lim_{\Delta y \to 0} \left(j\frac{\partial v}{\partial y} + \frac{\partial u}{\partial y} \right) \frac{\Delta y}{j\Delta y}$$

or

$$\frac{df}{dz} = -j\frac{\partial u}{\partial y} + \frac{\partial v}{\partial y} \tag{2.26}$$

There are now two expressions, given by Equations 2.25 and 2.26, for the derivative df/dz. Equating their real and imaginary parts, we get the *Cauchy-Riemann conditions* for the existence of a unique derivative of $f(z)$. These are

$$\frac{\partial u}{\partial x} = \frac{\partial v}{\partial y} \quad \text{and} \quad \frac{\partial v}{\partial x} = -\frac{\partial u}{\partial y} \tag{2.27}$$

We say that if a function $f(z) = u(x,y) + jv(x,y)$ satisfies the Cauchy-Riemann conditions at some point $z = z_0$, then $f(z)$ has a unique derivative at z_0. It is an *analytic function* at z_0. Thus the Cauchy-Riemann conditions are necessary for the analyticity of $f(z)$. They are also sufficient, provided that the partial derivatives in Equation 2.27 are continuous at the point (x_0,y_0).

Example 2.9 Given $f(z) = \sin z$, is $f(z)$ analytic at all points of the complex plane? Since $\sin z = \sin x \cosh y + j \cos x \sinh y$, as in Example 2.7, we identify

$$u(x,y) = \sin x \cosh y, \quad \text{and} \quad v(x,y) = \cos x \sinh y$$

To test for analyticity, we find

$$\frac{\partial u}{\partial x} = \cos x \cosh y \qquad \frac{\partial v}{\partial y} = \cos x \cosh y$$

$$\frac{\partial v}{\partial x} = -\sin x \sinh y \qquad \frac{\partial u}{\partial y} = \sin x \sinh y$$

Therefore, the Cauchy-Riemann conditions are satisfied at every finite point in a z-plane where these partial derivatives are defined. ∎

Example 2.10 Given $f(z) = e^{-z}$, is $f(z)$ analytic at all points of the complex plane? Since $e^{-z} = e^{-(x+jy)} = e^{-x}(\cos y - j \sin y)$, we identify

$$u(x,y) = e^{-x} \cos y \quad \text{and} \quad v(x,y) = -e^{-x} \sin y$$

Thus,

$$\frac{\partial u}{\partial x} = -e^{-x} \cos y = \frac{\partial v}{\partial y}$$

and

$$\frac{\partial u}{\partial y} = -e^{-x} \sin y = -\frac{\partial v}{\partial x}$$

Again, the Cauchy-Riemann conditions are satisfied at all points in the complex plane for which $|z|$ is finite. ∎

Example 2.11 Given $f(z) = \ln z$ as in Example 2.8, is $f(z)$ analytic? With

$$u(x,y) = \tfrac{1}{2} \ln (x^2 + y^2)$$

and

$$v(x,y) = \tan^{-1} \left(\frac{y}{x}\right) + 2n\pi$$

we compute the partial derivatives:

$$\frac{\partial u}{\partial x} = \frac{\partial v}{\partial y} = \frac{x}{x^2 + y^2} = \frac{\cos \theta}{r}$$

and

$$\frac{\partial u}{\partial y} = -\frac{\partial v}{\partial x} = \frac{y}{x^2 + y^2} = \frac{\sin \theta}{r}$$

Thus the Cauchy-Riemann conditions are satisfied at all finite points other than $r = 0$ ($x = y = 0$). The origin $x = y = 0$ is called a *singular point* for $f(z) = \ln z$. ∎

A point in the z-plane at which $f(z)$ is not analytic is called a *singular point* (or a *singularity*) of $f(z)$. There are several types of singularities. We say that $f(z)$ has an *isolated* singularity at $z = z_0$ if in the neighborhood of $z = z_0$, no matter how small, there are no other singularities. In other words, $f(z)$ is analytic throughout the neighborhood of $z = z_0$ except at $z = z_0$.

The function $f(z)$ has a *pole of order n* at $z = z_0$ (also called a *removable singularity*) if $(z - z_0)^n f(z)$ is analytic at z_0. If no integer n can be found, then $z = z_0$ is an *essential* singularity.

Example 2.12

$$f(z) = \frac{z - 2}{z^2(z + 1)}$$

has isolated singularities at $z = 0$ and at $z = -1$. The singularity at $z = 0$ is a pole of order 2, and the singularity at $z = -1$ is a pole of order 1 (a *simple* pole). ∎

Example 2.13 The function $f(z) = z^{p-1}$, $0 < p < 1$ has an essential singularity at $z = 0$, while the function $f(z) = \csc z$ has isolated singularities on the real axis, at an infinite number of points $z_n = n\pi$, where n is any positive or negative integer. ∎

Finally, there are singularities of complex functions called branch points. Consider the function $f(z) = z^{1/2}$. In polar notation,

$$f(z) = r^{1/2}e^{j\theta/2} \tag{2.28}$$

If $\theta = 0, f(z) = r^{1/2}$, while if $\theta = 2\pi, f(z) = -r^{1/2}$. That is, the function $f(z) = z^{1/2}$ will change sign if the angle θ increases by 2π. This if further illustrated by referring to Figure 2.6.

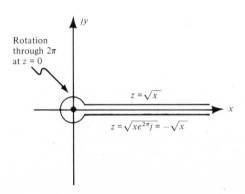

FIGURE 2.6.

As z varies along the "upper" branch, $f(z) = \sqrt{z}$ varies as $\sqrt{x}$, where we have chosen the positive sign for convenience. When θ increases by 2π about the circle of radius r, then, on the "lower" branch

$$f(z) = \sqrt{xe^{2\pi j}} = -\sqrt{x}$$

That is, $f(z) = z^{1/2}$ is multiple valued, with $z = 0$ being the *branch point* of the function, where the branching multiple values occur.

Suppose that we have a function $(z - z_0)^p$, where p is a rational fraction. Let $z = z_0 + \rho e^{j\theta}$, so that $(z - z_0)^p = \rho^p e^{jp\theta}$. Then, when θ increases by 2π, the argument of $(z - z_0)^p$ changes by $e^{jp\theta}$. Since p is not an integer, $e^{jp\theta} \neq 1$, so $z = z_0$ is a branch point of the function $f(z) = (z - z_0)^p$. If $p = 1/3$, say, we could increase θ by 6π and thereby recover the original sign of $(z - z_0)^{1/3}$.

The function $f(z) = \ln z$ has a branch point at $z = 0$ and infinitely many branches. To show this, write $z = re^{j\theta}e^{2\pi jn}$, where n is an integer. Then

$$\ln z = \ln r + j(\theta + 2\pi n) \tag{2.29}$$

Even if we set $\theta = 0$, we can pick any value $n = 0, \pm 1, \pm 2$, etc. The *principal branch* of the function $f(z) = \ln z$ is the one for which $n = 0$. The function thereby defined for which $r^2 = x^2 + y^2$ and $\theta = \tan^{-1}(y/x)$ is analytic at all points for which r and θ are defined. The interval over which $\tan \theta$ is defined is $-\pi/2 \le \theta \le \pi/2$, on the principal branch.

There are essential singularities in the complex plane. Consider the function $f(z) = e^{1/z}$. There is no integer n such that $f(z)(z - 0)^n$ is analytic at $z = 0$. Hence $z = 0$ is an essential singularity of $f(z) = e^{1/z}$.

We close this section on singularities with a few additional examples and define, in this way, Riemann surfaces or sheets.

Example 2.14   Let $f(z) = z^{1/3}$. With $z = re^{j\theta}e^{2jn\pi}$, there are three roots to $z^{1/3}$. These are

$$z_1 = r^{1/3}e^{j\theta/3}$$
$$z_2 = r^{1/3}e^{j\theta/3}e^{2j\pi/3}$$
$$z_3 = r^{1/3}e^{j\theta/3}e^{4j\pi/3}$$

If we move along the line $\theta = 0$ and rotate about the point $z = 0$ through 2π radians, we move from the value z_1 to z_2. A further rotation of 2π radians then gives us the value z_3. Here the point $z = 0$ is, once again, a branch point, with the surface in the complex z-plane being defined as a Riemann surface of three sheets. In this example there are only three distinct sheets since, given z_3, a further rotation of 2π radians will yield the original value z_1.   ∎

Example 2.15   Let $f(z) = \ln z$. With $z = re^{j\theta}e^{2jn\pi}$, as previously discussed, we have

$$\ln z = \ln r + j\theta + 2jn\pi$$

a multiple-valued function. Further, for any θ and n, $\ln z$ has an essential singularity at $|z| = r = 0$. On setting $\theta = 0$ for convenience, it is seen that a rotation through 2π produces a different value of $\ln z$ at any $r = r_0 \neq 0$. An infinite number of sheets make up the Riemann surface for the function $f(z) = \ln z$; the principal value of the function, as previously mentioned, is defined for $\theta = n = 0$.   ∎

Example 2.16 Let $f(z) = e^{-k\sqrt{z}}$, where k is real. This function has a branch point at $z = 0$ as does $f(z) = z^{1/2}$, and for the same reason. As $z \rightarrow 0$, we have along the axis (for which $z = x$) that $f(z)$ takes on the two values

$$f(x) = e^{-k\sqrt{x}}$$

and

$$f(x) = e^{k\sqrt{x}}$$

after a rotation from $\theta = 0$ to $\theta = 2\pi$. ∎

Example 2.17 It is somewhat difficult to picture Riemann surfaces, or sheets on a Riemann surface. Consider again the function $f(z) = z^{1/2}$, and Figure 2.7. It provides some pictorial understanding of the behavior of functions of a complex variable with a branch point. (A picture of an *n-sheeted* Riemann surface requires a lively imagination.) The cut along the line $y = 0$ splits the surface $f(z) = z^{1/2}$ into the two sheets which, in our case, exist for $x > 0$. Obviously, if we move along the imaginary axis, by setting $f(z) = z^{1/2} = \sqrt{jy}$ (for $x = 0$), we have, for $\theta = \pi/2$,

$$\sqrt{jy} = \sqrt{e^{j\pi/2}y}$$

on one sheet and

$$\sqrt{e^{5\pi j/2}y} = \sqrt{-jy}$$

when a rotation of 2π radians is made about $y = 0$. ∎

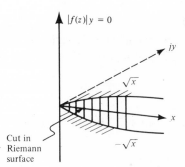

FIGURE 2.7 A branch point of Example 2.17.

Singularities and their classifications are important to the engineer for the following basic reason: Their locations and their types determine the nature of the response of a system.

2.5 LAPLACE'S EQUATION

We now have expressions for the real part of $f(z)$, either $u(x,y)$ or $u(r,\theta)$, as well as for the imaginary part of $f(z)$, either $v(x,y)$ or $v(r,\theta)$. These are of importance in many problems of science and engineering; among these are problems in electrostatics and magnetostatics. We now derive Laplace's equation in rectangular coordinates, as related to such problems.

The Cauchy-Riemann equations are, again,

$$\frac{\partial u}{\partial x} = \frac{\partial v}{\partial y} \quad \text{and} \quad \frac{\partial v}{\partial x} = -\frac{\partial u}{\partial y} \tag{2.27}$$

If these equations hold, then $f(z)$ is analytic so that $f(z)$, and therefore $u(x,y)$ and $v(x,y)$, have derivatives of any order that are finite, single valued, and continuous. Thus we can form

$$\frac{\partial^2 u}{\partial x^2} = \frac{\partial^2 v}{\partial x \partial y} \tag{2.30a}$$

and

$$\frac{\partial^2 v}{\partial y \partial x} = -\frac{\partial^2 u}{\partial y^2} \tag{2.30b}$$

The legitimacy of the interchange of the order of differentiation is guaranteed when both u and v and their derivatives of any order are continuous. By eliminating the expression

$$\frac{\partial^2 v}{\partial x \partial y} = \frac{\partial^2 v}{\partial y \partial x}$$

from Equations 2.30a and 2.30 b, we get

$$\frac{\partial^2 u}{\partial x^2} + \frac{\partial^2 u}{\partial y^2} = 0 \tag{2.31a}$$

The expression given in Equation 2.31a is known as Laplace's equation in two dimensions. The partial differential operator is usually denoted by ∇^2 ("del square"), i.e.,

$$\nabla^2 \equiv \frac{\partial^2}{\partial x^2} + \frac{\partial^2}{\partial y^2}$$

so that Equation 2.31a can be written as

$$\nabla^2 u = 0 \tag{2.31b}$$

By elimination of u from Equation 2.30 it is equally easy to show that

$$\nabla^2 v = 0 \tag{2.31c}$$

Thus, if a function $f(z) = u(x,y) + jv(x,y)$ is analytic in some region of the complex plane, both u and v satisfy Laplace's equation throughout that same region.

Example 2.18   Consider $f(z) = \sin z$, where we found earlier

$$u(x,y) = \sin x \cosh y$$

and

$$v(x,y) = \cos x \sinh y$$

We calculate

$$\frac{\partial^2 u}{\partial x^2} = -\sin x \, \cosh y$$

and

$$\frac{\partial^2 u}{\partial y^2} = \sin x \, \cosh y$$

Consequently, $\nabla^2 u = 0$.

Similarly,

$$\frac{\partial^2 v}{\partial x^2} = -\cos x \, \sinh y$$

and

$$\frac{\partial^2 v}{\partial y^2} = \cos x \, \sinh y$$

Therefore $\nabla^2 v = 0$.

Both u and v satisfy Laplace's equation at all finite points in the z-plane. ∎

Example 2.19 As an example of an electrostatic problem, let $u(x,y)$ represent a voltage in the region $0 \le x \le \infty$ and in $0 \le y \le b$. See Figure 2.8. If there is no free charge in the given region, then the voltage obeys Laplace's equation, $\nabla^2 u(x,y) = 0$. Physically we require that the voltage be finite everywhere, so that $\lim_{x \to \infty} u(x,y) \to 0$. Then solutions to $\nabla^2 u = 0$ are

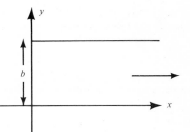

FIGURE 2.8 A two-dimensional electrostatic potential.

$$u_1(x,y) = e^{-kx} \sin ky$$
$$u_2(x,y) = e^{-kx} \cos ky$$

If, in addition, it is required, as a boundary condition, that $\lim_{y \to 0} u(x,y) \equiv 0$, then

$$u(x,y) = u_0 e^{-kx} \sin ky$$

where u_0 is an arbitrary constant voltage, evaluated by given boundary conditions. ∎

Example 2.20 Let $u(x,y)$ be a potential in the region $0 \le x \le a$, $0 \le y \le b$ as shown in Figure 2.9. Given that $u(0,y) = u(a,y) = 0$ and that $u(x,0) = 0$ and that $u(x,b) = V(x)$, a prescribed voltage, we can find $u(x,y)$ at any interior point of the rectangle as follows:

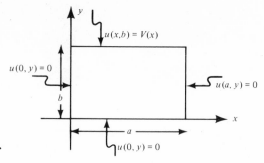

FIGURE 2.9   A two-dimensional potential.

Let

$$u(x,y) = (A \sin kx + B \cos kx)(C \sinh ky + D \cosh ky)$$

where each of the individual products, and therefore the sum of such products, is a solution to Laplace's equation. Since $u(0,y) \equiv 0$, $B \equiv 0$, while, since $u(x,0) = 0$, $D \equiv 0$. The expression for $u(x,y)$ then reduces to

$$u(x,y) = A \sin kx \sinh ky$$

Since the condition $u(a,y) = 0$ must be satisfied, we require that

$$\sin ka = 0$$

which means that

$$k \equiv k_n = \frac{n\pi}{a}$$

Then a sum of terms of the form

$$u(x,y) = \sum_{n=0}^{\infty} A_n \sin \frac{n\pi x}{a} \sinh \frac{n\pi y}{a}$$

is also a solution. Now the one remaining boundary condition to be satisfied is that

$$u(x,b) = V(x) = \sum A_n' \sin \frac{n\pi x}{a}$$

where $A_n' \equiv A_n \sinh (n\pi b)/a$. In the last expression we recognize the familiar Fourier series; therefore the coefficients A_n' can be obtained in the usual way as

$$A_n' = \frac{2}{a} \int_0^a V(x') \sin \frac{n\pi x'}{a} \, dx'$$

Thus,

$$u(x,y) = \frac{2}{a} \sum \sin \frac{n\pi x}{a} \frac{\sinh \dfrac{n\pi y}{a}}{\sinh \dfrac{n\pi b}{a}} \int_0^a V(x') \sin \frac{n\pi x'}{a} \, dx' \qquad \blacksquare$$

As a further illustration of the use of analytic functions in solving Laplace's equation, let us examine the function

$$f(z) = z^{\pm n} \tag{2.32}$$

where we shall require that $|f(z)| \to 0$ as $|z| \to \infty$. Written in polar coordinates, it is

$$f(re^{j\theta}) = r^{\pm n} e^{jn\theta} \tag{2.33}$$

On extracting real and imaginary parts, and multiplying by arbitrary constants, we obtain

$$u(r,\theta) = (Ar^n + Br^{-n})(C \cos n\theta + D \sin n\theta) \tag{2.34a}$$

as a solution to $\nabla^2 u(r,\theta) = 0$. Further, a summation of such terms, written as

$$u(r,\theta) = \sum (A_n r^n + B_n r^{-n})(C_n \cos n\theta + D_n \sin n\theta) \tag{2.34b}$$

is also a solution. (Verify!)

We shall, as before, consider $u(r,\theta)$ to be a voltage with boundary conditions given that permit evaluation of the arbitrary constants. A few examples are presented in the following.

Example 2.21 A cylinder of infinite length and of radius a is oriented along the z-axis. The function $u(a,\theta) = u_0 \cos^2 \theta$ is the given electrostatic potential on the surface of the cylinder. It is postulated that $u(r,\theta)$ is finite and continuous for all r and θ and that $\lim_{r \to \infty} u(r,\theta) \to u_0$. We wish to find $u(r,\theta)$ for all r,θ given these boundary conditions.

In $0 \leq r \leq a$, set

$$u(r,\theta) = \sum_{n=0}^{\infty} r^n(A_n \cos n\theta + B_n \sin n\theta)$$

and in $a \leq r \leq \infty$, set

$$u(,\theta) = \sum_{n=0}^{\infty} r^{-n}(C_n \cos n\theta + D_n \sin n\theta)$$

Since $\cos^2 \theta = \frac{1}{2}(1 + \cos 2\theta)$, the boundary condition $u(a,\theta) = u_0 \cos^2 \theta$ cannot be satisfied unless $B_n \equiv D_n \equiv 0$ for all n. At $r = a$, then, since $u(a,\theta)$ is continuous, we have

$$a^n A_n = a^{-n} C_n$$

or

$$C_n = A_n a^{2n}$$

The boundary condition at $r = a$ is now applied to find the only remaining arbitrary constant, namely, A_n. The boundary condition reads

$$u(a,\theta) = \frac{u_o}{2}(1 + \cos 2\theta) = \sum A_n a^n \cos n\theta$$

from which

$$A_n = \frac{u_0}{2\pi a^n} \int_0^{2\pi} (1 + \cos 2\theta) \cos n\theta \, d\theta$$

or

$$A_n = \frac{u_0}{2\pi a^n}(2\pi\delta_{n,0} + \pi\delta_{n,2})$$

where

$$\delta_{n,p} = \begin{cases} 1 & p = n \\ 0 & p \neq n \end{cases}$$

is called the Kronecker delta. Thus,

$$A_0 = u_0$$

and

$$A_2 = \frac{u_0}{2a^2}$$

are the only nonvanishing constants. Consequently, the potential is given by

$$u(r,\theta) = \begin{cases} u_0(1 + \dfrac{r^2}{2a^2}\cos 2\theta) & 0 \leq r \leq a \\[2ex] u_0(1 + \dfrac{a^2}{2r^2}\cos 2\theta) & a \leq r \leq \infty \end{cases}$$ ∎

Example 2.22   An infinitely long conducting cylinder of radius a, with its axis coincident with the z-axis, has the following normal derivative of the voltage prescribed at $r = a$:

$$\left.\frac{\partial u}{\partial r}\right)_{r=a} = \frac{u_0}{a}\sin 3\theta$$

We want to find $u(r,\theta)$ for $r \geq a$ if $\lim_{r\to\infty} u(r,\theta) = 0$.

To satisfy this last requirement, we must have

$$u(r,\theta) = \sum_n r^{-n}(A_n \sin n\theta + B_n \cos n\theta)$$

Then

$$\left.\frac{\partial u}{\partial r}\right)_{r=a} = -\sum_n na^{-(n+1)}(A_n \sin n\theta + B_n \cos n\theta)$$

Unless $B_n \equiv 0$ for all n, the boundary conditions cannot be satisfied. Thus, with $B_n \equiv 0$, we have

$$\frac{u_0}{a}\sin 3\theta = -\sum_n na^{-(n+1)}A_n \sin n\theta$$

Only the constant A_3 will have a nonzero value. It is given by

$$-3a^{-4}A_3 = \frac{u_0}{a}$$

that is,

$$A_3 = -\frac{u_0}{3}a^3$$

so that

$$u(r,\theta) = -\frac{u_0}{3}\left(\frac{a}{r}\right)^3 \sin 3\theta \qquad (a \leq r \leq \infty)$$ ∎

2.6   LAPLACE AND FOURIER TRANSFORMS

It is now shown that, by examining certain solutions of Laplace's equation, we can introduce the Laplace transform and the Fourier transform in a formal sense. These transforms are discussed in greater detail in subsequent chapters. Here we introduce them formally in order to stress their connection with complex variable theory.

Consider the function

$$f(z) = e^{-kz} \tag{2.35}$$

with $z = x + jy$ and $k > 0$ and real. Then

$$u(x,y) = e^{-kx} \cos ky$$

and (2.36)

$$v(x,y) = -e^{-kx} \sin ky$$

It is easy to verify that either $u(x,y)$ or $v(x,y)$ satisfies Laplace's equation in two dimensions. For example,

$$\frac{\partial^2 u}{\partial x^2} + \frac{\partial^2 u}{\partial y^2} = (k^2 - k^2)e^{-kx} \cos ky \equiv 0 \tag{2.37}$$

It is also easy to show that the function

$$f(z) = e^{-k(x+jy)}$$

satisfies the equation

$$\nabla^2 f(z) = 0 \tag{2.38}$$

Next, consider the function $G(z) = G(x,y)$, defined by

$$G(x,y) \equiv \int_0^\infty a(k)e^{-k(x+jy)} \, dk \tag{2.39}$$

where $a(k)$ is a function of the parameter k. Let us show that $G(x,y)$ is itself a solution to Laplace's equation. Taking its second partial derivatives with respect to x and y, we obtain

$$\frac{\partial^2 G}{\partial x^2} = \int_0^\infty a(k)k^2 e^{-k(x+jy)} \, dk$$

$$\frac{\partial^2 G}{\partial y^2} = \int_0^\infty a(k)(-k^2)e^{-k(x+jy)} \, dk \tag{2.40}$$

and, therefore,

$$\nabla^2 G = \frac{\partial^2 G}{\partial x^2} + \frac{\partial^2 G}{\partial y^2} = 0 \qquad (2.41)$$

Now let $G(x,0) = A(x)$ be a boundary condition at $y = 0$. Therefore, from Equation 2.39 we get

$$G(x,0) = A(x) = \int_0^\infty a(k)e^{-kx} \, dk \qquad (2.42)$$

Equation 2.42 defines the *Laplace transform* $A(x)$ of the function $a(k)$, provided that the integral appearing on the right-hand side exists.*

A function derived from $u(x)$ (in Equation 2.36) by forming

$$u(x,y) = \int_0^\infty a(k)e^{-kx} \cos ky \, dk \qquad (2.43)$$

also satisfies Laplace's equation. If $u(0,y) = F_1(y)$, then

$$F_1(y) = \int_0^\infty a(k) \cos ky \, dk \qquad (2.44)$$

is defined as the *Fourier cosine transform* of $a(k)$. We can similarly define a function $F_2(y)$ derived from $v(x,y)$ as $x \to 0$. This function is

$$F_2(y) = \int_0^\infty a(k) \sin ky \, dk \qquad (2.45)$$

and is a *Fourier sine transform* of $a(k)$.

These transforms are discussed in succeeding chapters. For now, however, it is sufficient to note that, at least formally, there is a close connection between integrals formed by applying boundary conditions to solutions of Laplace's equation and familiar transforms that are of extreme importance in the analysis of systems.

2.7 INTEGRATION IN THE COMPLEX PLANE

We assume that certain properties of integration are familiar to the student. For a real variable x we recall that

$$\int_a^b f(x) \, dx = \int_a^c f(x) \, dx + \int_c^b f(x) \, dx \qquad (2.46)$$

and

$$\int_a^b f(x) \, dx = -\int_b^a f(x) \, dx \qquad (2.47)$$

---

*The usual notation for the Laplace transform is

$$F(s) = \int_0^\infty f(t)e^{-st} \, dt$$

and we use it in subsequent chapters.

Further, as $\Delta x_i \to 0$,

$$\sum_i f(x_i)\Delta x_i \to \int_a^b f(x)\, dx \tag{2.48}$$

Equations 2.46 and 2.47 carry over into the complex plane with the understanding that the interval $[a,b]$ is specified along a curve C in the plane. Thus a and b can, in general, be complex.

There are two theorems of crucial importance for such integrations in the complex plane. They are called Cauchy's first and second (or residue) theorems.

Cauchy's first integral theorem asserts that if a function $f(z)$ is analytic throughout some region R of the complex plane and at all points on a curve C bounding R, then the integral of $f(z)$ around a closed curve C vanishes,

$$\oint_C f(z)\, dz = 0 \tag{2.49}$$

Proof The closed simple curve C (a simple curve is one that does not cross itself) is taken for clarity. Figure 2.10(a) shows the region R bounded by C, and Figure 2.10(b) shows a curve Γ which is a jagged line approximation to C. Now consider Figure 2.11, an enlarged version of a few of the elementary squares shown in Figure 2.10(b).

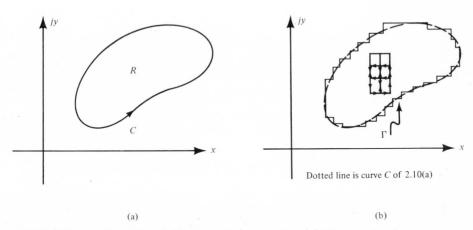

(a)   (b)

FIGURE 2.10 A region R bounded by (a) a simple curve C and (b) its approximation.

If the curve C of Figure 2.10(a) is traversed in a counterclockwise (positive) direction, then each of the small squares of Figure 2.11 must be traversed in a counterclockwise direction. By Equation 2.47, all contributions from paths in the interior of the approximating curve Γ will cancel one another. The result is that the integral around C is replaced by an integral around Γ that will be an approximation to the integral around C. There will be a sum of such integrals along Γ, taken along straight-line segments, and the sum of the contributions from each of the straight-line segments will be the value of the integral along Γ. By Equation 2.48, as each of the $\Delta x_i \to 0$, the

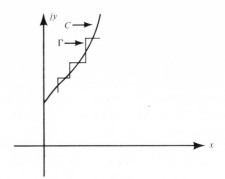

FIGURE 2.11   An enlarged portion of curve C.

integral over Γ will be equal to the integral over C. All of this means that rather than the Equation 2.49, we can examine an integral of the form

$$\oint_{C'} f(z)\, dz$$

where the path C' is shown in Figure 2.12. Now, with $f(z) = u + jv$, and $dz = dx + jdy$,

$$\oint_{C'} f(z)\, dz = \oint_{C'} (udx - vdy) + j \oint_{C'} (vdx + udy) \equiv I_1 + I_2 \qquad (2.50)$$

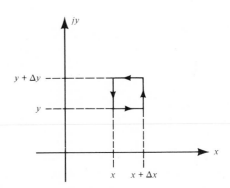

FIGURE 2.12   A curve enclosing an area $\Delta x \Delta y$.

We consider the two integrals I_1 and I_2 separately. For I_1 we have

$$I_1 = \int_x^{x+\Delta x} u(y,x')\, dx' - \int_y^{y+\Delta y} v(x + \Delta x, y')\, dy' + \int_{x+\Delta x}^x u(y + \Delta y, x')\, dx'$$
$$- \int_{y+\Delta y}^y v(x,y')\, dy' \qquad (2.51)$$

By Equation 2.48 we have

$$I_1 = -\int_x^{x+\Delta x} [u(y + \Delta y, x') - u(y,x')]\, dx' - \int_y^{y+\Delta y} [v(x + \Delta x, y') - v(x,y')]\, dy' \qquad (2.52)$$

A Taylor series expansion of $u(y + \Delta y, x')$ about $\Delta y = 0$, and one of $v(x + \Delta x, y')$ about $\Delta x = 0$ yields

$$I_1 = \int_x^{x+\Delta x} -\frac{\partial u}{\partial y}\, dx' \, \Delta y - \int_y^{y+\Delta y} \frac{\partial v}{\partial x}\, dy' \, \Delta x \tag{2.53}$$

or, as $\Delta x \to \Delta y \to 0$,

$$I_1 = -\left[\frac{\partial u}{\partial y} + \frac{\partial v}{\partial x}\right]\Delta x \,\Delta y \tag{2.54}$$

But

$$\frac{\partial u}{\partial y} \equiv -\frac{\partial v}{\partial x}$$

by the Cauchy-Riemann equations, so that

$$I_1 \equiv 0 \tag{2.55}$$

For I_2 we have, in a similar way,

$$I_2 = \left[\frac{\partial u}{\partial x} - \frac{\partial v}{\partial y}\right]\Delta x \,\Delta y \tag{2.56}$$

Again, by the Cauchy-Riemann conditions, $I_2 \equiv 0$.

Since $\oint_{C'} f(z)\, dz \equiv 0$, a sum of such integrals is also zero. But the sum of such integrals is the value along the curve Γ of Figure 2.10(b) and as $\Delta x \to \Delta y \to 0$, the value of the integral along Γ becomes equal to the value along C. Thus we have proved that

$$\oint_C f(z)\, dz \equiv 0 \tag{2.49}$$

Cauchy's second integral theorem, or the residue theorem, gives an expression for the value of $f(z)$ at $z = z_0$. It can be written as

$$f(z_0) = \frac{1}{2\pi j} \oint_{\Gamma_1} \frac{f(\zeta)}{\zeta - z_0}\, d\zeta \tag{2.57}$$

where $f(\zeta)$ is analytic within some region R and at all points on curve C bounding R, and where the point z_0 is within R. The relation given in Equation 2.57 will be proved for curve C, shown in Figure 2.13.

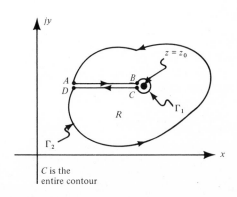

FIGURE 2.13 A curve C bounding R in which the point $z = z_0$ is excluded.

C is the entire contour

Proof   The contour C is chosen so that the point $z = z_0$ is not within R. Now, $f(\zeta)$ is analytic everywhere within R and on C. With the point $z = z_0$ excluded as shown, the function $\phi(\zeta) \equiv f(\zeta)/(\zeta - z_0)$ is also analytic throughout R and on C. Thus, by Cauchy's first integral theorem,

$$\oint_C \phi(\zeta)\, d\zeta = 0 \tag{2.58}$$

The contour C is such that

$$\oint_C \phi(\zeta)\, d\zeta = \int_A^B \phi(\zeta)\, d\zeta + \oint_{\Gamma_1} \phi(\zeta)\, d\zeta + \int_C^D \phi(\zeta)\, d\zeta + \oint_{\Gamma_2} \phi(\zeta)\, d\zeta = 0 \tag{2.59}$$

Now, as $A \to D$ and $B \to C$ (i.e., as these points coincide),

$$\int_A^B \phi(\zeta)\, d\zeta + \int_C^D \phi(\zeta)\, d\zeta \equiv 0 \tag{2.60}$$

by Equation 2.47 of integration. Thus,

$$0 = \oint_{\Gamma_1} \phi(\zeta)\, d\zeta + \oint_{\Gamma_2} \phi(\zeta)\, d\zeta \tag{2.61}$$

Note that the integrals over Γ_2 and Γ_1 are taken in the counterclockwise and clockwise senses, respectively.

Again, by Equation 2.47 we have

$$\oint_{\Gamma_1} \phi(\zeta)\, d\zeta = \oint_{\Gamma_2} \phi(\zeta)\, d\zeta \tag{2.62}$$

The points ζ on the contour Γ_1 are given by $\zeta = z_0 + \rho e^{j\theta}$, where ρ is the radius of the circle surrounding z_0. Thus, as previously defined, the function $\phi(\zeta)$ becomes, on Γ_1,

$$\phi(\zeta) = \frac{f(z_0 + \rho e^{j\theta})}{e^{j\theta}} \tag{2.63}$$

With $d\zeta = j\rho e^{j\theta}\, d\theta$ the integral $\oint_{\Gamma_1} \phi(\zeta)\, d\zeta$ now is given by

$$I = j \int_0^{2\pi} \frac{f(z_0 + \rho e^{j\theta})}{\rho e^{j\theta}} \rho e^{j\theta}\, d\theta \tag{2.64}$$

We investigate $\lim_{\rho \to 0} I$. It is

$$\lim_{\rho \to 0} I = j f(z_0) \int_0^{2\pi} d\theta = 2\pi j f(z_0) \tag{2.65}$$

The final result of substituting Equation 2.65 into Equation 2.62 and dividing both sides by $2\pi j$ is the desired result, i.e.,

$$f(z_0) = \frac{1}{2\pi j} \oint \frac{f(\zeta)}{\zeta - z_0}\, d\zeta \tag{2.66}$$

The reason for calling Cauchy's second integral theorem the residue theorem is as follows: The function $f(\zeta)/(\zeta - z_0)$ is analytic at all points of region R except at the point $\zeta = z_0$. There,

$$\lim_{\zeta \to z_0} \frac{(\zeta - z_0)f(\zeta)}{(\zeta - z_0)} = f(z_0) \tag{2.67}$$

is analytic and for any fixed z_0 becomes a constant. According to a previous definition, the function $\phi(\zeta) = f(\zeta)/(\zeta - z_0)$ has a pole of order 1 at the point $\zeta = z_0$ and $f(z_0)$ is called its *residue* at $\zeta = z_0$. Thus, Equation 2.66 can be written as

$$2\pi j[\operatorname{Res} f(\zeta)]_{\zeta=z_0} = \oint \frac{f(\zeta)}{\zeta - z_0} \, d\zeta \tag{2.68}$$

By using Equation 2.67 it is now a simple matter to find the residue at a pole of order n. Treating z as a variable, and knowing that $f(z)$ is analytic, we then know that $f(z)$ has derivatives of any order. Thus it is permissible to form

$$\frac{df}{dz} = \frac{1}{2\pi j} \oint \frac{f(\zeta)}{(\zeta - z)^2} \, d\zeta \tag{2.69}$$

and

$$\frac{1}{2}\frac{d^2f}{dz^2} = \frac{1}{2\pi j} \cdot \oint \frac{f(\zeta)}{(\zeta - z)^3} \, d\zeta \tag{2.70}$$

and, in general,

$$\frac{1}{(n-1)!}\frac{d^{n-1}f(z)}{dz^{n-1}} = \frac{1}{2\pi j} \oint \frac{f(\zeta)}{(\zeta - z)^n} \, d\zeta \tag{2.71}$$

Now, the function $\phi(\zeta) = f(\zeta)/(\zeta - z)^n$ has a pole of order n at $\zeta = z$, since $f(\zeta)$ is analytic at $\zeta = z$. Thus the residue at a pole of order n is given by

$$\operatorname{Res}_n = \lim_{\zeta \to z} \left[\frac{1}{(n-1)!}\frac{d^{n-1}f(\zeta)}{d\zeta^{n-1}} \right] \tag{2.72}$$

The foregoing discussion is easily extended to the case of several poles within some region R bounded by a curve C. Consider the integral

$$I = \frac{1}{2\pi j} \oint_C \frac{f(\zeta) \, d\zeta}{(\zeta - z_1)(\zeta - z_2) \cdots (\zeta - z_n)} \tag{2.73}$$

where each of the z_i ($i = 1, \ldots, n$) is *distinct*. The residue at $\zeta = z_1$ is defined, on letting $\phi(\zeta) = f(\zeta)/(\zeta - z_1)(\zeta - z_2) \cdots (\zeta - z_n)$, as

$$\lim_{\zeta \to z_1} (\zeta - z_1)\phi(\zeta) = \frac{f(z_1)}{(z_1 - z_2)(z_1 - z_3) \cdots (z_1 - z_n)} \tag{2.74}$$

since $(\zeta - z_1)\phi(\zeta)$ is analytic at z_1. For the residue at z_2 we find

$$[\operatorname{Res}]_{z=z_2} = \frac{f(z_2)}{(z_2 - z_1)(z_2 - z_3) \cdots (z_2 - z_n)} \tag{2.75}$$

and so forth. Thus, by the residue theorem,

$$2\pi j \sum_{i=1}^{n} [\text{Res}]_{z=z_i} = \oint \frac{f(\zeta)\, d\zeta}{\prod_i (\zeta - z_i)} \tag{2.76}$$

when each of the z_i is a distinct pole. Equation 2.76 is an extension of Equation 2.68.

Here are several examples of finding residues by the methods discussed. There are cases for which L'Hôpital's rule becomes necessary.

Example 2.23   Find the residue of

$$f(z) = \frac{1}{z - 3}$$

at $z = 3$. In this case we have

$$\lim_{z \to 3} (z - 3)f(z) = 1$$

Thus the residue is equal to unity at $z = 3$.   ∎

Example 2.24   Find the sum of the residues of the function

$$f(z) = \frac{z - 2}{(z + 3)(z - 5)}$$

at $z = -3$ and at $z = 5$. The residue at $z = -3$ is

$$\lim_{z \to -3} (z + 3)f(z) = \lim_{z \to -3} \frac{z - 2}{z - 5} = \frac{5}{8}$$

The residue at $z = 5$ is calculated according to

$$\lim_{z \to 5} (z - 5)f(z) = \lim_{z \to 5} \frac{z - 2}{z + 3} = \frac{3}{8}$$

Thus the sum of the residues is

$$\frac{5}{8} + \frac{3}{8} = 1.$$ ∎

Example 2.25   Find the residue of

$$f(z) = \frac{1 + \sin z}{1 - \cos z}$$

at $z = 0$. Here it is first necessary to determine the order of the pole of $f(z)$ as $z \to 0$. Since $\cos z = 1 - (z^2/2!) + \cdots$ then, as $z \to 0$, $(1 - \cos z) \approx z^2/2$, and there is a second-order pole at $z = 0$. The function $(1 + \sin z)$ is analytic at $z = 0$ so that the residue is determined by calculating

$$\left[2 \frac{d}{dz} (1 + \sin z) \right]_{z=0} = 2$$ ∎

Example 2.26 Find the residue of $f(z) = \cot z$ at $z = n\pi$, where n is an integer. Since $\cot z = \cos z/\sin z$, and since, for $z = n\pi$, $\sin z \equiv 0$, there is an infinite number of poles of the function cot z. For n fixed, however, we require

$$\lim_{z \to n\pi} (z - n\pi)f(z) = \lim_{z \to n\pi} (z - n\pi) \frac{\cos z}{\sin z}$$

which is an indeterminate form; L'Hôpital's rule must be applied by differentiating both numerator and denominator with respect to z. Then

$$\lim_{z \to n\pi} \frac{(z - n\pi)}{\sin z} \cos z = \left. \frac{\cos z}{\cos z} \right)_{n\pi} = 1$$

which is the value of the residue. ■

Example 2.27 Find the residue of

$$f(z) = \frac{\sin z}{(z - \pi/2)^3}$$

at $z = \pi/2$. There is a pole of order 3 at $z = \pi/2$. Thus the residue is found by calculating

$$\frac{1}{2!} \left[\frac{d^2}{dz^2} \sin z \right]_{z=\pi/2} = -\frac{1}{2}$$ ■

Example 2.28 Find the residue of $f(z) = e^{az}/(1 + e^z)$ at $z = j\pi$. There is a pole of first order at $z = e^{j\pi}$ since $1 + e^{j\pi} \equiv 0$. Therefore we need to calculate

$$\lim_{z \to j\pi} \frac{(z - j\pi)e^{az}}{1 + e^z}$$

Again, as $z \to j\pi$, there is an indeterminate form. Upon applying L'Hôpital's rule, we get

$$e^{aj\pi} \lim_{z \to j\pi} \frac{(z - j\pi)}{1 + e^z} = e^{aj\pi} \lim_{z \to j\pi} \left(\frac{1}{e^z} \right) = e^{aj\pi} e^{-j\pi}$$

or, since $e^{-j\pi} \equiv -1$,

$$\text{Res } f(z)_{z=j\pi} = -e^{aj\pi}$$ ■

2.8 THE TAYLOR SERIES

From Cauchy's residue theorem, as in Equation 2.57,

$$f(z) = \frac{1}{2\pi j} \oint \frac{f(\zeta)}{\zeta - z} d\zeta \qquad (2.57)$$

and the fact that $f(z)$ is analytic throughout the region R, and therefore has derivatives of any order throughout R, we can develop a Taylor series expansion of $f(z)$ about a point z_0 in R. We proceed as follows: Select a point z_0 within R and write

$$\frac{1}{\zeta - z} = \frac{\zeta - z_0}{(\zeta - z)(\zeta - z_0)} = \frac{1}{\zeta - z_0} \frac{1}{(1 - (z - z_0)/(\zeta - z_0))} \qquad (2.77)$$

For $|z - z_0| < |\zeta - z_0|$, the quantity

$$(\zeta - z)^{-1} = (\zeta - z_0)^{-1} \sum_{l=0}^{\infty} \frac{(z - z_0)^l}{(\zeta - z_0)^l} \tag{2.78}$$

is a uniformly and absolutely convergent series. Thus,

$$f(z) = \frac{1}{2\pi j} \oint \frac{f(\zeta)}{\zeta - z_0} \sum_{l=0}^{\infty} \frac{(z - z_0)^l}{(\zeta - z_0)^l} \, d\zeta \tag{2.79}$$

can be written as

$$f(z) = \sum_{l=0}^{\infty} a_l (z - z_0)^l \tag{2.80}$$

where the coefficients a_1 are given by

$$a_l = \frac{1}{l!} \frac{d^l f}{dz_0^{\,l}} = \frac{1}{2\pi j} \oint \frac{f(\zeta)}{(\zeta - z_0)^{l+1}} \, d\zeta \tag{2.81}$$

Equation 2.80, with the coefficients given by Equation 2.81, is a Taylor series expansion of $f(z)$ about the point $z = z_0$.

Example 2.29   We compute the Taylor series expansion of $\cos z$ about the point $z = z_0 = \pi/2$. We have

$$\cos z = \cos \frac{\pi}{2} + \frac{d}{dz} (\cos z)_{z=\pi/2} \left(z - \frac{\pi}{2} \right) + \frac{1}{2!} \frac{d^2}{dz^2} (\cos z)_{z=\pi/2} \left(z - \frac{\pi}{2} \right)^2$$

$$+ \frac{1}{3!} \frac{d^3}{dz^3} (\cos z)_{z=\pi/2} \left(z - \frac{\pi}{2} \right)^3 + \cdots,$$

which, upon simplification, becomes

$$\cos z \approx -\left(z - \frac{\pi}{2} \right) + \frac{1}{6} \left(z - \frac{\pi}{2} \right)^3 + \cdots \qquad\blacksquare$$

Example 2.30   When $z_0 = 0$, the Taylor series is called a Maclaurin series. Thus, for example, the Maclaurin series of the following functions can be written by inspection:

(a) $e^z = 1 + z + \dfrac{z^2}{2!} + \cdots$

(b) $\sin z = z - \dfrac{z^3}{3!} + \dfrac{z^5}{5!} + \cdots$

(c) $\tan z = z + \dfrac{z^3}{3} + \dfrac{2z^5}{15} + \dfrac{17z^7}{315} + \cdots$ $\qquad\blacksquare$

2.9   THE EVALUATION OF DEFINITE INTEGRALS THROUGH CONTOUR INTEGRATION

In this section we use contour integrals to evaluate real, definite integrals. Considerable stress is placed on the reasons for the choice of a given contour.

Given an integral of the form

$$I(a,b, \ldots) = \int_0^{2\pi} f(a,b, \ldots, \theta) \, d\theta \tag{2.82}$$

where $a, b, \ldots$ are real parameters, it is shown that conversion of I into an equivalent integral in the complex plane allows an easy evaluation of the equivalent integral by the Cauchy residue theorem.

Example 2.31   Consider the integral I, defined by

$$I(a,b,\pi) = \int_0^{2\pi} \frac{d\theta}{(a + b \cos \theta)}$$

where a and b are real, and $b < a$. To reduce the expression for I to an equivalent contour integral, set $z = e^{j\theta}$. The path (or contour) of integration in the complex plane will, then, be a circle of unit radius. Since $\cos \theta = (e^{j\theta} + e^{-j\theta})/2$, we have

$$\cos \theta = (z + z^{-1})/2 = (z^2 + 1)/2z$$

Further, with $z = e^{j\theta}$, $dz = je^{j\theta} \, d\theta$, so that

$$d\theta = dz/jz$$

The integral I becomes, equivalently,

$$I = \oint \frac{2 \, dz}{j[2az + b(z^2 + 1)]}$$

or

$$I = \frac{2}{jb} \oint \frac{dz}{\left(z^2 + \dfrac{2a}{b}z + 1\right)} = \frac{2}{jb} \oint \frac{dz}{(z - z_+)(z - z_-)}$$

and where the poles of the integrand are at the points

$$z_+ = -\frac{a}{b} + \sqrt{\left(\frac{a}{b}\right)^2 - 1}$$

and

$$z_- = -\frac{a}{b} - \sqrt{\left(\frac{a}{b}\right)^2 - 1}$$

Since $b < a$ by assumption, both poles are real, and

$$|z_+| < 1, \quad |z_-| > 1$$

Thus only the root z_+ is within a circle of unit radius. Therefore the application of the Cauchy residue theorem leads to the result

$$I = \frac{2}{jb} 2\pi j \text{ Res}\left[\frac{1}{z - z_-}\right]_{z=z_+}$$

that is,

$$I = \frac{4\pi}{b} \frac{1}{z_+ - z_-}$$

On inserting the expressions for z_+ and z_-, the answer is

$$I = \frac{2\pi}{\sqrt{a^2 - b^2}}$$

a function of a, b, π as was expected. Note, again, that with $a > b$, I is real.   ■

There are several interesting shortcuts that may be used to evaluate an integral if the value of another allied integral is known.

Example 2.32   Consider the integral

$$I' = \int_0^{2\pi} \frac{d\theta}{(a + b \cos \theta)^2}$$

with $a > b$, and a, b real. We have just evaluated the integral given in Example 2.31. Consider the quantity a as a variable and differentiate the allied integral

$$I = \int_0^{2\pi} \frac{d\theta}{(a + b \cos \theta)}$$

with respect to a. The result is

$$\frac{\partial I}{\partial a} = -\int_0^{2\pi} \frac{d\theta}{(a + b \cos \theta)^2}$$

Thus the integral I' is the negative of $\partial I / \partial a$. But from the previous example,

$$-\frac{\partial I}{\partial a} = \frac{2\pi a}{(a^2 - b^2)^{3/2}}$$

so that

$$I' = \int_0^{2\pi} \frac{d\theta}{(a + b \cos \theta)^2} = \frac{2\pi a}{(a^2 - b^2)^{3/2}}$$ ■

2.10   THE EVALUATION OF REAL DEFINITE INTEGRALS OVER INFINITE OR SEMI-INFINITE INTERVALS

In this section integrals of the form $\int_0^\infty f(x) \, dx$ or of the form $\int_{-\infty}^\infty f(x) \, dx$ are considered, where $f(x)$ is a function of the real variable x, and may, in general, depend on

additional constant parameters. Several examples are given, each of which involves a
different contour in the complex plane. Stress is placed on the physical context in which
such integrals may arise, as well as the reasons for the choice of a given contour.
Let

$$I(a,t) = \int_{-\infty}^{\infty} \frac{e^{j\omega t}}{\omega^2 + a^2} \, d\omega \tag{2.83}$$

Here, ω is an angular frequency, t is the time, with $t \gtrless 0$, and a is a positive constant
parameter. Far more effort will be devoted to a discussion of integrals of this form in
Chapter 4 on Fourier transforms; it is sufficient to state here that Equation 2.83 is of
the form of an exponential Fourier transform over the domain of the frequency ω.

The first task in evaluating the integral in Equation 2.83 by use of complex
variable theory is to choose a contour. Since ω covers the interval $[-\infty, \infty]$, and ω is
real, one part of the contour must involve the real axis. Then the contour can be closed
by means of a semicircle in either the upper or the lower half-plane. If, as mentioned
previously, we require that the integral be taken in the positive (counterclockwise)
direction about the contour, then we should choose a path which is closed in the upper
half-plane. Thus, we consider a contour as shown in Figure 2.14.

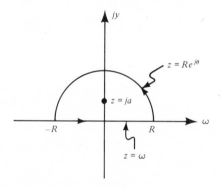

FIGURE 2.14 A contour for the evaluation of the integral in Equation 2.83.

We have, for $-R \le z \le R$, $z = \omega$, while on the arc over which $0 \le \theta \le \pi$,
$z = Re^{j\theta}$. We eventually allow R to approach infinity. We examine the integral

$$J(a,t) = \oint \frac{e^{jzt}}{z^2 + a^2} \, dz \tag{2.84}$$

about the contour C. The integrand of Equation 2.84 contains singularities at points
$z^2 + a^2 = 0$, i.e., at the points $z = \pm ja$. Only the singularity at $z = ja$ is within the
contour. Thus the residue at $z = ja$ is

$$\left[\frac{e^{jzt}}{z + ja} \right]_{z=ja} = \frac{e^{-a|t|}}{2ja} \tag{2.85}$$

and, consequently, by Cauchy's residue theorem,

$$J(a,t) = \frac{\pi e^{-a|t|}}{a} \tag{2.86}$$

We now have

$$\frac{\pi e^{-a|t|}}{a} = \oint \frac{e^{jzt}}{z^2 + a^2} \, dz \tag{2.87}$$

and must determine the contribution of the right-hand side of Equation 2.87 from the individual portions of contour C. We have

$$\oint \frac{e^{jzt} \, dz}{z^2 + a^2} = \int_{-R}^{R} \frac{e^{j\omega t}}{\omega^2 + a^2} \, d\omega + j \int_{0}^{\pi} \frac{e^{jtRe^{j\theta}}Re^{j\theta}}{R^2 e^{2j\theta} + a^2} \, d\theta \tag{2.88}$$

Consider the second of the two integrals on the right-hand side of Equation 2.88 as $R \rightarrow \infty$ in absolute value. The inequality

$$\left| j \int_{0}^{\pi} \frac{e^{jtRe^{j\theta}}Re^{j\theta}}{(R^2 e^{2j\theta} + a^2)} \, d\theta \right| \leq R^{-1} \int_{0}^{\pi} e^{-Rt\sin\theta} \, d\theta \tag{2.89}$$

holds, and as $R \rightarrow \infty$, the right-hand side of Equation 2.89 vanishes.*

Thus, as $R \rightarrow \infty$,

$$\oint \frac{e^{jzt}}{z^2 + a^2} \, dz = \int_{-\infty}^{\infty} \frac{e^{j\omega t}}{\omega^2 + a^2} \, d\omega \tag{2.90}$$

so that

$$\frac{\pi e^{-a|t|}}{a} = \int_{-\infty}^{\infty} \frac{e^{j\omega t}}{\omega^2 + a^2} \, d\omega \tag{2.91}$$

Note that the choice of $a > 0$ indicates that as $|t| \rightarrow \infty$, $I(a,t)$ is bounded.

There is additional information in Equation 2.91. The left-hand side is real, whereas the right-hand side can be written as

$$\int_{-\infty}^{\infty} \frac{e^{j\omega t}}{\omega^2 + a^2} \, d\omega = \int_{-\infty}^{\infty} \frac{\cos \omega t}{\omega^2 + a^2} \, d\omega + j \int_{-\infty}^{\infty} \frac{\sin \omega t}{\omega^2 + a^2} \, d\omega \tag{2.92}$$

Equating real and imaginary parts of both sides yields the two expressions

$$\frac{\pi e^{-a|t|}}{a} = \int_{-\infty}^{\infty} \frac{\cos \omega t}{\omega^2 + a^2} \, d\omega \tag{2.93}$$

and

$$0 = \int_{-\infty}^{\infty} \frac{\sin \omega t}{\omega + a^2} \, d\omega \tag{2.94}$$

where, because the integrand of Equation 2.93 is an even function of t, the absolute

---

*In any integral of the form $\int_{0}^{\pi} f(Re^{j\theta}) \, d\theta$, if $f(Re^{j\theta})$ varies with R as $R^{-(1+k)}$, where $k > 0$, then $\lim_{R \rightarrow \infty} \int_{0}^{\pi} f(Re^{j\theta}) \, d\theta \rightarrow \lim_{R \rightarrow \infty} R^{-k} \rightarrow 0$. That is, if $f(Re^{j\theta})$ varies inversely with R to any power greater than 1, the integral vanishes when evaluated over the semicircular arc.

value of t is required on the left-hand side. The expression in Equation 2.93 shows us that an exponential pulse $\pi e^{-a|t|}/a$ can be synthesized from the summation, or integration, over frequency components given on the right-hand side.

A few remarks on the integrals of even and odd functions are in order. A function satisfying $f(x) = f(-x)$ is even, while an odd function is such that $f(x) = -f(-x)$. Now, an odd function, when integrated over an even interval (from $-\infty$ to $+\infty$ here), will be identically zero. Thus only the integral of an even function has a nonzero value when evaluated over an even interval.

Example 2.33 The integral

$$I(\omega) = \int_0^\infty \frac{\sin \omega t}{t}\, dt$$

for $t \geq 0$ is now investigated. By setting $\omega t = x$, we have

$$I(\omega) = \int_0^\infty \frac{\sin x}{x}\, dx$$

From the appearance of this expression, it can be surmised immediately that the value of I will be independent of ω. Now, $\sin x/x$ is an even function of x. Thus we can write

$$I(\omega) = \frac{1}{2} \int_{-\infty}^\infty \frac{\sin x}{x}\, dx$$

or

$$I(\omega) = \frac{1}{2} \operatorname{Im} \int_{-\infty}^\infty \frac{e^{jx}}{x}\, dx$$

To evaluate this integral, consider the associated integral

$$J = \oint \frac{e^{jz}}{z}\, dz$$

Here the integrand has a pole at the point $z = 0$. According to both Cauchy's first and second integral theorems, the function under consideration must be analytic on all points C of the contour. This means, in choosing C, that the point $z = 0$ must be excluded from the contour; this, in turn, leads to the contour shown in Figure 2.15.

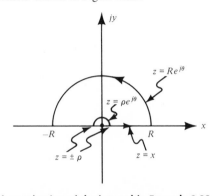

FIGURE 2.15 The contour for evaluation of the integral in Example 2.33.

With C now chosen, it is easy to see that there are no singularities within the region bounded by C, nor is there a singularity on C. By Cauchy's first integral theorem, we write immediately

$$J = 0 = \oint \frac{e^{jz}}{z} \, dz$$

The contributions from the four parts of C must now be found. We have

$$0 = \int_{-R}^{-\rho} \frac{e^{jx}}{x} \, dx + j \int_{\pi}^{0} \frac{e^{j\rho e^{j\theta}} \rho e^{j\theta}}{\rho e^{j\theta}} \, d\theta + \int_{\rho}^{R} \frac{e^{jx}}{x} \, dx + j \int_{0}^{\pi} \frac{e^{jRe^{j\theta}} Re^{j\theta}}{Re^{j\theta}} \, d\theta$$

The value of the second term of the right-hand side, as $\rho \to 0$, is $-\pi j$; the first and third terms are combined, so that

$$0 = -j\pi + \int_{-R}^{R} \frac{e^{jx}}{x} \, dx + j \int_{0}^{\pi} e^{jRe^{j\theta}} \, d\theta$$

The absolute value of the integral over θ satisfies the inequality

$$\left| j \int_{0}^{\pi} e^{jRe^{j\theta}} \, d\theta \right| \leq \int_{0}^{\pi} e^{-R \sin \theta} \, d\theta$$

Further, since $\sin \theta$ is an even function about $\pi/2$, we have

$$\int_{0}^{\pi} e^{-R \sin \theta} \, d\theta = 2 \int_{0}^{\pi/2} e^{-R \sin \theta} \, d\theta$$

and $\sin \theta \geq 2\theta/\pi$ for all θ in $0 \leq \theta \leq \pi/2$. Thus,

$$2 \int_{0}^{\pi/2} e^{-R \sin \theta} \, d\theta \leq 2 \int_{0}^{\pi/2} e^{-2R\theta/\pi} \, d\theta = \frac{\pi}{R} (1 - e^{-R})$$

Clearly, as $R \to \infty$, the last result approaches zero. Thus,

$$0 = -j\pi + \int_{-\infty}^{\infty} \frac{e^{jx}}{x} \, dx$$

That is,

$$I(\omega) = \frac{1}{2} \operatorname{Im} \int_{-\infty}^{\infty} \frac{e^{jx}}{x} \, dx = \frac{\pi}{2}$$

or, finally,

$$\int_{0}^{\infty} \frac{\sin \omega t}{t} \, dt = \frac{\pi}{2}$$ ∎

Example 2.34 We examine now the integral

$$I(t,\tau) = \int_{-\infty}^{\infty} \frac{e^{j\omega t}}{\cosh \omega \tau} \, d\omega$$

where $\tau > 0$ is some fixed time and, again, ω is the angular frequency over which the integration is made. We evaluate the quantity $I(t,\tau)$ by considering the associated integral

$$J(t,\tau) = \oint_C \frac{e^{jzt}}{\cosh z\tau} \, dz$$

about some contour C. The function $\cosh z\tau$ has zeros at the points z_n that satisfy the relation

$$z_n\tau = (2n + 1)j\pi/2$$

for any integer n, $n \geq 0$. To evaluate the integral $I(t,\tau)$ in terms of the contour integral $J(t,\tau)$, a part of the path of integration must be, again, the real axis for which $z = \omega$. If the path is then closed by a semicircle of radius Ω and Ω is allowed to approach infinity, an infinite number of poles will be enclosed by the contour, thus requiring the calculation of an infinite number of residues. There is, however, a contour that can be constructed that encloses only one pole. Obviously, such a path makes application of the Cauchy residue theorem a much easier task! The contour is shown in Figure 2.16. Only one pole, corresponding to $n = 0$, is now enclosed by the contour C.

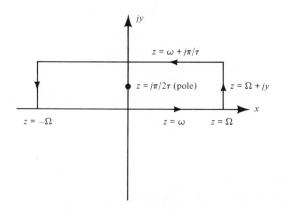

FIGURE 2.16   A contour C for evaluating the integral of Example 2.33.

Application of Cauchy's residue theorem gives the result

$$J(t,\tau) = 2\pi j \, \mathrm{Res}\left[\frac{e^{jzt}}{\cosh z\tau}\right]_{z=j\pi/2\tau}$$

The residue is calculated as follows:

$$\mathrm{Res} = \lim_{z \to j\pi/2\tau} \frac{(z - j\pi/2\tau)e^{jzt}}{\cosh z\tau}$$

and, on application of L'Hôpital's rule, has the value

$$\mathrm{Res} = -\frac{je^{-\pi t/2\tau}}{\tau}$$

so that

$$J(t,\tau) = \frac{2\pi e^{-\pi t/2\tau}}{\tau}$$

The integral around the contour C is now written as

$$\frac{2\pi}{\tau} e^{-\pi t/2\tau} = \int_{-\Omega}^{\Omega} \frac{e^{j\omega t}}{\cosh \omega\tau} \, d\tau + j \int_{0}^{\pi/\tau} \frac{e^{j(\Omega + jy)t}}{\cosh (\Omega + jy)} \, dy$$

$$+ \int_{\Omega}^{-\Omega} \frac{e^{j(\omega + j\pi/\tau)t}}{\cosh (\omega + j\pi/\tau)\tau} \, d\omega + j \int_{\pi/\tau}^{0} \frac{d^{j(-\Omega + jy)t}}{\cosh (-\Omega + jy)} \, dy$$

As $\Omega \to \infty$, the second and fourth integrals in the above expression approach zero as $e^{-\Omega}$. In the third of the integrals, the identity $\cosh (\omega + j\pi/\tau)\tau = \cosh \omega\tau$ is used, so that, as $\Omega \to \infty$,

$$\frac{2\pi}{\tau} e^{-\pi t/2\tau} = \int_{-\infty}^{\infty} \frac{e^{j\omega t}}{\cosh \omega\tau} (1 + e^{-\pi t/\tau}) \, d\omega$$

or

$$\frac{\pi}{\tau \cosh (\pi t/2\tau)} = \int_{-\infty}^{\infty} \frac{e^{j\omega t}}{\cosh \omega\tau} \, d\omega$$

On equating real and imaginary parts of both sides of the last equation, we find that

$$\frac{\pi}{\tau \cosh (\pi t/2\tau)} = \int_{-\infty}^{\infty} \frac{\cos \omega t}{\cosh \omega\tau} \, d\omega$$

and that

$$0 = \int_{-\infty}^{\infty} \frac{\sin \omega t}{\cosh \omega\tau} \, d\omega \qquad \blacksquare$$

2.11 ESSENTIAL SINGULARITIES. BRANCH POINTS

Thus far we have considered integrals having only simple poles or which were singularity-free in choosing contours for evaluation. We now look at a few examples of integrands that contain essential singularities or branch points and at the choice of contours for evaluating such integrals.

Example 2.35   Consider

$$J = \oint_{C} \frac{z^{p-1}}{1 + z} \qquad 0 < p < 1$$

We use a knowledge of the value of J to evaluate the integral

$$I = \int_{0}^{\infty} \frac{x^{p-1}}{1 + x} \, dx \qquad 0 < p < 1$$

The quantity $f(z) = z^{p-1}/(1 + z)$ has an essential singularity at the point $z = 0$. There is also a first-order pole of the function $f(z)$ at $z = -1$. Since there is an essential singularity at $z = 0$, the contour C must be chosen so that we avoid enclosing the point $z = 0$ within the region R bounded by C. The limits of integration on the integral I also indicate that we should take the positive real axis to be a part of C. The contour shown in Figure 2.17 is suitable for evaluating

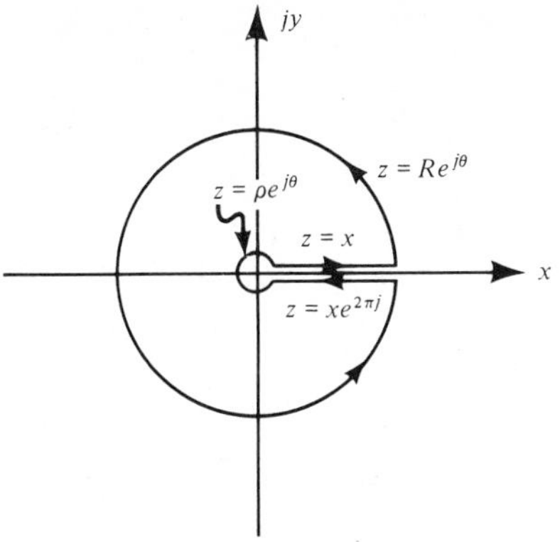

FIGURE 2.17 A contour for use in evaluating the integral given in Example 2.35.

the integral J. Since $z = 0$ is excluded from contour C, the only singularity within the region bounded by C (or on C) is the pole at $z = -1$. Thus we write

$$J = 2\pi j \ \text{Res}\left[\frac{z^{p-1}}{1+z}\right]_{z=-1}$$

or, since $e^{j\pi} = -1$,

$$J = 2\pi j \ e^{j\pi(p-1)}$$

On writing

$$\oint_C \frac{z^{p-1}}{1+z} \, dz = \int_\rho^R \frac{x^{p-1}}{1+x} \, dx + j \int_0^{2\pi} \frac{R^p e^{jp\theta}}{1+Re^{j\theta}} \, d\theta +$$
$$+ \int_R^\rho \frac{(xe^{2\pi j})^{p-1}}{1+x} \, dx + j \int_{2\pi}^0 \frac{\rho^p e^{jp\theta}}{1+\rho e^{j\theta}} \, d\theta$$

and allowing $R \to \infty$ and $\rho \to 0$, we have that the second and fourth integrals vanish, as previously discussed. Therefore,

$$\oint_C \frac{z^{p-1}}{1+z} \, dz = (1 - e^{2\pi j(p-1)}) \int_0^\infty \frac{x^{p-1}}{1+x} \, dx$$

On inserting the value of the integral J, and simplifying, we obtain

$$\int_0^\infty \frac{x^{p-1}}{1+x} \, dx = \frac{\pi}{\sin p\pi} \qquad (0 < p < 1) \qquad \blacksquare$$

Example 2.36 Consider the integral

$$J = \oint \frac{e^{jz}}{\sqrt{z}} \, dz$$

to be evaluated about the contour shown. From this, the value of the integral

$$I = \int_0^\infty \frac{e^{jx}}{\sqrt{x}} \, dx$$

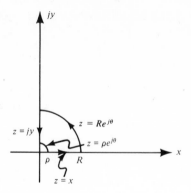

FIGURE 2.18   Contour for J in Example 2.36.

will be determined. Since there are no singularities within the contour,

$$J = 0 = \oint \frac{e^{jz}}{\sqrt{z}}\, dz$$

Therefore,

$$0 = \int_\rho^\infty \frac{e^{jx}}{\sqrt{x}}\, dx + jR^{1/2}\int_0^{\pi/2} e^{jRe^{j\theta}} e^{j\theta/2}\, d\theta + \sqrt{j}\int_R^\rho \frac{e^{-y}}{\sqrt{y}}\, dy +$$

$$+ \rho^{1/2}\int_{\pi/2}^0 e^{j\rho e^{j\theta}} e^{j\theta/2}\, d\theta$$

The second and fourth integrals vanish as $R \to \infty$ and $\rho \to 0$, respectively. Noting that $\sqrt{j} = (1 + j)/\sqrt{2}$, we have

$$I = \int_0^\infty \frac{\cos x + j\, \sin x}{\sqrt{x}}\, dx = \frac{1 + j}{\sqrt{2}}\int_0^\infty \frac{e^{-y}}{\sqrt{y}}\, dy$$

Hence

$$\int_0^\infty \frac{\cos x}{\sqrt{x}}\, dx = \int_0^\infty \frac{\sin x}{\sqrt{x}}\, dx = \frac{1}{\sqrt{2}}\int_0^\infty \frac{e^{-y}}{\sqrt{y}}\, dy$$

On setting $y = w^2$, we get

$$\int_0^\infty \frac{\cos x}{\sqrt{x}}\, dx = \int_0^\infty \frac{\sin x}{\sqrt{x}}\, dx = \sqrt{2}\int_0^\infty e^{-w^2}\, dw$$

or

$$\int_0^\infty \frac{\cos x}{\sqrt{x}}\, dx = \int_0^\infty \frac{\sin x}{\sqrt{x}}\, dx = \sqrt{\frac{\pi}{2}}$$

because

$$\int_0^\infty e^{-w^2}\, dw = \frac{1}{2}\int_{-\infty}^\infty e^{-w^2}\, dw = \frac{\sqrt{\pi}}{2}$$

Note that this last expression is the integral of an unnormalized Gaussian curve that has important applications in probability theory and diffusion theory, discussed in later chapters. ■

In the preceding examples, real integrals of the general form $\int_0^\infty x^{a-1}f(x)\,dx$ were evaluated using specific contours. The reason for the different choices is associated with the convergence of integrals over the arc of Figure 2.17 on which $z = Re^{j\theta}$. There is a theorem that will allow us to use the contour of Figure 2.17, provided that $x^{a-1}f(x)$ satisfies the requirements

$$\lim_{x\to 0} x^{a-1}f(x) \to 0$$

and

$$\lim_{x\to\infty} x^{a-1}f(x) \to 0$$

together with the condition that $f(x)$ is finite for $x > 0$. The theorem reads as follows:

$$\int_0^\infty x^{a-1}f(x)\,dx = \frac{\pi}{\sin a\pi} \sum \text{Res}\,(-z)^{a-1}f(z) \tag{2.96}$$

at the poles of $(-z)^{a-1}f(z)$, and where the contour is that of Figure 2.17. The theorem holds provided that, with $-z = \lambda e^{j\theta}$, say, the angle θ is in the interval $-\pi \le \theta \le \pi$. Let us prove this result.

Proof Consider

$$J = \oint_C (-z)^{a-1}f(z)\,dz \tag{2.97}$$

about the contour shown in Figure 2.17. We can write

$$(-z)^{a-1} = e^{(a-1)\ln(-z)} \tag{2.98}$$

and if we set $z = \lambda e^{j\theta}$, with $|\pm z| = \lambda$,

$$(-z)^{a-1} = e^{(a-1)(\ln|z| + j\theta)} \tag{2.99}$$

The range of θ is in $-\pi \le \theta \le \pi$, as required.

The integrand $(-z)^{a-1}f(z)$ is analytic on C and within R bounded by C except, possibly, at the poles of $f(z)$. By the Cauchy residue theorem,

$$J = \oint_C (-z)^{a-1}f(z)\,dz = 2\pi j \sum \text{Res}\,(f(z)) \tag{2.100}$$

There remains the question of the contributions to the integral from the various parts of the contour. On the circle surrounding $z = 0$ it is easy to show that, with $z = \rho e^{j\theta}$,

$$\lim_{\rho\to 0} -j \int_{-\pi}^{\pi} (\rho e^{j\theta})^{a-1}f(\rho e^{j\theta})e^{j\theta}\,d\theta = 0 \tag{2.101}$$

while on the circle of radius R, with $z = Re^{j\theta}$,

$$\lim_{R\to\infty} j \int_{-\pi}^{\pi} (Re^{j\theta})^{a-1}f(Re^{j\theta})Re^{j\theta}\,d\theta = 0 \tag{2.102}$$

The remaining two integrals associated with the contour C are on the x-axis. We have $-z = xe^{-\pi j}$ and $-z = xe^{\pi j}$ along the lines from ρ to R and R to ρ, respectively. Thus,

$$\lim_{\substack{\rho \to 0 \\ R \to \infty}} \oint_C (-z)^{a-1} f(z) \, dz = \int_0^\infty x^{a-1} (e^{-(a-1)\pi j} - e^{(a-1)\pi j}) f(x) \, dx \qquad (2.103)$$

Equating the expressions given in Equations 2.100 and 2.103 proves the required result of Equation 2.96.

2.12 THE LAURENT EXPANSION; MORE ON RESIDUES

There are functions $f(z)$ that are analytic in some *annular* region of the complex plane bounded by a contour C. See Figure 2.19. These may be expanded in a convergent series within the region of analyticity; the resulting expression is called a Laurent expansion of the function $f(z)$.

Consider the Cauchy residue theorem in the form

$$f(z) = \frac{1}{2\pi j} \oint_C \frac{f(\zeta)}{\zeta - z} \, d\zeta \qquad (2.104)$$

where the contour C is shown in Figure 2.19(b).

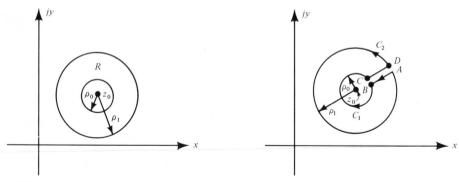

FIGURE 2.19 (a) The annular region of analyticity and (b) the contour for establishing the Laurent series.

Two circles, concentric with the point z_0 and of radius ρ_0 and ρ_1, are drawn. A cut is made in the contour as shown. Then, for any point z in the annular ring bounded by the circles of radius ρ_0 and ρ_1, it is clear that

$$\rho_0 < |z| < \rho_1 \qquad (2.105)$$

Equation 2.104 then becomes

$$2\pi j f(z) = \int_A^B \frac{f(\zeta)}{\zeta - z} \, d\zeta + \oint_{C_1} \frac{f(\zeta)}{\zeta - z} \, d\zeta + \int_C^D \frac{f(\zeta)}{\zeta - z} \, d\zeta + \oint_{C_2} \frac{f(\zeta)}{\zeta - z} \, d\zeta \qquad (2.106)$$

When A coincides with D and C with B, we have

$$2\pi j f(z) = -\oint_{C_1} \frac{f(\zeta)}{\zeta - z} \, d\zeta + \oint_{C_2} \frac{f(\zeta)}{\zeta - z} \, d\zeta \tag{2.107}$$

Let us write

$$f(z) = f_1(z) + f_2(z) \tag{2.108}$$

where

$$f_1(z) = \frac{1}{2\pi j} \oint_{C_1} \frac{f(\zeta)}{z - \zeta} \, d\zeta \tag{2.109}$$

and

$$f_2(z) = \frac{1}{2\pi j} \oint_{C_2} \frac{f(\zeta)}{\zeta - z} \, d\zeta \tag{2.110}$$

On any point on the contour C_1, $|z| > |\zeta|$, since $\zeta = \rho_0 e^{j\theta}$ on C_1. We use the identity

$$z - \zeta = (z - z_0)\left(1 - \frac{\zeta - z_0}{z - z_0}\right) \tag{2.111}$$

and the fact that

$$\left|\frac{\zeta - z_0}{z - z_0}\right| < 1 \tag{2.112}$$

to recognize that the quantity

$$\frac{1}{z - \zeta} = \frac{1}{z - z_0}\left(1 - \frac{\zeta - z_0}{z - z_0}\right)^{-1} \tag{2.113}$$

can be expanded in a uniformly and absolutely convergent series according to

$$(z - \zeta)^{-1} = (z - z_0)^{-1} \sum_n \left(\frac{\zeta - z_0}{z - z_0}\right)^n \tag{2.114}$$

Then $f_1(z)$ becomes

$$f_1(z) = \frac{1}{2\pi j} \oint_{C_1} \sum_{n=0}^{\infty} \frac{f(\zeta)}{(z - z_0)^{n+1}} (\zeta - z_0)^n \, d\zeta \tag{2.115}$$

or, on interchanging the order of integration and summation,

$$f_1(z) = \sum a_n (z - z_0)^{-(n+1)} \tag{2.116}$$

where the constants a_n are given by

$$a_n = \frac{1}{2\pi j} \oint_{C_1} f(\zeta)(\zeta - z_0)^n \, d\zeta \tag{2.117}$$

Consider the expression for $f_2(z)$ given by Equation 2.110. On C_2, $|\zeta| > |z|$, so that

$$(\zeta - z) = (\zeta - z_0)\left(1 - \frac{z - z_0}{\zeta - z_0}\right) \tag{2.118}$$

At every point on C_2,

$$\left|\frac{z - z_0}{\zeta - z_0}\right| < 1$$

so that we can expand the quantity

$$\left(1 - \frac{z - z_0}{\zeta - z_0}\right)^{-1}$$

in a uniformly and absolutely convergent series. The result is

$$(\zeta - z)^{-1} = \sum_{n=0}^{\infty} \frac{(z - z_0)^n}{(\zeta - z_0)^{n+1}} \tag{2.119}$$

Hence

$$f_2(z) = \sum_{n=0}^{\infty} b_n(z - z_0)^n \tag{2.120}$$

where the coefficients b_n are given by

$$b_n = \frac{1}{2\pi j} \oint_{C_2} \frac{f(\zeta)}{(\zeta - z_0)^{n+1}} \, d\zeta \tag{2.121}$$

The uniformly and absolutely convergent expansion of $f(z)$ then becomes

$$f(z) = \sum_{n=0}^{\infty} a_n(z - z_0)^{-(n+1)} + \sum_{n=0}^{\infty} b_n(z - z_0)^n \tag{2.122}$$

in the annular region $\rho_0 \le |z| \le \rho_1$. This expression may be made more compact by letting $n = -m$ in the series involving the coefficients a_n. We then have

$$f(z) = \sum_{m=0}^{-\infty} a_{-m}(z - z_0)^{m+1} + \sum_{m=0}^{\infty} b_m(z - z_0)^m \tag{2.123}$$

This can be written, denoting a_{-m} by b_m for negative m, as the *Laurent series*

$$f(z) = \sum_{m=-\infty}^{\infty} b_m(z - z_0)^m \tag{2.124}$$

where, for every integer m, positive or negative, b_m is given by

$$b_m = \frac{1}{2\pi j} \oint_{C} \frac{f(\zeta)}{(\zeta - z_0)^{m+1}} \, d\zeta \tag{2.125}$$

Consider the series in Equation 2.125, written as

$$f(z) = \frac{b_{-k}}{(z - z_0)^k} + \frac{b_{-k+1}}{(z - z_0)^{k-1}} + \cdots + \frac{b_{-1}}{z - z_0} + b_0 + b_1(z - z_0)$$

$$+ \cdots + b_p(z - z_0)^p \tag{2.126}$$

Suppose that $f(z)$ has a pole of first order at $z = z_0$. Then

$$\lim_{z \to z_0} (z - z_0)f(z) = b_{-1} \tag{2.127}$$

since it can be shown that $b_{-m} \equiv 0$ for $m > 1$. The importance of the Laurent expansion for our purposes can now be seen. It provides a quick way of finding the residue of a function within some annulus.

Example 2.37   Find the Laurent expansion of $f(z) = (z - 2)^{-1}$ for $|z| < 2$. We have, for $|z| < 2$, that

$$\frac{1}{z - 2} = \frac{-1}{2\left(1 - \dfrac{z}{2}\right)}$$

and since $|z/2| < 1$,

$$\left(1 - \frac{z}{2}\right)^{-1} = \sum_{n=0}^{\infty} \left(\frac{z}{2}\right)^n$$

Thus the Laurent expansion of $f(z)$ is

$$f(z) = \sum_{n=0}^{\infty} a_n z^n \qquad |z| < 2$$

where

$$a_n = -(2)^{-(n+1)}$$

It is observed here that there is no term a_{-1}/z. Thus the function $(z - 2)^{-1}$ is analytic at $z = 0$.

∎

Example 2.38   Find the Laurent expansion of $(z - 2)^{-1}$ for $z > 2$.
 We have, for $|z| > 2$, that

$$(z - 2)^{-1} = \frac{1}{z}\left(1 - \frac{2}{z}\right)^{-1}$$

and since $|2/z| < 1$ in this case,

$$(z - 2)^{-1} = \sum \frac{2^n}{z^{n+1}}$$

The coefficient of $z^{-1} (n = 0)$ is unity. Thus the residue of $f(z) = 1/(z - 2)$ at $z = 2$ is unity.

∎

Example 2.39   Find the Laurent expansion of $f(z) = 1/\sin z$ about $z = 0$. Since

$$\frac{1}{\sin z} = \frac{1}{z - \dfrac{z^3}{6} + \dfrac{z^5}{120} + \cdots}$$

there is a pole of first order at $z = 0$, i.e.,

$$\lim_{z \to 0} \frac{z}{\sin z} = 1$$

The Laurent series therefore must start with the term a_{-1}/z and will be of the form

$$\frac{a_{-1}}{z} + a_0 + a_1 z + a_2 z^2 + \cdots$$

with the coefficients $a_{-m} \equiv 0$ for $m > 1$. We therefore have

$$\frac{1}{z - \dfrac{z^3}{6} + \dfrac{z^5}{120} + \cdots} = \frac{a_{-1}}{z} + a_0 + a_1 z + a_2 z^2 + a_3 z^3$$

or, alternatively,

$$1 = \left(z - \frac{z^3}{6} + \frac{z^5}{120} + \cdots \right)\left(\frac{a_{-1}}{z} + a_0 + a_1 z + a_2 z^2 + a_3 z^3 + \cdots \right)$$

Equating coefficients of like powers of z on both sides gives us the first coefficients in the Laurent expansion. These are $a_{-1} = 1$, $a_0 = 0$, $a_1 = 1/3!$, $a_2 = 0$, $a_3 = -1/3! + 1/5!$, ... so that the Laurent expansion of $1/\sin z$ about $z = 0$ is

$$\frac{1}{\sin z} = \frac{1}{z} + \frac{z}{3!} + \left(-\frac{1}{3!} + \frac{1}{5!} \right)z^3 + \cdots$$

and the residue of $1/\sin z$ at $z = 0$ is unity, $a_{-1} = 1$.   ∎

Example 2.40   Let

$$f(z,t) = e^{\frac{z}{2}(t - 1/t)} = \sum_{n=-\infty}^{\infty} a_n(z) t^n$$

Let $t = e^{j\phi}$ so that

$$e^{\frac{z}{2}(t - 1/t)} = e^{jz \sin \phi}$$

Then

$$e^{jz \sin \phi} = \sum_{n=-\infty}^{\infty} a_n e^{jn\phi}$$

It remains to determine the coefficients a_n. We have by Equation 2.21 that, when the expansion is about $z_0 = 0$, then

$$a_n(z) = \frac{1}{2\pi j} \oint \frac{f(\zeta)}{\zeta^{n+1}} \, d\zeta$$

where, in our case,

$$f(\zeta) = e^{j\zeta \sin \phi}$$

Thus, since $\zeta = t = e^{j\phi}$, $d\zeta = je^{j\phi} \, d\phi$ and the integral is over a circle of unit radius, with $0 \le \phi \le 2\pi$. We find that

$$a_n(z) = \frac{1}{2\pi} \int_0^{2\pi} e^{jz \sin \phi} e^{-jn\pi} \, d\phi$$

This expression is an integral representation for the Bessel function $J_n(z)$; that is, $a_n(z) \equiv J_n(z)$. Bessel functions will be discussed further when we consider Fourier transforms in two spatial dimensions.   ∎

2.13   CONCLUDING REMARKS

In this chapter it has been our intent to introduce sufficient material to make inversion theorems for Laplace and Fourier transforms understandable. The Cauchy residue theorem is, in fact, totally remarkable, in that it reduces the problem of evaluating integrals, which may appear formidable, to a straightforward algebraic process.

In engineering, as previously mentioned, a knowledge of the location and nature of singularities is important in the analysis of complex systems. Questions of control and of stability of systems are intimately related to the nature of singularities in a (complex) frequency plane. The behavior of distributed linear systems, as well as the more familiar lumped-parameter systems, can be handled more easily with a knowledge of contour integration.

PROBLEMS

2-1   Evaluate (a) j^j; (b) $j^{1/j}$; (c) $\ln (\ln j)$; (d) $(1 + j)^j$.

2-2   Evaluate (a) $(1 - j)^6$; (b) $(1 + j\sqrt{3})^{1/3}$; (c) $\sqrt[5]{j}$; (d) $\sqrt[3]{-j}$.

2-3   Show on the complex plane the locus of points satisfying (a) Re $(z)^2 \geq 1$; (b) $2 \leq z - 1$; (c) Im $1/z < 1$.

2-4   In system theory the complex variable (used in Laplace transforms) is $s = \sigma + j\omega$. Find the $2n$ roots of

$$(-1)^n s^{2n} + 1 = 0$$

and show their location in the s-plane.

2-5   The equation in Problem 2-4 arises in filter theory and design. Consider only those roots $s_1, s_2, \ldots s_n$ whose real part is negative ($\sigma < 0$). Form the nth *Butterworth polynomial* defined as

$$B_n(s) = (s - s_1)(s - s_2) \cdots (s - s_n)$$

Obtain $B_1(s)$, $B_2(s)$, $B_3(s)$, and $B_4(s)$. Next form the transfer function

$$H_n(s) = \frac{1}{B_n(s)} \qquad (n = 1,2,3,4) \qquad s = j\omega$$

and plot $|H_n(\omega)|$ versus ω, yielding the magnitude response of these Butterworth filters.

2-6   Find $u(x,y)$ and $v(x,y)$ if $f(z)$ is given by (a) $\cos z$; (b) $\cosh z$; (c) $\tan z$.

2-7   Show that the Cauchy-Riemann equations in the polar representation are

$$\frac{\partial u}{\partial r} = \frac{1}{r} \frac{\partial v}{\partial \theta}$$

and

$$\frac{\partial v}{\partial r} = -\frac{1}{r}\frac{\partial u}{\partial \theta}$$

2-8   Determine whether or not the Cauchy-Riemann equations hold, and, in each case, the region of analyticity for (a) $f(z) = \sec z$; (b) $f(z) = \tan z$; (c) $f(z) = \tanh z$.

2-9   For $f(z)$ given by $r^n(\cos n\theta + j \sin n\theta)$ determine whether or not the Cauchy-Riemann are satisfied, and the region of analyticity.

2-10   Letting ψ denote either $u(r,\theta)$ or $v(r,\theta)$, show that

$$\frac{1}{r}\frac{\partial}{\partial r}\left(r\frac{\partial \psi}{\partial r}\right) + \frac{1}{r^2}\frac{\partial^2 \psi}{\partial \theta^2} = 0$$

is Laplace's equation expressed in polar coordinates.

2-11   For an infinitely long cylinder of radius a along the z-axis, find the potential $u(r,\theta)$ for $0 \le r \le \infty$ and $0 \le \theta \le 2\pi$ if

(a) $\lim\limits_{r\to\infty} u(r,\theta) = \dfrac{u_0}{2}$, $u(a,\theta) = u_0\,(\cos^2\theta - \sin\theta)$

(b) $\lim\limits_{r\to\infty} u(r,\theta) = 0$, $u(a,\theta) = u_0\,(\cos 2\theta - \sin 2\theta)$

2-12   For two concentric cylinders of radii a and b, find $u(r,\theta)$ in $a \le r \le b$ if $u(a,\theta) = u_0 \cos \theta$ and $u(b,\theta) = (u_0 a/b) \sin \theta$.
Hint   Set $u = u_1 + u_2$, where $u_1(a,\theta) = u_0 \cos \theta$ and $u_1(b,\theta) \equiv 0$, and where $u_2(b,\theta) = (u_0 a/b) \sin \theta$ and $u_2(a,\theta) \equiv 0$. This problem illustrates the *principle of superposition* of solutions.

2-13   Integrate $\dfrac{z+1}{z^2(z+z)}$ around the circle $|z| = 1$.

2-14   Integrate $1/\sinh z$ around: (a) $|z| = 1$; (b) $|z| = 4$.

2-15   Find the residue of $f(z)$ at the points indicated if $f(z)$ is given by

(a) $\dfrac{1}{z(z-b)}$ at $z = 0,\ b$

(b) $\dfrac{z}{z^2+1}$ at $z = \pm j$

(c) $1/(\sin z - z)$ at $z = 0$

2-16   Find the sum of the residues of the function $f(z) = e^{jz}/(z^2 + a^2)$ at the poles $z = \pm ja$.

2-17   Verify the final result of Example 2.32 by letting $z = e^{j\theta}$ and then evaluating the resulting integral by Cauchy's residue theorem.

2-18   Evaluate the integral $\displaystyle\int_0^{2\pi} \frac{\sin^2\theta\,d\theta}{a + b\cos\theta}$ for a and b real and $a > b > 0$.

2-19   Evaluate the integral $\displaystyle\int_0^{2\pi} \frac{\cos 2\theta}{a + b\cos\theta}\,d\theta$ for $a > b > 0$.

2-20   Evaluate each of the following integrals by considering a contour integral in the complex plane.

(a) $\displaystyle\int_{-\infty}^{\infty} \frac{e^{j\omega t}}{(\omega^2 \tau^2 + 1)^2}\, d\omega$

(b) $\displaystyle\int_{-\infty}^{\infty} \frac{e^{j\omega t}}{(\omega^2 - \omega_0^2 + 2a\omega)}\, d\omega$ for a, ω_0 real and positive. Note that in the corresponding integral involving the integrand $e^{jzt}/(z^2 - \omega_0^2 + 2az)$, there occurs the factor $z^2 + 2az - \omega_0^2$. The roots of this quadratic equation are at the points $z_1 = -a + \sqrt{a^2 + \omega_0^2}$ and $z_2 = -a - \sqrt{a^2 + \omega_0^2}$, and these are on the real axis. Thus you should choose a contour as shown in Figure 2.20.

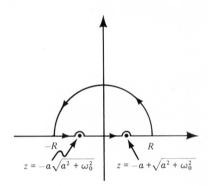

FIGURE 2.20   Problem 2-20(b).

(c) $\displaystyle\int_{0}^{\infty} \frac{\cos \omega t \sin \omega \tau}{\omega}\, d\omega \quad (t < \tau)$

(d) $\displaystyle\int_{0}^{\infty} \frac{\sin \omega t \sin \omega \tau}{(\omega^2 - \omega_0^2)}\, d\omega \quad \text{for both} \quad \begin{pmatrix} t > \tau \\ t < \tau \end{pmatrix}$

(e) $\displaystyle\int_{0}^{\infty} \frac{e^{j\omega t}}{\sqrt{\omega}(\omega + \tau^{-1})}\, d\omega$

Hint   Use the contour of Figure 2.17.

(f) $\displaystyle\int_{0}^{\infty} \frac{\omega^{-(1/2)} \sin \omega t}{(\omega^2 \tau^2 + 1)^2}\, d\omega \quad \text{for both} \ (t, \tau) > 0$

Hint   Use the contour of Figure 2.17.

2-21   Use contour integration to evaluate

(a) $\displaystyle I = \int_{0}^{\infty} \frac{dx}{1 + x^2}$

(b) $\displaystyle I = \int_{0}^{\infty} \frac{dx}{1 + x^4}$

2-22   Find the Laurent expansion of $f(z)$ if $f(z)$ is given by

(a) $z/(z^2 - 1)$ for $|z| > 1$

(b) $(z - 1)^{-1}(2 - z)^{-1}$ in $1 < |z| < 2$

(c) $(z - 1)^{-1}(2 - z)^{-1}$ for $|z| > 2$

2-23 In each of the cases, identify the residues, if any. Find the Laurent expansions of $f(z)$ if $f(z)$ is given by

(a) $e^z z^{-2}$ at $z = 0$

(b) $\dfrac{1 - \sin z}{\cos z}$ about $z = \pi/2$ (let $z = \rho - \pi/2$ and expand about $\rho = 0$)

2.24 Consider the function $f(z)$ to be analytic in the right half of the complex plane and on the imaginary axis. Such functions are commonly encountered in the analysis and design of lumped-parameter stable systems.

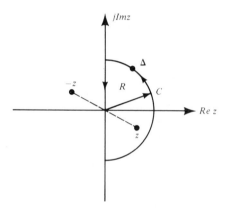

FIGURE 2.21 Problem 2-24.

(a) Use the contour of integration C_1 as shown in Figure 2.21. Use Cauchy's integral theorem to write the expression for $f(z)$ where z is a point within C and δ is on C. Next write an expression for $f(-z)$.

(b) Add and subtract these two expressions to obtain two integral expressions for $f(z)$.

(c) Simplify further the expressions for $f(z)$ if the contributions to the integrals on the semi-circular path vanish. These expressions are the *Hilbert transforms* of $f(z)$, relating $f(z)$ to its real and imaginary parts.

2-25 One useful form of the Hilbert transforms (see Problem 2-24) is

$$X(\omega) = -\frac{2\omega}{\pi} \int_0^\infty \frac{R(\eta)\, d\eta}{\omega^2 - \eta^2}$$

where $Z(j\omega) = R(\omega) + jX(\omega)$ is the rectangular form of an impedance $Z(s)$ for $s = j\omega$, and $R(\omega)$ and $X(\omega)$ are, respectively, the real and the imaginary parts of $Z(j\omega)$.

(a) Investigate the behavior of $X(\omega)$ for large frequencies ($\omega \to \infty$). Show that this behavior is that of a capacitive reactance, where the value of the capacitor C is given by

$$\frac{\pi}{2C} = \int_0^\infty R(\eta)\, d\eta$$

This result is known as the *resistance integral formula*.

(b) Repeat for $\omega \to 0$. Show that then the behavior is inductive, with

$$\frac{\pi L}{2} = \int_0^\infty \frac{R(\eta)}{\eta^2} \, d\eta$$

2-26 An alternate way to derive the resistance integral formula is given in the following steps

(a) Let $Z(s)$ be analytic in the right half of the complex plane and also let $Z(s) \to 1/Cs$ as $s \to \infty$. Use Cauchy's integral formula to integrate $\oint Z(s) \, ds$ where the contour or integration consists of the entire $j\omega$-axis and a large semicircle in the right half of the s-plane.

(b) In part (a) establish that the contribution to the contour integral along the $j\omega$-axis is

$$j \int_{-\infty}^\infty Z(j\omega) \, d\omega = 2j \int_0^\infty R(\omega) \, d\omega$$

(c) Establish that, around the semicircle, the contribution to the integral is $-j\pi/C$.

(d) From parts (a), (b), and (c), establish the final result, as given in Problem 2-25.

SELECTED BIBLIOGRAPHY

1. R. V. Churchill, *Introduction to Complex Variables and Applications*. New York: McGraw-Hill Book Co., Inc., 1948.
2. E. A. Guillemin, *The Mathematics of Circuit Analysis*. New York: John Wiley & Sons, Inc., and M.I.T. Press, 1949.
3. W. Kaplan, *Advanced Mathematics for Engineers*. Reading, Mass.: Addison-Wesley Publishing Co., Inc., 1981.
4. W. Kaplan, *Operational Methods for Linear Systems*. Reading, Mass.: Addison-Wesley Publishing Co., Inc., 1962.
5. E. Kreyszig, *Advanced Engineering Mathematics* (4th ed.). New York: John Wiley & Sons, Inc., 1979.
6. N. W. McLachlan, *Complex Variable Theory and Transform Calculus*. Cambridge, England: Cambridge University Press, 1953.
7. E. T. Whittaker and G. N. Watson, *Modern Analysis*. New York: Macmillan Book Co., Inc., 1943.
8. C. R. Wylie, *Advanced Engineering Mathematics* (4th ed.). New York: McGraw-Hill Book Co., Inc., 1975.

CHAPTER 3

The
Laplace
Transform
And
Its
Inversion

3.1 INTRODUCTION

In this chapter we study the Laplace transform and some of its applications in engineering. After defining the Laplace transform, we discuss briefly the conditions for its existence and then find the Laplace transform of a few simple functions. Several theorems follow, each of which enables us to find further transforms. In this way a table of Laplace transforms can be constructed, such as given in Appendix D.

The inversion of Laplace transforms is then considered. This operation involves an integral defined in a region of the complex plane, and much of the work of Chapter 2 is directly applicable; in particular, Cauchy's residue theorem is important here.

Applications of the Laplace transform to both total and partial differential equations as they occur in engineering are discussed, with emphasis on the physical context in which such equations arise.

3.2 THE LAPLACE TRANSFORM

Given a function $f(t)$, which is piecewise continuous and is of exponential order, the function $F(s)$

$$F(s) = \mathscr{L}\{f(t)\} \equiv \int_{0_-}^{\infty} f(t)e^{-st}dt \qquad (3.1)$$

exists, and is called the Laplace transform of $f(t)$. The function $f(t)$ is of exponential order if $|f(t)| \leq Me^{\alpha t}$ for all t and where M is real and bounded and α is real.

Also, we are dealing with $f(t)$ which is considered to be zero for $t < 0$. Such functions, common in engineering, are sometimes designated by $f(t)u(t)$, where $u(t)$ is the unit step function, given by

$$u(t) = \begin{cases} 1 & t > 0 \\ 0 & t < 0 \end{cases} \tag{3.2}$$

See Figure 3.1.

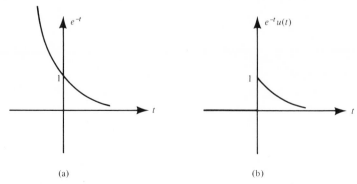

(a)   (b)

FIGURE 3.1   (a) $f(t) = e^{-t}$; (b) $f(t)u(t) = e^{-t}u(t)$.

Note that, since the quantity st must be dimensionless in the term e^{-st}, it follows that s is a frequency. We take s to be complex, in general, and write

$$s = \sigma + j\omega$$

The s-plane is shown in Figure 3.2.

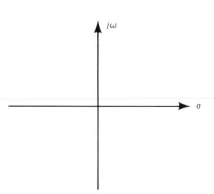

FIGURE 3.2   The complex s-plane.

If, then, we define

$$G(s) = \int_{0-}^{\infty} |f(t)| e^{-st} dt \le M \int_{0-}^{\infty} e^{-(s-\alpha)t} dt \tag{3.3}$$

we find that for Re $s > \alpha$,

$$G(s) \le \frac{M}{s - \alpha} \tag{3.4}$$

Thus the conditions for the existence of a unique Laplace transform $F(s)$ of a function

$f(t)$ are that $f(t)$ be piecewise continuous, that it be of exponential order, and, finally, that Re $s > \alpha$, where α is some real positive constant.

It follows directly from Equation 3.1 that if $f(t) = f_1(t) + f_2(t)$, then

$$\mathcal{L}\{f_1(t) + f_2(t)\} = \mathcal{L}\{f_1(t)\} + \mathcal{L}\{f_2(t)\} \tag{3.5}$$

Also, if a is a constant,

$$\mathcal{L}\{af(t)\} = a\mathcal{L}\{f(t)\} \tag{3.6}$$

i.e., the Laplace transform is a linear operation.

In the remainder of this section, several examples of the calculation of Laplace transforms are given.

Example 3.1   Let $f(t) = e^{-at}$ with a complex and with Re $a > 0$. Then, according to Equation 3.1,

$$\mathcal{L}\{e^{-at}\} = \int_{0_-}^{\infty} e^{-(s+a)t} dt$$

The integral is easily evaluated and yields

$$\mathcal{L}\{e^{-at}\} = \frac{1}{s + a}$$

provided that Re $\{s + a\} > 0$. ∎

Example 3.2   If we now let the real part of a be identically zero, so that $a \equiv j\omega$ is purely imaginary, then

$$\mathcal{L}\{e^{-j\omega t}\} = \frac{1}{s + j\omega}$$

while

$$\mathcal{L}\{e^{j\omega t}\} = \frac{1}{s - j\omega}$$ ∎

Example 3.3   It is now an easy matter to find the Laplace transforms of the trigonometric functions $\cos \omega t$ and $\sin \omega t$. We have

$$\cos \omega t = \frac{e^{j\omega t} + e^{-j\omega t}}{2}$$

Using Equations 3.5 and 3.6 and the previous example, we have

$$\mathcal{L}\{\cos \omega t\} = \frac{s}{s^2 + \omega^2}$$

The transform of $\sin \omega t$ becomes, similarly,

$$\mathcal{L}\{\sin \omega t\} = \mathcal{L}\left\{\frac{1}{2j}(e^{j\omega t} - e^{-j\omega t})\right\} = \frac{\omega}{s^2 + \omega^2}$$ ∎

Example 3.4   The Laplace transform of the hyperbolic cosine and sine are now found. The use of exponential representations of the hyperbolic sine and cosine yields

$$\mathcal{L}\{\cosh at\} = \frac{s}{s^2 - a^2}$$

and

$$\mathcal{L}\{\sinh at\} = \frac{a}{s^2 - a^2}$$ ∎

Example 3.5   We calculate

$$\mathcal{L}\{t^n\} = \int_{0-}^{\infty} t^n e^{-st} dt$$

where n is an integer. Let $st = x$ so that $t^n dt = x^n dx/s^{n+1}$. Then

$$\mathcal{L}\{t^n\} = \frac{1}{s^{n+1}} \int_{0-}^{\infty} e^{-x} x^n dx$$

By successive integration by parts, the identity

$$n! = \int_{0-}^{\infty} e^{-x} x^n dx$$

is established,* with the result that

$$\mathcal{L}\{t^n\} = \frac{n!}{s^{n+1}}$$

In particular, for $n = 0$ we have

$$\mathcal{L}\{u(t)\} = \frac{1}{s}$$

where the unit step function $u(t)$ is previously defined.†   ∎

We now introduce the Dirac delta function and show its relationship to the unit step function.

In Appendix A, the Dirac delta function, or the unit impulse function, is discussed in some detail. Our purpose here is to find the Laplace transform of the "function" $\delta(t - t_0)$. Here, $\delta(t - t_0)$ is a function that is zero for all $t \neq t_0$, and at $t = t_0$, $\delta(t - t_0) \rightarrow \infty$ such that

---

*The quantity $\int_{0}^{\infty} e^{-x} x^n dx$ is often taken to be the defining relation for the gamma function, i.e.,

$\Gamma(n + 1) = \int_{0}^{\infty} e^{-x} x^n dx$, or $\Gamma(n + 1) = n!$ for integer n.

†The function $u(t)$ is sometimes called the Heaviside unit step function in honor of Oliver Heaviside, a British engineer who developed a "transform" calculus that has been refined to the Laplace transform. His feuds with mathematicians over his supposed lack of rigor are well documented and provide interesting reading.

$$\int_0^\infty \delta(t - t_0) = 1 \tag{3.7}$$

Further,

$$\int_{-\infty}^\infty f(t)\, \delta(t - t_0)\, dt = f(t_0) \tag{3.8}$$

i.e., the delta function picks out (or "sifts") $f(t)$ and finds its value at $t = t_0$.

With the above remarks in mind, it is clear that

$$\mathcal{L}\{\delta(t - t_0)\} = \int_{0_-}^\infty \delta(t - t_0)e^{-st}dt = e^{-st_0} \tag{3.9}$$

Note that, if $t_0 = 0$, $\mathcal{L}\{\delta(t)\} = 1$.

The connection with the unit step function is made reasonable by examination of Figure 3.3(a,b). In Figure 3.3(a), $f(t) \equiv 0$ for $t \leq t_0$ and $f(t) = 1$ for $t \geq t_0 + \tau$. In

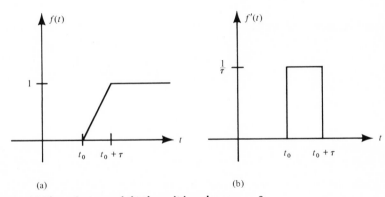

(a)   (b)

FIGURE 3.3   (a) The unit step and (b) the unit impulse as $\tau \to 0$.

Figure 3.3(b) the derivative of the function $f(t)$ is shown. As $\tau \to 0$, $f(t) \to u(t - t_0)$, while $f'(t) \to \delta(t - t_0)$.

As mentioned previously, further information concerning the delta function can be found in Appendix A.

3.3   LAPLACE TRANSFORMS OF DERIVATIVES AND INTEGRALS

We consider the transform

$$\mathcal{L}\left\{\frac{df}{dt}\right\} = \int_{0_-}^\infty \frac{df(t)}{dt} e^{-st}dt \tag{3.10}$$

An integration by parts gives

$$\mathcal{L}\left\{\frac{df}{dt}\right\} = f(t)e^{-st}\Big|_{0_-}^\infty + s\int_{0_-}^\infty f(t)e^{-st}dt \tag{3.11}$$

Since $f(t)$ is of exponential order, the first term on the right-hand side of Equation 3.11 vanishes as $t \to \infty$. We use Equation 3.10 to obtain

$$\mathcal{L}\left\{\frac{df}{dt}\right\} = sF(s) - f(0_-) \tag{3.12}$$

Here is another of the valuable properties of the Laplace transform; namely, the initial condition on the function $f(t)$ is a "built-in" consequence of finding the Laplace transform of the first derivative.

We now calculate

$$\mathcal{L}\left\{\frac{d^2f}{dt^2}\right\} = \mathcal{L}\left\{\frac{d}{dt}\left(\frac{df}{dt}\right)\right\} \tag{3.13}$$

If we temporarily designate the first derivative of f by $g(t)$, i.e.,

$$\frac{df}{dt} = g(t) \tag{3.14}$$

then from Equation 3.12 we get

$$\mathcal{L}\left\{\frac{d^2f}{dt^2}\right\} = sG(s) - g(0_-) \tag{3.15}$$

where

$$G(s) = \mathcal{L}\{g(t)\} = \mathcal{L}\left\{\frac{df}{dt}\right\} = sF(s) - f(0_-) \tag{3.16}$$

Therefore,

$$\mathcal{L}\left\{\frac{d^2f}{dt^2}\right\} = s[sF(s) - f(0_-)] - f'(0_-) = s^2F(s) - sf(0_-) - f'(0_-) \tag{3.17}$$

The Laplace transform of the nth derivative of $f(t)$ is calculated in the same way. The result is

$$\mathcal{L}\left\{\frac{d^nf}{dt^n}\right\} = s^nF(s) - s^{n-1}f(0_-) - s^{n-2}f'(0_-) - \cdots - f^{(n-1)}(0_-) \tag{3.18}$$

where $F(s) = \mathcal{L}\{f(t)\}$ and

$$\lim_{t\to 0_-}\frac{d^kf}{dt^k} \equiv f^{(k)}(0_-), \qquad (k = 0, \ldots n - 1) \tag{3.19}$$

A question might arise at this point (if not earlier) about the lower limit of the integral defining the Laplace transform: Since the Laplace transform could have been defined originally with 0_+ as the lower limit, what happens if $f(0_-) \neq f(0_+)$? The answer is very simple.* Either one of these choices (0_- or 0_+) is valid, provided we are consistent throughout all the following derivations. It is easier, however, to work with

---

*Here, the notation $f(0_-)$ should be interpreted as "the limit of $f(t)$ as t approaches zero (from the left) through negative values."

0_- as the lower limit in the Laplace integral, because this choice *automatically* gives the correct answers even when $f(0_-) \neq f(0_+)$. The following example illustrates this point.[1]

Example 3.6 In the network shown in Figure 3.4, the capacitor is uncharged until $t = 0$, at

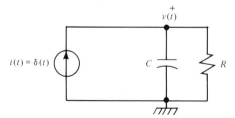

FIGURE 3.4 Example 3.6.

which time the current source $i(t) = \delta(t)$ is applied. The differential equation describing the system for $t > 0$ is

$$C\frac{dv}{dt} + \frac{1}{R}v = \delta(t)$$

Apply the Laplace transform to this equation, using 0_- as the lower limit. We obtain

$$C[sV(s) - v(0_-)] + \frac{1}{R}V(s) = 1$$

Since $v(0_-) = 0$ (i.e., the capacitor is uncharged until $t = 0$), the transformed equation becomes

$$CsV(s) + \frac{1}{R}V(s) = 1$$

If we want to use the Laplace transform with 0_+ as the lower limit, we obtain

$$C[sV(s) - v(0_+)] + \frac{1}{R}V(s) = 0$$

The right-hand side of this equation is zero because

$$\int_{0_+}^{\infty} \delta(t)e^{-st}dt = 0$$

since the impulse $\delta(t)$ occurs outside the limits of the integral. We still need to evaluate $v(0_+)$. This is done as a separate "subproblem," based on physical considerations. The current $i(t) = \delta(t)$ amounts to one unit of charge placed instantly on the capacitor. Therefore, $q(0_+) = 1$ and $v(0_+) = q(0_+)/C = 1/C$. Upon inserting this value into the transformed equation, we get

$$C\left[sV(s) - \frac{1}{C}\right] + \frac{1}{R}V(s) = 0$$

or

$$CsV(s) + \frac{1}{R} V(s) = 1$$

precisely as in the previous calculation.   ∎

There are functions whose transforms can be expressed as derivatives or integrals of the function $F(s)$, defined by Equation 3.1. Consider

$$\mathcal{L}\{tf(t)\} = \int_0^\infty tf(t)e^{-st}dt \qquad (3.20)$$

Now, on writing once again the relation

$$F(s) = \int_{0_-}^\infty f(t)e^{-st}dt \qquad (3.1)$$

and on differentiating both sides of Equation 3.1 with respect to s, we have

$$\frac{dF(s)}{ds} = -\int_{0_-}^\infty tf(t)e^{-st}dt \qquad (3.21)$$

Thus, we get from Equations 3.20 and 3.21 the theorem

$$\mathcal{L}\{tf(t)\} = -\frac{dF(s)}{ds} \qquad (3.22)$$

Multiplication of $f(t)$ by t corresponds to the negative of the derivative of $F(s)$ with respect to s. We illustrate by means of a few examples.

Example 3.7   We have already established that

$$\mathcal{L}\{\cos \omega t\} = \frac{s}{s^2 + \omega^2}$$

Then, from the theorem given in Equation 3.22, we get

$$\mathcal{L}\{t \cos \omega t\} = -\frac{d}{ds}\left(\frac{s}{s^2 + \omega^2}\right)$$

or

$$\mathcal{L}\{t \cos \omega t\} = \frac{s^2 - \omega^2}{(s^2 + \omega^2)^2} \qquad \blacksquare$$

Example 3.8   In similar fashion, since

$$\mathcal{L}\{e^{-at}\} = \frac{1}{s + a}$$

$$\mathcal{L}\{te^{-at}\} = -\frac{d}{ds}\left(\frac{1}{s + a}\right)$$

or

$$\mathcal{L}\{te^{-at}\} = \frac{1}{(s + a)^2} \qquad \blacksquare$$

Example 3.9   We now find

$$\mathcal{L}\{t^n f(t)\} = \int_{0_-}^{\infty} t^n f(t) e^{-st} dt$$

From Equation 3.1 we have

$$\frac{d^n F(s)}{ds^n} = (-1)^n \int_0^{\infty} t^n f(t) e^{-st} dt$$

so that

$$\mathcal{L}\{t^n f(t)\} = (-1)^n \frac{d^n F(s)}{ds^n} \qquad\blacksquare$$

We now turn to the case for which a Laplace transform is expressible as an integral of the transform function $F(s)$. We calculate

$$\mathcal{L}\left\{\frac{f(t)}{t}\right\} = \int_{0_-}^{\infty} \frac{f(t)}{t} e^{-st} dt \tag{3.23}$$

The integral

$$I(s) = \int_s^{\infty} e^{-\xi t} d\xi \tag{3.24}$$

has the value, for Re $\xi > 0$, of

$$I(s) = \frac{1}{t} e^{-st} \tag{3.25}$$

Thus we can write

$$\mathcal{L}\left\{\frac{f(t)}{t}\right\} = \int_{0_-}^{\infty} \int_s^{\infty} e^{-\xi t} f(t) d\xi \, dt \tag{3.26}$$

Assuming that interchange of the order of integration is allowed, we have

$$\mathcal{L}\left\{\frac{f(t)}{t}\right\} = \int_s^{\infty} \int_{0_-}^{\infty} e^{-\xi t} f(t) dt \, d\xi \tag{3.27}$$

or

$$\mathcal{L}\left\{\frac{f(t)}{t}\right\} = \int_s^{\infty} F(\xi) d\xi \tag{3.28}$$

Thus the Laplace transform of $f(t)/t$ is equal to the integral of $F(s)$ over the range $s \le \xi \le \infty$, where ξ is a dummy variable of integration.

Example 3.10   Since

$$\mathcal{L}\{\sin \omega t\} = \frac{\omega}{s^2 + \omega^2}$$

then

$$\mathcal{L}\left\{\frac{\sin \omega t}{t}\right\} = \int_s^\infty \frac{\omega \, d\xi}{\xi^2 + \omega^2}$$

Setting $\xi/\omega = x$ converts the last integral into

$$\mathcal{L}\left\{\frac{\sin \omega t}{t}\right\} = \int_{s/\omega}^\infty \frac{dx}{1 + x^2}$$

so that

$$\mathcal{L}\left\{\frac{\sin \omega t}{t}\right\} = \frac{\pi}{2} - \tan^{-1}\left(\frac{s}{\omega}\right) = \tan^{-1}\left(\frac{\omega}{s}\right) \qquad \blacksquare$$

Example 3.11   Find the Laplace transform of $(1/t)(e^{-at} - e^{-bt})$. We write

$$f_1(t) = e^{-at}, \quad f_2(t) = e^{-bt}$$

Then

$$\mathcal{L}\left\{\frac{e^{-at} - e^{-bt}}{t}\right\} = \int_s^\infty (F_1(\xi) - F_2(\xi)) d\xi$$

where $F_1(\xi) = 1/(\xi + a)$ and $F_2(\xi) = 1/(\xi + b)$. Thus,

$$\mathcal{L}\left\{\frac{e^{-at} - e^{-bt}}{t}\right\} = \ln\left(\frac{s + b}{s + a}\right) \qquad \blacksquare$$

3.4   SHIFTING THEOREMS

In this section two theorems of considerable usefulness are proved. Consider first a function $f(t)$, whose Laplace transform is $F(s)$. We inquire into the connection between $F(s)$ and the Laplace transform of the function $e^{-\lambda t}f(t)$. We have

$$\mathcal{L}\{e^{-\lambda t}f(t)\} = \int_{0_-}^\infty f(t)e^{-\lambda t}e^{-st} dt \qquad (3.29)$$

or

$$\mathcal{L}\{e^{-\lambda t}f(t)\} = \int_{0_-}^\infty f(t)e^{-(s+\lambda)t} dt \qquad (3.30)$$

But Equation 3.30 is nothing more than the definition, from Equation 3.1, of the function $F(s + \lambda)$

$$F(s + \lambda) = \int_{0_-}^\infty f(t)e^{-(s+\lambda)t} dt \qquad (3.31)$$

Thus the shifting theorem in the s-domain is: If

$$F(s) = \mathcal{L}\{f(t)\} \qquad (3.32a)$$

then

$$F(s + \lambda) = \mathcal{L}\{e^{-\lambda t}f(t)\} \qquad (3.32b)$$

The relations shown in Equation 3.32 hold provided, again, that $f(t)$ and $e^{-\lambda t}f(t)$ are of exponential order. If $f(t)$ is of exponential order, then $e^{-\lambda t}f(t)$ is clearly of exponential order for Re $\lambda > 0$. If Re $\lambda < 0$, then $e^{\lambda t}f(t)$ has a Laplace transform $F(s - \lambda)$ provided that, if $\lim_{t \to \infty} f(t) \to e^{at}$, then Re $s >$ Re $(\lambda + a)$.

Example 3.12 If $f(t) = \cos \omega_0 t$, find $\mathscr{L}\{e^{-\lambda t}f(t)\}$. Since $\mathscr{L}\{\cos \omega_0 t\} = s/(s^2 + \omega_0^2)$, the theorem immediately yields the result

$$\mathscr{L}\{e^{-\lambda t} \cos \omega_0 t\} = \frac{s + \lambda}{(s + \lambda)^2 + \omega_0^2}$$

∎

Example 3.13 Given $\mathscr{L}\{t\}^2 = 2/s^3$. Then, by applying the s-domain shifting theorem,

$$\mathscr{L}\{e^{-\lambda t}t^2\} = \frac{2}{(s + \lambda)^3}$$

∎

Example 3.14 Let $f(t)$ be a square pulse, as shown in Figure 3.5. Then

$$\mathscr{L}\{f(t)\} = \int_{0_-}^{t_0} e^{-st}dt = \frac{1}{s}(1 - e^{-st_0})$$

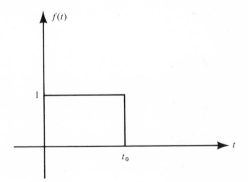

FIGURE 3.5 Example 3.14.

The Laplace transform of $e^{-\lambda t}f(t)$, with $f(t)$ as above, is

$$\mathscr{L}\{e^{-\lambda t}f(t)\} = \frac{1}{s + \lambda}(1 - e^{-(s+\lambda)t_0})$$

This example also illustrates the fact that the Laplace transform of a function that is nonzero over only a portion of the t-axis can be found.

∎

The second shifting theorem deals with a time-shifted function. Here the explicit use of the unit step function is helpful. First, let us define a shifted unit step function as

$$u(\cdot) = \begin{cases} 1 & (\cdot) > 0 \\ 0 & (\cdot) < 0 \end{cases} \tag{3.33}$$

Therefore,

$$u(t - \tau) = \begin{cases} 1 & t > \tau \\ 0 & t < \tau \end{cases} \qquad (3.34)$$

and is shown in Figure 3.6.

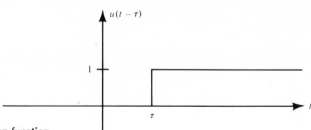

FIGURE 3.6   A shifted unit step function.

Now consider the original time function $f(t)u(t)$ whose Laplace transform is $F(s)$. The time-shifted (time-delayed) function is then $f(t - \tau)u(t - \tau)$, as shown in Figure 3.7(b). We wish to find the Laplace transform of the time-shifted function. Setting up the defining integral, we have

$$\mathcal{L}\{f(t - \tau)u(t - \tau)\} = \int_{0_-}^{\infty} f(t - \tau)u(t - \tau)e^{-st}dt \qquad (3.35)$$

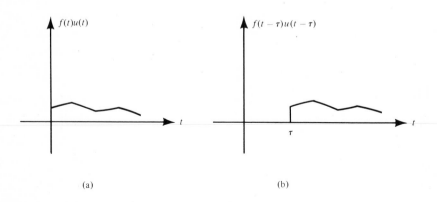

FIGURE 3.7   (a) Original, nonshifted and (b) time-shifted functions.

Because $u(t - \tau) = 0$ for $0 < t < \tau$ and $u(t - \tau) = 1$ for $t > \tau$, the last integral becomes

$$\mathcal{L}\{f(t - \tau)u(t - \tau)\} = \int_{\tau}^{\infty} f(t - \tau)e^{-st}dt \qquad (3.36)$$

A change of variables

$$t - \tau = w, \quad dt = dw \qquad (3.37)$$

yields the value of the integral as

$$\mathscr{L}\{f(t - \tau)u(t - \tau)\} = e^{-s\tau}F(s) \tag{3.38}$$

In words, we say that the Laplace transform of a time-shifted function is obtained by multiplying the Laplace transform of the original time function, $F(s)$, by $e^{-s\tau}$.

Example 3.15   Consider a shifted square pulse, as shown in Figure 3.8 and compared with the nonshifted pulse in Example 3.14. Its Laplace transform is obtained by using Equation 3.38,

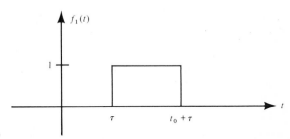

FIGURE 3.8   A shifted square pulse.

$$F_1(s) = \mathscr{L}\{f_1(t)\} = e^{-s\tau}\left(\frac{1 - e^{-st_0}}{s}\right)$$

where $F(s)$ is the Laplace of the original nonshifted pulse, as in Example 3.14. As a check on our result we can evaluate $F_1(s)$ directly by using Equation 3.1.

$$F_1(s) = \int_{0_-}^{\infty} f_1(t)e^{-st}dt = \int_{0_-}^{t_0+\tau} e^{-st}dt = \frac{e^{-s\tau} - e^{-s(t_0+\tau)}}{s} \qquad \blacksquare$$

3.5   INITIAL AND FINAL VALUE THEOREMS

The initial value theorem of the Laplace transform theory states concisely that

$$\lim_{s\to\infty} sF(s) = \lim_{t\to 0_-} f(t) \tag{3.39}$$

and it provides information about $\lim_{t\to 0_-} f(t)$ directly from $F(s)$. The proof of the theorem follows from the definition of the Laplace transform of the derivative of $f(t)$. We have, from a previous derivation,

$$\mathscr{L}\left\{\frac{df}{dt}\right\} = sF(s) - f(0_-) = \int_{0_-}^{\infty} \frac{df}{dt}e^{-st}dt \tag{3.40}$$

Now, as $s \to \infty$,

$$\lim_{s\to\infty} \int_{0_-}^{\infty} \frac{df}{dt}e^{-st}dt \to 0 \tag{3.41}$$

for all $t > 0$ if $f(t)$ and its derivative are Laplace transformable. Thus,

$$\lim_{s\to\infty} sF(s) = f(0_-) \tag{3.42}$$

or

$$\lim_{s \to \infty} sF(s) = \lim_{t \to 0_-} f(t) \tag{3.43}$$

The final value theorem of the Laplace transform theory is given by

$$\lim_{s \to 0} sF(s) = \lim_{t \to \infty} f(t) \tag{3.44}$$

provided these limits exist. Again, the behavior of $f(t)$ for $t \to \infty$ may be inferred directly from its transform. To prove the theorem it is necessary again to write

$$sF(s) - f(0_-) = \int_{0_-}^{\infty} \frac{df}{dt} e^{-st} dt \tag{3.45}$$

As $s \to 0$, we get

$$\lim_{s \to 0} \int_{0_-}^{\infty} \frac{df}{dt} e^{-st} dt \to \int_{0_-}^{\infty} \frac{df}{dt} dt = \lim_{t \to \infty} f(t) - f(0_-) \tag{3.46}$$

Thus,

$$\lim_{s \to 0} sF(s) = \lim_{t \to \infty} f(t) \tag{3.47}$$

Concisely, the condition for the validity of this theorem should be stated in terms of $F(s)$. This condition is: $sF(s)$ must be analytic for all Re $s \geq 0$.

A few illustrations of the use of these theorems are now given, including cases for which the theorems do not hold. We start with the latter.

Example 3.16   Let

$$F(s) = \frac{s}{s^2 + \omega_0^2}$$

Even though we have formally

$$\lim_{s \to 0} sF(s) = 0$$

the final value theorem does not apply because $F(s)$ is not bounded for $s = \pm j\omega_0$ (Re $s = 0$). Indeed, the corresponding time function is $f(t) = \cos \omega_0 t$, and $\lim_{t \to \infty} f(t)$ is undefined.   ∎

Example 3.17   Let $f(t) = \cos \omega t$. As $t \to 0$, we know that $\lim_{t \to \infty} \cos \omega t \to 1$. The initial value theorem correctly gives this result:

$$\lim_{s \to \infty} sF(s) = \lim_{s \to \infty} \frac{s^2}{s^2 + \omega^2} = 1$$ ∎

Example 3.18   (a) Find $\lim_{t \to \infty} e^{-at}$ ($a > 0$) by use of the final value theorem. Here

$$F(s) = \frac{1}{s + a}$$

and

$$\lim_{s \to 0,} sF(s) = 0 = \lim_{t \to \infty} e^{-at}$$ ∎

(b) Find $\lim_{t \to 0} e^{-at}$, ($a > 0$), by the initial value theorem. We have immediately that

$$\lim_{s \to \infty} \frac{s}{s + a} = 1$$ ∎

There are other possible applications of the initial and final value theorems. Consider, for example, the Laplace transform function

$$F(s) = \frac{\omega}{s^2 + \omega^2} \tag{3.48}$$

Now,

$$F(s) = \frac{\omega}{s^2} \left(1 + \frac{\omega^2}{s^2} \right)^{-1} \tag{3.49}$$

and if $\left| \dfrac{\omega}{s} \right| < 1$ (i.e., we are letting $s \to \infty$), then we can expand $F(s)$ in a convergent series according to

$$F(s) = \frac{\omega}{s^2} \left(1 - \frac{\omega^2}{s^2} + \frac{\omega^4}{s^4} + \cdots + (-1)^n \frac{\omega^{2n}}{s^{2n}} \right) \tag{3.50}$$

Inverting term by term, by using Example 3.5, we find that

$$f(t) = \omega t - \frac{\omega^3 t^3}{3!} + \frac{\omega^5 t^5}{5!} + \cdots \tag{3.51}$$

The expression for $f(t)$ is the series expansion of a sine function, i.e.,

$$f(t) = \sin \omega t \tag{3.52}$$

Thus the range of validity of the initial and final value theorems can be extended somewhat, as shown by the above example.

3.6   THE CONVOLUTION INTEGRAL

In this section we discuss one of the most important theorems of the Laplace transform theory. Of equal importance is its physical significance.

Let $f(t)$ be given as

$$f(t) = \int_{0_-}^{t} f_1(\tau) f_2(t - \tau) d\tau \tag{3.53}$$

the *convolution* of the two functions $f_1(t)$ and $f_2(t)$. Then

$$\mathcal{L}\{f(t)\} = F(s) = F_1(s) F_2(s) \tag{3.54}$$

where $F_1(s) = \mathcal{L}\{f_1(t)\}$ and $F_2(s) = \mathcal{L}\{f_2(t)\}$.

Proof   With

$$\mathcal{L}\{f(t)\} = \int_{0_-}^{\infty} e^{-st} \int_{0_-}^{t} f_1(\tau) f_2(t - \tau) d\tau \, dt \tag{3.55}$$

the integration spans an area in the (t, τ)-plane bounded by the lines $t = \tau$ and the entire t-axis. This part of the (t, τ)-plane is shown in Figure 3.9. We can span the area shown equally well by letting t run over the interval $\tau \le t \le \infty$ and then requiring τ to be in the interval $0 \le \tau \le \infty$. This simply amounts to interchanging the order of

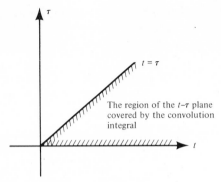

FIGURE 3.9   The (t,τ)-plane in the convolution integral.

integration in Equation 3.55 and assuming that $\mathcal{L}\{f(t)\}$ will have a definite limit independent of the order of integration. With the interchange,

$$\mathcal{L}\{f(t)\} = \int_{0_-}^{\infty} f_1(\tau) \int_{\tau}^{\infty} e^{-st} f_2(t - \tau) dt \, d\tau \tag{3.56}$$

In the integral over t appearing in Equation 3.56, the quantity τ is held constant. Now, by letting $t - \tau = u$, we have

$$\int_{\tau}^{\infty} e^{-st} f_2(t - \tau) dt = \int_{0}^{\infty} e^{-s(u+\tau)} f_2(u) du \tag{3.57}$$

and then Equation 3.56 becomes

$$\mathcal{L}\{f(t)\} = \int_{0_-}^{\infty} f_1(t) e^{-st} dt \int_{0_-}^{\infty} f_2(u) e^{-su} du \tag{3.58a}$$

But this expression is the product of $F_1(s)$ and $F_2(s)$, where

$$F_1(s) = \int_{0_-}^{\infty} f_1(t) e^{-st} dt, \quad F_2(s) = \int_{0_-}^{\infty} f_2(t) e^{-st} dt \tag{3.58b}$$

so that

$$F(s) = F_1(s) F_2(s) \tag{3.59}$$

That is, the Laplace transform of a convolution of two time functions is simply the product of the Laplace transforms of these two functions.

The importance of Equation 3.59 is examined at length in subsequent sections of this chapter.

3.7   THE CONVOLUTION INTEGRAL AND LINEAR SYSTEM RESPONSE

In this section we begin with a discussion of a simple system response and then generalize the results in order to show that there is an intimate connection between the convolution integral and that response. Consider an *RL* circuit containing a voltage source, as shown in Figure 3.10. All initial conditions are zero: $i(0_-) = i'(0_-) = 0$. The response under these conditions is called the *zero-state* response.

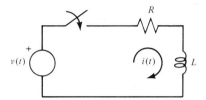

FIGURE 3.10   An *RL* circuit.

The switch is closed at $t = 0$ and application of the Kirchhoff's voltage law then gives

$$L \frac{di}{dt} + Ri = v(t) \tag{3.60}$$

Applying the Laplace transform to Equation 3.60 we get

$$(Ls + R) I(s) = V(s) \tag{3.61}$$

or

$$I(s) = G(s) V(s) \tag{3.62}$$

where

$$G(s) = \frac{1}{Ls + R} = \frac{1}{L} \frac{1}{(s + R/L)} \tag{3.63}$$

Consequently, the zero-state current response corresponding to Equation 3.62 is the convolution of $g(t)$ and $v(t)$ and given by

$$i(t) = \int_{0_-}^{t} g(\tau) v(t - \tau) d\tau \tag{3.64}$$

where

$$g(t) = \frac{1}{L} e^{-(R/L)t} u(t) \tag{3.65}$$

according to Equation 3.63.

This method is now generalized. Let an input $p(t)$ act upon a system whose output is $y(t)$. Then, if the system is linear and time invariant, the input–output relationship is an nth-order differential equation of the form

$$a_0 \frac{d^n y}{dt^n} + a_1 \frac{d^{n-1} y}{dt^{n-1}} + \cdots + a_n y = b_0 \frac{d^m p}{dt^m} + b_1 \frac{d^{m-1} p}{dt^{m-1}} + \cdots + b_m p \tag{3.66a}$$

where, in most physical systems, $n \geq m$.

If we designate the right-hand side (containing the known input and its known derivatives) by $f(t)$, and use the linear operator M as*

$$M = a_0 \frac{d^n}{dt^n} + \cdots + a_n \tag{3.66b}$$

then we have

$$M\{y(t)\} = f(t) \tag{3.66c}$$

as the differential equation describing our system.

We want to find the zero-state response; this is the solution of Equation 3.66 where the system has been in the zero state just before the application of the input. In other words, we find the solution by assuming all initial conditions to be zero:

$$y(0_-) = \frac{dy}{dt}(0_-) = \cdots = \frac{d^{n-1}y}{dt^{n-1}}(0_-) = 0 \tag{3.66d}$$

Let the Laplace transform of $y(t)$ be $Y(s)$, and that of $f(t)$ be $F(s)$. Then Equation 3.66c, when the Laplace transform of both sides is taken, has the form

$$P(s)Y(s) = F(s) \tag{3.67}$$

where $P(s)$ is a polynomial in s whose degree n is that of the highest order derivative appearing in M. We cast Equation 3.67 into the form

$$Y(s) = G(s)F(s) \tag{3.68}$$

where $G(s) \equiv P^{-1}(s)$. Then, from the convolution theorem, the response $y(t)$ can be written down immediately; it is

$$y(t) = \int_{0_-}^{t} f(\tau)g(t - \tau)d\tau \tag{3.69}$$

where $g(t)$ is the function whose Laplace transform is $G(s)$.

What we have established is the following: The response of any linear time-invariant[†] system can be written as a convolution integral of the form given in Equation 3.69.

It is now shown that if a linear time-invariant system is driven with an input $f(t)$, it is necessary only to find the response of the system to a unit impulse function in order to find its zero-state response $y(t)$. This fact follows directly from the convolution theorem. Let the differential equation describing the zero-state response be, once again,

$$M\{y(t)\} = f(t) \tag{3.66c}$$

and let a function $g(t)$ obey the differential equation

$$M\{g(t)\} = \delta(t) \tag{3.70a}$$

i.e., $g(t)$ is the impulse response of the system. Also,

---

*M is a linear operator if it satisfies the conditions $M\{y_1 + y_2\} = M\{y_1\} + M\{y_2\}$ and $M\{ay\} = aM\{y\}$, for constant a.

†By time-invariant we mean that g is only a function of the difference $(t - \tau)$, and not of both t and τ, $g(t, \tau)$, which is the general case with time-variant systems.

$$M\{g(t - \tau)\} = \delta(t - \tau) \tag{3.70b}$$

We stipulate the solution to Equation 3.66 as follows:

$$y(t) = \int_{-\infty}^{\infty} f(\tau)g(t - \tau)d\tau \tag{3.71}$$

and proceed to prove its validity. The operator M operates only on the time variable t. Invoking the rule for differentiation under an integral sign, we have, therefore,

$$M\{y(t)\} = \int_{-\infty}^{\infty} f(\tau)M\{g(t - \tau)\}\,d\tau \tag{3.72}$$

But by Equation 3.70b the right-hand side of Equation 3.72 reduces to

$$M\{y(t)\} = \int_{-\infty}^{\infty} f(\tau)\,\delta(t - \tau)d\tau \tag{3.73}$$

which, by the "sifting" property of the delta function, becomes

$$M\{y(t)\} = f(t) \tag{3.66c}$$

That is, Equation 3.71 is a solution to Equation 3.66, provided only that the function $g(t - \tau)$ satisfies Equation 3.70 and certain initial conditions, to be established below. The connection between Equations 3.71 and 3.69 is readily established. If there is a switch in the system that introduces the forcing function into the system at $t = 0$, then the quantity $f(\tau)$ appearing in Equation 3.71 is identically zero for $\tau \leq 0$. With this in mind, we see that Equation 3.71 reduces to

$$y(t) = \int_{0_-}^{\infty} f(\tau)g(t - \tau)d\tau \tag{3.74}$$

The range of τ in this integral can be split so that $y(t)$ becomes

$$y(t) = \int_{0_-}^{t} f(\tau)g_<(t - \tau)d\tau + \int_{t}^{\infty} f(\tau)g_>(t - \tau)d\tau \tag{3.75}$$

where we have indicated by the notation $g_{\lessgtr}$ that the solution to the equation $M\{g(t - \tau)\} = \delta(t - \tau)$ may differ according to whether $\tau \lessgtr t$.

Consider the integrals

$$I_< = \int_{0_-}^{t} f(\tau)g_<(t - \tau)d\tau \tag{3.76a}$$

and

$$I_> = \int_{t}^{\infty} f(\tau)g_>(t - \tau)d\tau \tag{3.76b}$$

According to Equation 3.75 we can express $y(t)$ as

$$y(t) = I_< + I_>$$

where $I_<$ depends on the course of events up to the time t ($\tau \leq t$) and $I_>$ depends on events which take place after the time t ($\tau \geq t$). Since physical systems are *causal* (*nonanticipative*), the output $y(t)$ cannot possibly depend on what will happen to the system in the future. This causality argument then reduces Equation 3.75 to

$$y(t) = \int_{0_-}^{t} f(\tau)g(t - \tau)d\tau \tag{3.77}$$

the convolution integral of a driving function and the unit impulse response.

Thus we have shown that it is necessary only to find the solution to

$$M\{g(t - \tau)\} = \delta(t - \tau) \tag{3.70}$$

in order to write the zero-state solution of

$$M\{y(t)\} = f(t) \tag{3.66c}$$

as a convolution integral for linear time-invariant systems.

A somewhat different approach to this proof is given in Problem 3-7.

The question of initial conditions for the impulse response $g(t - \tau)$ is now examined for second-order operators M. Consider again the pair of equations

$$M\{y(t)\} = f(t) \tag{3.66c}$$

and

$$M\{g(t - \tau)\} = \delta(t - \tau) \tag{3.70b}$$

Let

$$M \equiv \frac{d^2}{dt^2} + a \frac{d}{dt} + b$$

where a,b are constants. The zero-state response of this second-order linear system is written as

$$y(t) = \int_{0_-}^{t} f(\tau)g(t - \tau)d\tau \tag{3.77}$$

and we have by differentiation

$$\frac{dy}{dt} = f(t)g(t - t) + \int_{0_-}^{t} f(\tau) \frac{dg}{dt} d\tau \tag{3.78}$$

We shall set $g(t - t) \equiv 0$, so that a second differentiation yields

$$\frac{d^2y}{dt^2} = \left[f(t) \frac{dg(t - \tau)}{dt} \right]_{t=\tau} + \int_{0}^{t} f(\tau) \frac{d^2g}{dt^2} d\tau \tag{3.79}$$

Then

$$M\{y\} \equiv \frac{d^2y}{dt^2} + a \frac{dy}{dt} + by = f(t) \tag{3.80}$$

is indeed satisfied if $\left. \dfrac{dg}{dt} \right]_{t=\tau} = 1$, and if $M\{g\} = 0$ for $t \neq \tau$. Thus, in constructing unit impulse responses for second-order linear systems we solve the differential equation (Equation 3.66c) subject to the conditions

$$g(t - \tau)]_{t=\tau} = 0 \quad \text{and} \quad \frac{dg}{dt}\bigg]_{t=\tau} = 1 \tag{3.81}$$

The second condition then means that the second derivative of $g(t - \tau)$ with respect to t evaluated at $t = \tau$ will have a delta function discontinuity at $t = \tau$.

It was shown in Chapter 1 that an nth-order differential equation can be represented as a family of n first-order differential equations in matrix form. Thus we do not discuss higher order equations. Our preoccupation with second-order differential equations is rather natural, however, since the underlying physical law governing many linear (and nonlinear) systems is related to Newton's second law, which is, in vector form, a second-order differential equation.

We consider now several examples of system responses, written as convolution integrals.

Example 3.19 Let $y(t)$ satisfy the differential equation of an RLC circuit driven by an exponential, namely,

$$\frac{d^2y}{dt^2} + 4\frac{dy}{dt} + 4y = e^{-2t}u(t)$$

with $y(0_-) = 0$ and $y'(0_-) = 0$. The zero-state response is given by the convolution integral

$$y(t) = \int_{0_-}^{t} e^{-2\tau}g(t - \tau)d\tau$$

where

$$\frac{d^2g}{dt^2} + 4\frac{dg}{dt} + 4g = \delta(t - \tau)$$

The unit impulse response function $g(t - \tau)$ will satisfy the initial conditions

$$g(t - \tau)]_{t=\tau} = 0, \quad \frac{dg}{dt}(t - \tau)\bigg]_{t=\tau} = 1$$

Laplace transforming the equation for g, we obtain

$$(s^2 + 4s + 4)G(s) = e^{-s\tau}$$

or

$$G(s) = \frac{e^{-s\tau}}{(s + 2)^2}$$

Using the shifting theorem, we find that, since

$$\mathcal{L}\{te^{-2t}u(t)\} = 1/(s + 2)^2$$

then

$$g(t - \tau) = (t - \tau)e^{-2(t-\tau)}u(t - \tau)$$

and then

$$y(t) = \int_{0_-}^{t} (t - \tau)e^{-2(t-\tau)}e^{-2\tau}d\tau = e^{-2t}\int_{0_-}^{t} (t - \tau)d\tau$$

or

$$y(t) = \frac{t^2}{2} e^{-2t}u(t) \qquad \blacksquare$$

Example 3.20   Let y(t) satisfy the differential equation of an *LC* circuit, driven by a sinusoidal input, i.e.,

$$\frac{d^2y}{dt^2} + \omega_0^2 y = \sin \omega_0 tu(t)$$

with $y(0_-) = y'(0_-) = 0$. The zero-state solution is given by

$$y(t) = \int_{0_-}^{t} \sin \omega_0 \tau g(t - \tau)d\tau$$

where the unit impulse response is the solution to

$$\frac{d^2g}{dt^2} + \omega_0^2 g = \delta(t - \tau)$$

On Laplace transforming, we have

$$G(s) = \frac{e^{-s\tau}}{s^2 + \omega_0^2}$$

so that, on applying the shifting theorem,

$$g(t - \tau) = \frac{1}{\omega_0} \sin \omega_0(t - \tau)u(t - \tau)$$

Thus,

$$y(t) = \frac{1}{\omega_0} \int_{0_-}^{t} \sin \omega_0 \tau \sin \omega_0(t - \tau)d\tau \qquad \blacksquare$$

Example 3.21   Consider the differential equation

$$\frac{d^2y}{dt^2} + 2a \frac{dy}{dt} + \omega_0^2 y = e^{-\lambda t}u(t)$$

where $\omega_0^2 - a^2 > 0$ and where $\lambda > 0$, with a real. Let the initial conditions be $y(0_-) = 1$ and $y'(0_-) = 0$. We now need not only the zero-state response, but also the zero-input response. The sum of the two constitutes the complete response. To solve such a differential equation (representing in this case the current in an *RLC* circuit driven by an exponential pulse), we take the Laplace transform and obtain

$$s^2 Y(s) - sy(0_-) - y'(0_-) + 2a[sY(s) - y(0_-)] + \omega_0^2 Y(s) = \frac{1}{s + \lambda}$$

or

$$(s^2 + 2as + \omega_0^2)Y(s) = \frac{1}{s + \lambda} + s + 2a$$

That is,

$$Y(s) = \frac{s + 2a}{s^2 + 2as + \omega_0^2} + \frac{1}{(s^2 + 2as + \omega_0^2)} \frac{1}{(s + \lambda)}$$

The first term is the zero input (homogeneous solution) and the second term is recognized as the transform of the convolution integral

$$\int_0^t \frac{e^{-a(t-\tau)} \sin \bar{\omega}(t - \tau)}{\bar{\omega}} e^{-\lambda\tau} d\tau, \qquad \bar{\omega}^2 = \omega_0^2 - a^2 > 0$$

representing the zero-state part of the solution. ∎ ■

3.8 THE LAPLACE TRANSFORM OF PERIODIC FUNCTIONS

Let $f(t) = f(t + T)$ be a piecewise continuous periodic function, for $t > 0$, of period T. Then its Laplace transform is

$$\mathcal{L}\{f(t)\} = \frac{\int_{0_-}^T f(t)e^{-st} dt}{1 - e^{-sT}} \tag{3.82}$$

Proof We have

$$\mathcal{L}\{f(t)\} = \int_{0_-}^\infty f(t)e^{-st} dt$$

which can be written as

$$\mathcal{L}\{f(t)\} = \int_{0_-}^T f(t)e^{-st} dt + \int_T^{2T} f(t)e^{-st} dt + \cdots + \int_{(n-1)T}^{nT} f(t)e^{-st} dt + \cdots \tag{3.83}$$

or

$$\mathcal{L}\{f(t)\} = \sum_{n=0}^\infty \int_{nT}^{(n+1)T} f(t)e^{-st} dt \tag{3.84}$$

Consider the integral, for integer p,

$$\int_{pT}^{(p+1)T} f(t)e^{-st} dt$$

and let $u = t - pT$. Then

$$\int_{pT}^{(p+1)T} f(t)e^{-st} dt = e^{-spT} \int_0^T e^{-su} f(u + pT) du \tag{3.85}$$

But by the definition of periodicity, $f(u + pT) \equiv f(u)$ for all p. Thus,

$$\int_p^{(p+1)T} f(t)e^{-st} dt = e^{-spT} \int_0^T f(u)e^{-su} du \tag{3.86}$$

so that

$$\mathcal{L}\{f(t)\} = \sum_{n=0}^{\infty} e^{-snT} \int_0^T f(u)e^{-su}du \qquad (3.87)$$

and with

$$\sum_{n=0}^{\infty} e^{-snT} = \frac{1}{1 - e^{-sT}} \qquad (3.88)$$

Equation 3.87 yields the desired result in Equation 3.82. This result expresses the transform of the periodic function as the ratio of the transform of only the *first period* and the factor $(1 - e^{-sT})$. The following waveforms are some of the common periodic functions in engineering and science.

Example 3.22 Find the Laplace transform of $f(t)$, a train of square pulses, as shown in Figure 3.11.

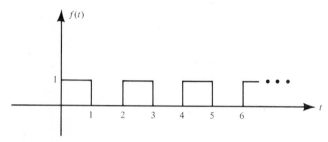

FIGURE 3.11   Example 3.22.

We write

$$\mathcal{L}\{f(t)\} = \frac{\int_0^1 e^{-st}dt}{1 - e^{-2s}} = \frac{(1 - e^{-s})}{s(1 - e^{-2s})} = \frac{1}{s(1 + e^{-s})} \qquad \blacksquare$$

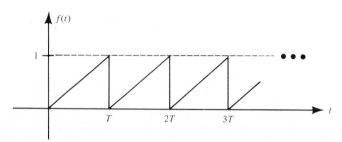

FIGURE 3.12   Example 3.23.

Example 3.23 The sawtooth wave shown has a period T, for which the periodic function $f(t) = t/T$. Thus,

$$\mathcal{L}\{f(t)\} = \frac{1}{1 - e^{-sT}} \int_0^T \frac{t}{T} e^{-st}dt$$

Evaluation of the integral yields the result

$$\mathcal{L}\{f(t)\} = \frac{Ts + 1 - e^{-Ts}}{Ts^2(1 - e^{-Ts})}$$ ∎

Example 3.24   The fully rectified sine wave, shown in Figure 3.13, has the Laplace transform

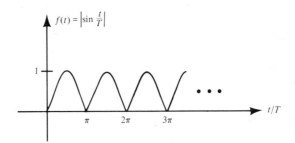

FIGURE 3.13   Example 3.24.

$$\mathcal{L}\{f(t)\} = \frac{1}{1 - e^{-s\pi T}} \int_0^{\pi T} \sin\left(\frac{t}{T}\right) e^{-st} dt = \frac{T^{-1}}{s^2 + T^{-2}} \cdot \frac{1 + e^{-s\pi T}}{1 - e^{-s\pi T}}$$ ∎

Example 3.25   The half-wave rectified sine function, shown in Figure 3.14, has the Laplace transform

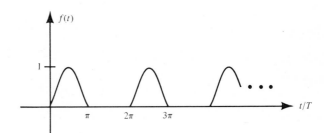

FIGURE 3.14   Example 3.25.

$$\mathcal{L}\{f(t)\} = \frac{1}{1 - e^{-2\pi sT}} \int_0^{\pi T} \sin(T^{-1}t) e^{-st} dt = \frac{T}{s^2 + T^2} \cdot \frac{1}{1 - e^{-s\pi T}}$$ ∎

3.9   THE LAPLACE INVERSION THEOREM

Often it is necessary to find $f(t)$ when $F(s)$, its Laplace transform, is given. That is, if $F(s)$ is known in the relation

$$F(s) = \int_{0_-}^{\infty} f(t)e^{-st} dt \qquad (3.89)$$

and $f(t)$ is unknown, we want to invert Equation 3.89 to find $f(t)$.

Theorem   The function $f(t)$ can be found from

$$\mathcal{L}^{-1}\{F(s)\} \equiv f(t) = \frac{1}{2\pi j} \int_{\gamma - j\infty}^{\gamma + j\infty} e^{st} F(s)\,ds \qquad (3.90)$$

where γ is real and is to the right of all the poles of $F(s)$ in the s-plane.

Let us sketch a proof of the theorem, making use of an integral representation of the unit impulse function.

Proof   Write $F(s)$ as in Equation 3.89 and form

$$\oint_c F(s)e^{st}\,ds = \oint e^{st} \int_0^\infty e^{-st} f(t)\,dt\,ds \qquad (3.91)$$

where C is an appropriate contour, shown in Figure 3.15. Assuming convergence of the double integral on the right, we have, on interchanging the order of integration,

$$\oint_c F(s)e^{st}\,ds = \int_0^\infty f(t) \oint_c e^{-s(t-\tau)}\,ds\,dt \qquad (3.92)$$

Now, an integral representation of the delta function is given by (see Appendix A)

$$2\pi\delta(t - \tau) = \int_{-\infty}^\infty e^{j\omega(t-\tau)}\,d\omega \qquad (3.93)$$

or, alternatively, by

$$2\pi j\delta(t - \tau) = \oint e^{s(t-\tau)}\,ds \qquad (3.94)$$

for an appropriately chosen contour. Thus,

$$2\pi j \int_0^\infty f(t)\delta(t - \tau)\,dt = \oint_C e^{st} F(s)\,ds \qquad (3.95)$$

or

$$f(t) = \frac{1}{2\pi j} \oint_C e^{st} F(s)\,ds \qquad (3.96)$$

The contour must be such that all of the poles of $F(s)$ are enclosed. If this were not the case, full information concerning the nature of $f(t)$ would be lacking. The contour is chosen as shown in Figure 3.15, being traversed in a counterclockwise manner; then, as was shown in Chapter 2, the integral over the arc Γ will go to zero as $R \to \infty$. Then we are left with

$$f(t) = \frac{1}{2\pi j} \int_{\gamma - j\infty}^{\gamma + j\infty} e^{st} F(s)\,ds \qquad (3.97)$$

If $F(s)$ contains essential singularities, the contour must be deformed so as to exclude such points by making appropriate cuts.

The use of the Cauchy residue theorem in Equation 3.97 will play a major role.

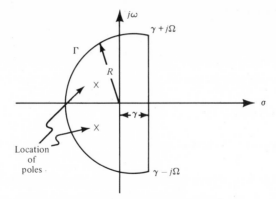

FIGURE 3.15 The contour for inversion when $F(s)$ has poles only.

3.10 HEAVISIDE'S EXPANSION THEOREM

In many practical problems $F(s)$ will be given as a rational function

$$F(s) = \frac{P(s)}{Q(s)} \tag{3.98}$$

where $P(s)$ and $Q(s)$ are polynomials in s with no common factors. For physical reasons, $Q(s)$ is generally of higher degree than $P(s)$. Suppose that $F(s)$ has only distinct first-order poles. Then $Q(s)$, if of degree n, can be factored as the product

$$Q(s) = \prod_{i=1}^{n} (s - s_i) \tag{3.99}$$

The function $f(t)$ is then given by

$$f(t) = \sum_{i=1}^{n} \frac{P(s_i)}{Q'(s_i)} e^{s_i t} \tag{3.100}$$

where $Q'(s_i)$ denotes the first derivative of $Q(s)$ evaluated at $s = s_i$. The form of Equation 3.100 is attributed to Heaviside.

Proof By the inversion theorem, we have here

$$f(t) = \frac{1}{2\pi j} \int_{\gamma - j\infty}^{\gamma + j\infty} e^{st} \frac{P(s)}{Q(s)} ds \tag{3.101}$$

where, as stated previously, γ is to the right of all the poles of $P(s)/Q(s)$. The residue at a given pole at, say, $s = s_k$ is found by the expression

$$\text{Res } (s = s_k) = \lim_{s \to s_k} (s - s_k) \frac{P(s)e^{st}}{(s - s_k) \prod_i{}' (s - s_i)} \tag{3.102}$$

where $\prod'$ means that $i \neq k$; in other words,

$$\Pi' = (s - s_1)(s - s_2) \ldots (s - s_{k-1})(s - s_{k+1}) \ldots \qquad (3.103)$$

It is easy to show that

$$\Pi'(s_k - s_i) = \frac{d}{ds} Q(s) \bigg]_{s=s_k} = Q'(s_k) \qquad (3.104)$$

and therefore the residue in Equation 3.102 is

$$\text{Res} (s = s_k) = \frac{P(s_k)}{Q'(s_k)} e^{s_k t} \qquad (3.105)$$

The sum of such residues when multiplied by $2\pi j$ is, according to the Cauchy residue theorem, the value of $f(t)$. Thus, the theorem follows.

Example 3.26   Given

$$F(s) = \frac{1}{(s + a)(s + b)}$$

find $f(t)$. We have

$$f(t) = \frac{1}{2\pi j} \int_{\gamma - j\infty}^{\gamma + j\infty} \frac{e^{st}}{(s + a)(s + b)} \, ds$$

There are two poles, one at $s = -a$ and one at $s = -b$. Here $Q'(s) = 2s + a + b$. Thus, by the residue theorem or by the Heaviside expansion theorem, we have

$$f(t) = \frac{e^{-at}}{b - a} + \frac{e^{-bt}}{a - b} \qquad \blacksquare$$

Example 3.27   Given

$$F(s) = \frac{1}{(s + a)(s + b)^2}$$

find

$$f(t) = \frac{1}{2\pi j} \int_{\gamma - j\infty}^{\gamma + j\infty} \frac{e^{st}}{(s + a)(s + b)^2} \, ds$$

There is a first-order pole at $s = -a$ and a second-order pole at $s = -b$. The residue at the first-order pole is

$$\frac{e^{-at}}{(b - a)^2}$$

The residue at the second-order pole is

$$\text{Res} [s = -b] = \frac{d}{ds} \left(\frac{e^{st}}{s + a} \right)_{s=-b}$$

that is,

$$\text{Res}\,[s = -b] = \frac{te^{-bt}}{a - b} - \frac{e^{-bt}}{(a - b)^2}$$

and therefore

$$f(t) = \frac{e^{-at} - e^{-bt}}{(b - a)^2} + \frac{te^{-bt}}{a - b} \qquad \blacksquare$$

Example 3.28 Given

$$F(s) = \frac{e^{-s\tau}}{(s + a)(s + b)(s + c)}$$

find $f(t)$. We have

$$f(t) = \frac{1}{2\pi j} \int_{\gamma - j\infty}^{\gamma + j\infty} \frac{e^{s(t - \tau)}}{(s + a)(s + b)(s + c)}\, ds$$

The function $f(t)$ can be found from the Heaviside expansion theorem and the shifting theorem. The result is

$$f(t) = \left[\frac{e^{-a(t - \tau)}}{(b - a)(c - a)} + \frac{e^{-b(t - \tau)}}{(a - b)(c - b)} + \frac{e^{-c(t - \tau)}}{(a - c)(b - c)} \right] \cdot u(t - \tau) \qquad \blacksquare$$

Example 3.29 Given the equation of an RC circuit

$$\frac{dy}{dt} + \frac{y}{\tau} = be^{-at}u(t), \quad \text{with } y(0_-) = 1$$

Here τ is the time constant. Let $Y(s) = \mathcal{L}\{y(t)\}$. Then

$$\left(s + \frac{1}{\tau} \right) Y(s) = 1 + \frac{b}{s + a}$$

from which

$$Y(s) = \frac{1}{s + \dfrac{1}{\tau}} + \frac{b}{(s + a)\left(s + \dfrac{1}{\tau} \right)}$$

Then $y(t)$ is found from

$$y(t) = \frac{1}{2\pi j} \int_{\gamma - j\infty}^{\gamma + j\infty} e^{st} \left\{ \frac{1}{s + \tau^{-1}} + \frac{b}{(s + a)(s + \tau^{-1})} \right\} ds$$

The zero-input part of the response contains a single pole at $s = -\tau^{-1}$, while the zero-state part contains poles at $s = -a$ and at $s = -\tau^{-1}$. Thus, by the residue theorem,

$$y(t) = e^{-t/\tau}\left(1 + \frac{b\tau}{a\tau - 1} \right) - \frac{b\tau e^{-at}}{a\tau - 1} \qquad \blacksquare$$

Example 3.30 Find $y(t)$ if

$$\frac{d^2y}{dt^2} + 2a\frac{dy}{dt} + \omega_0^2 y = 0$$

with $\omega_0^2 - a^2 > 0$ and with $y(0_-) = 0$ and $y'(0_-) = 1$. The Laplace transform of this equation yields

$$Y(s) = \frac{1}{(s + a)^2 + \bar{\omega}^2}$$

with $\bar{\omega}^2 = \omega_0^2 - a^2 > 0$. Then

$$y(t) = \frac{1}{2\pi j} \int_{\gamma - j\infty}^{\gamma + j\infty} \frac{e^{st}}{(s + a)^2 + \bar{\omega}^2} ds$$

The integral has poles at $s = -a \pm j\bar{\omega}$, so that

$$y(t) = e^{-at} \left\{ \frac{e^{j\bar{\omega}t}}{2j\bar{\omega}} - \frac{e^{-j\bar{\omega}t}}{2j\bar{\omega}} \right\}$$

or

$$y(t) = \frac{e^{-at}}{\bar{\omega}} \sin \bar{\omega}t \qquad\blacksquare$$

It is very appropriate at this stage to recognize the equivalence between the inversion theorem (Heaviside's theorem) and the popular *partial fraction expansion* method. Recall that in the latter method the function $F(s) = P(s)/Q(s)$, as in Equations 3.98 and 3.99, has the partial fraction expansion

$$F(s) = \frac{P(s)}{Q(s)} = \sum_i \frac{K_i}{s - s_i} \tag{3.106}$$

when the poles of $F(s)$ are distinct. Recall also that

$$K_i = \frac{P(s)}{Q(s)} (s - s_i) \Bigg]_{s=s_i} \tag{3.107}$$

and, consequently,

$$f(t) = \sum_i K_i e^{s_i t} u(t) \tag{3.108}$$

This is identical to the results in Equations 3.100–3.105, if we recognize that in Equation 3.107 an actual cancellation of the term $(s - s_i)$ occurs and the resulting denominator is then

$$Q'(s_i) = \Pi' \tag{3.109}$$

For higher order poles, as in Example 3.27, the partial fraction expansion usually requires successive differentiation, as illustrated in the following example.

Example 3.31   Consider the same $F(s)$ as in Example 3.27:

$$F(s) = \frac{1}{(s + a)(s + b)^2}, \quad a \neq b$$

Its expansion will be

$$F(s) = \frac{K_1}{s + a} + \frac{K_{2,1}}{s + b} + \frac{K_{2,2}}{(s + b)^2}$$

Here K_1 and $K_{2,2}$ can be evaluated as before, namely,

$$K_1 = F(s)(s + a)]_{s=-a} = \frac{1}{(b - a)^2}$$

$$K_{2,2} = F(s)(s + b)^2]_{s=-b} = \frac{1}{a - b}$$

In most textbooks the expression for $K_{2,1}$ is given as

$$K_{2,1} = \frac{d}{ds}[F(s)(s + b)^2]_{s=-b}$$

and requires the indicated differentiation. Here we obtain

$$K_{2,1} = \frac{d}{ds}\left[\frac{1}{s + a}\right]_{s=-b} = \frac{-1}{(a - b)^2}$$

The function $f(t)$ is then

$$f(t) = (K_1 e^{-at} + K_{2,1}e^{-bt} + K_{2,2}te^{-bt})u(t)$$

in agreement with the results obtained previously. ∎

The differentiations required for the higher order poles can be avoided if we use an auxiliary function with first-order poles only. The higher order poles are restored by subsequent division. This novel method[3] is simple, purely algebraic, and recursive; hence it is also suitable for machine calculations. It is illustrated by the following example.

Example 3.32 Consider the same $F(s)$ as in the previous example. Form the auxiliary function $F_a(s)$ with first-order poles only.

$$F_a(s) = \frac{1}{(s + a)(s + b)}$$

It can be expanded in partial fractions using Equation 3.107. The result is

$$F_a(s) = \frac{1/(b - a)}{s + a} + \frac{1/(a - b)}{s + b}$$

One division of $F_a(s)$ by $(s + b)$ yields the original $F(s)$, that is,

$$\frac{1}{s + b}F_a(s) = \frac{1/(b - a)}{(s + b)(s + a)} + \frac{1/(a - b)}{(s + b)^2}$$

The first term on the right-hand side can be expanded again by Equation 3.107. Therefore we get

$$F(s) = \frac{1/(b-a)^2}{s+a} + \frac{-1/(b-a)^2}{s+b} + \frac{1/(a-b)}{(s+b)^2}$$

as before.   ∎

We now consider a few examples of the inversion of Laplace transforms when $F(s)$ contains essential singularities, or fractional powers of s.

Example 3.33   Let

$$F(s) = s^{-1}e^{-kx\sqrt{s}}$$

We are to find the function

$$f(x,t) = \frac{1}{2\pi j}\int_{\gamma-j\infty}^{\gamma+j\infty}\frac{1}{s}e^{st}e^{-kx\sqrt{s}}ds$$

There is a branch point at the origin of the complex s-plane. For this reason the contour for inversion of the transform will be as shown in Figure 3.16.

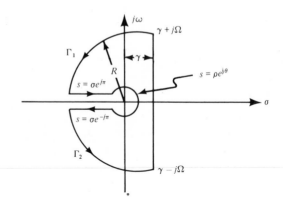

FIGURE 3.16   Example 3.33.

The integral about the contour shown and denoted by

$$I = \frac{1}{2\pi j}\oint\frac{e^{st}e^{-kx\sqrt{s}}}{s}ds$$

is identically zero since there are no singularities enclosed within the contour. As R (and Ω) $\to \infty$, the integrals along the arcs Γ_1 and Γ_2 approach zero, while as $\rho \to 0$, the integral around the circle of radius ρ approaches the value $-2\pi j$.

The integrals from R to ρ and from ρ to R, where $s = \sigma e^{j\pi}$ and $s = \sigma e^{-j\pi}$, respectively, combine, so that we have

$$I = 0 = \int_{\gamma-j\infty}^{\gamma+j\infty}\frac{e^{st}e^{-kx\sqrt{s}}}{s}ds - 2\pi j + 2j\int_0^\infty\frac{e^{-\sigma t}}{\sigma}\sin(kx\sigma^{1/2})d\sigma$$

or, after dividing by $2\pi j$,

$$f(x,t) = 1 - \frac{1}{\pi} \int_0^\infty \frac{e^{-\sigma t}}{\sigma} \sin(kx\sigma^{1/2})d\sigma$$

In order to bring the last integral into a standard form, we change variables by setting $\sigma = u^2$, so that

$$f(t) = 1 - \frac{2}{\pi} \int_0^\infty \frac{e^{-u^2 t}}{u} \sin(kxu)du$$

and note that

$$\int_0^{kx} \cos \beta u \, d\beta = \frac{1}{u} \sin(kxu)$$

On interchanging the order of integration,

$$f(x,t) = 1 - \frac{1}{\pi} \int_0^{kx} \int_{-\infty}^\infty e^{-u^2 t} \cos \beta u \, du \, d\beta$$

since the integrand is an even function of u. Let the integral J be defined by

$$J \equiv \int_{-\infty}^\infty e^{-u^2 t} \cos \beta u \, du = \text{Re} \int_{-\infty}^\infty e^{-u^2 t} e^{j\beta u} du$$

By completing the square in the exponent, it is seen that

$$J = \sqrt{\frac{\pi}{t}} e^{-\beta^2/4t}$$

so that

$$f(x,t) = 1 - \frac{1}{\sqrt{\pi t}} \int_0^{kx} e^{-\beta^2/4t} d\beta$$

A final change of variables $\beta^2/4t = \alpha^2$, so that $d\beta = 2\sqrt{t} \, d\alpha$, yields

$$f(x,t) = 1 - \frac{2}{\sqrt{\pi}} \int_0^{kx/2\sqrt{t}} e^{-\alpha^2} d\alpha$$

The error function is commonly defined as

$$\text{erf}\left(\frac{kx}{2\sqrt{t}}\right) \equiv \frac{2}{\sqrt{\pi}} \int_0^{kx/2\sqrt{t}} e^{-\alpha^2} d\alpha$$

while the complementary error function is defined as

$$\text{erfc}\left(\frac{kx}{2\sqrt{t}}\right) = 1 - \text{erf}\left(\frac{kx}{2\sqrt{t}}\right)$$

Finally, then

$$f(x,t) = \text{erfc}\left(\frac{kx}{2\sqrt{t}}\right)$$

We have worked out this example in some detail, not only because it illustrates a choice of contour in evaluating an inverse Laplace transform, but also because of the importance of the error function and its complement in problems of solid state diffusion theory, in probability theory, and in heat flow. These matters are discussed more thoroughly in a later section of this chapter. ∎

Example 3.34   Let

$$F(s) = s^{-1/2} e^{-kx\sqrt{s}}$$

We have to evaluate

$$f(x,t) = \frac{1}{2\pi j} \int_{\gamma-j\infty}^{\gamma+j\infty} \frac{e^{st}}{\sqrt{s}} e^{-kx\sqrt{s}} ds$$

Using the same contour as in the previous example, we can find $f(x,t)$ by writing, as before,

$$I = 0 = \oint_C \frac{e^{st}}{\sqrt{s}} e^{-kx\sqrt{s}} ds$$

As $R,\Omega \to \infty$, the integrals over Γ_1 and Γ_2 go to zero, while the integral about the circle surrounding the origin goes to zero as $\rho \to 0$. The integrals along the path $s = \sigma e^{\pm j\pi}$ combine so that we have

$$0 = \frac{1}{2\pi j} \int_{\gamma-j\infty}^{\gamma+j\infty} \frac{e^{st}}{\sqrt{s}} e^{-kx\sqrt{s}} ds - \frac{1}{\pi} \int_0^\infty \frac{e^{-\sigma t}}{\sigma^{1/2}} \cos(kx\sigma^{1/2}) d\sigma$$

Thus $f(x,t)$ is

$$f(x,t) = \frac{1}{\pi} \int_0^\infty \frac{e^{-\sigma t}}{\sigma^{1/2}} \cos(kx\sigma^{1/2}) d\sigma$$

Let $\sigma = u^2$ so that $\dfrac{d\sigma}{\sigma^{1/2}} = 2du$. Then

$$f(x,t) = \frac{1}{\pi} \int_{-\infty}^\infty e^{-u^2 t} \cos(kxu) du$$

The integral can be evaluated as in the previous example with the result

$$f(x,t) = \frac{1}{\sqrt{\pi t}} e^{-k^2 x^2/4t}$$ ∎

Example 3.35   Consider the following integral equation for $y(t)$:

$$y(t) = f(t) + \int_0^t g(t - \tau)y(\tau)d\tau$$

Such an equation, containing a convolution integral, occurs in several physical cases. It is called a Volterra integral equation. Specifically, let

$$y(t) = \sin \omega_0 t - \gamma \int_0^t y(\tau)e^{-a(t-\tau)} d\tau \qquad (a > 0)$$

with γ a constant parameter. Then, applying the Laplace transform, we get

$$Y(s) = \frac{\omega_0}{s^2 + \omega_0^2} - \gamma Y(s) \cdot \frac{1}{(s + a)}$$

or

$$Y(s) = \frac{\omega_0(s + a)}{(s^2 + \omega_0^2)(s + a + \gamma)}$$

Then

$$y(t) = \frac{\omega_0}{2\pi j} \int_{\gamma - j\infty}^{\gamma + j\infty} \frac{e^{st}(s + a)}{(s^2 + \omega_0^2)(s + a + \gamma)} \, ds$$

There are poles at the points $s = \pm j\omega_0$ and at $s = -(a + \gamma)$. Evaluation by means of the Cauchy residue theorem gives the result

$$y(t) = K_1 e^{-(a+\gamma)t} + K_2 \sin(\omega_0 t + \beta)$$

where K_1, K_2, and β are constants. ∎

3.11 FURTHER APPLICATIONS OF THE LAPLACE TRANSFORM

In earlier sections of this chapter various theorems in the Laplace transform theory were proved, with illustrations of their use. In the remainder of this chapter we consider a few applications in electrical engineering that involve partial differential equations for distributed (continuous) systems.

The Transmission Line

A transmission line can be modeled by means of the continuously distributed network shown in Figure 3.17. Here L, R, C, and G are the inductance, resistance, capacitance,

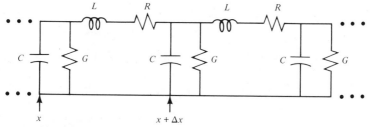

FIGURE 3.17 Model of a transmission line.

and conductance per unit length of the line. Upon applying Kirchhoff's voltage and current laws, respectively, to the section of line extending from x to $x + \Delta x$, we have

$$-\frac{\partial v}{\partial x} = L\frac{\partial i}{\partial t} + Ri \tag{3.110}$$

for the voltage drop in length $\Delta x \to 0$, and

$$-\frac{\partial i}{\partial x} = C\frac{\partial v}{\partial t} + Gv \tag{3.111}$$

as the current loss in the same length. Here $v = v(x,t)$ and $i = i(x,t)$.

It is our intent to study these two equations in some detail, in order to understand the operation of a transmission line.

On differentiating Equation 3.110 with respect to x, we obtain

$$-\frac{\partial^2 v}{\partial x^2} = L\frac{\partial^2 i}{\partial x\,\partial t} + R\left(-C\frac{\partial v}{\partial t} - Gv\right) \tag{3.112}$$

having substituted for $\partial i/\partial x$ from Equation 3.111. Also, Equation 3.111, when differentiated with respect to time, yields

$$-\frac{\partial^2 i}{\partial t\,\partial x} = C\frac{\partial^2 v}{\partial t^2} + G\frac{\partial v}{\partial t} \tag{3.113}$$

so that Equation 3.112 can be written as

$$\frac{\partial^2 v}{\partial x^2} = LC\frac{\partial^2 v}{\partial t^2} + (LG + RC)\frac{\partial v}{\partial t} + RGv \tag{3.114}$$

It is easy to show that the current $i(x,t)$ satisfies an equation of identical form. But if we can solve Equation 3.114, the current $i(x,t)$ can be found from Equation 3.111. Therefore we concentrate our efforts on Equation 3.114 and its special cases.

Equation 3.114 is a one-dimensional lossy wave equation, with the losses introduced through parameters R and G. As a first case we study the *lossless line,* defined by

$$R = G = 0 \tag{3.115}$$

In this case, on setting $(LC)^{-1} = c^2$, the square of the speed of propagation of the voltage wave on the line, we have the wave equation for the voltage $v(x,t)$ as

$$\frac{\partial^2 v}{\partial x^2} = \frac{1}{c^2}\frac{\partial^2 v}{\partial t^2} \tag{3.116}$$

The current $i(x,t)$ obeys an identical equation in the lossless case. Now let

$$\mathscr{L}\{v(x,t)\} \equiv V(x,s) = \int_{0_-}^{\infty} v(x,t)e^{-st}dt \tag{3.117}$$

be the Laplace transform of the voltage with respect to time. Then, Laplace transforming Equation 3.116 with respect to time, we obtain

$$\frac{d^2 V(x,s)}{dx^2} - \frac{s^2}{c^2} V(x,s) = 0 \tag{3.118}$$

if $v(x,0)$ and $v'(x,0)$ are zero, which we assume to be the case. The solution to Equation 3.118 can be written as

$$V(x,s) = V_1 e^{-sx/c} + V_2 e^{sx/c} \qquad (3.119)$$

where V_1 and V_2 are two constants that may be functions of s. We adopt the convention that $V_1 e^{-sx/c}$ is a forward traveling voltage wave, with $V_2 e^{sx/c}$ being a voltage traveling in the negative x-direction.

In the lossless case we have

$$-\frac{dV}{dx} = LsI(x,s) \qquad (3.120)$$

where $I(x,s) = \mathcal{L}\{i(x,t)\}$. The expression for the current can immediately be written as follows:

$$I(x,s) = \frac{1}{Lc} (V_1 e^{-sx/c} - V_2 e^{sx/c}) \qquad (3.121)$$

or, since $c = (LC)^{-1/2}$,

$$I(x,s) = \sqrt{\frac{C}{L}} (V_1 e^{-sx/c} - V_2 e^{sx/c}) \qquad (3.122)$$

The ratio $V(x,s)/I(x,s)$, an impedance $Z(x,s)$, is found to be

$$Z(x,s) = Z_c \frac{(V_1 e^{-sx/c} + V_2 e^{sx/c})}{(V_1 e^{-sx/c} - V_2 e^{sx/c})} \qquad (3.123)$$

where $Z_c = (L/C)^{1/2}$ is the characteristic impedance of a lossless line.

In transmission-line theory, it is usual to consider the voltage $V_2 e^{sx/c}$ as being the result of a reflection from an impedance discontinuity. In this case a voltage reflection coefficient $\rho = V_2/V_1$ is defined so that

$$Z(x,s) = Z_c \frac{(1 + \rho e^{2sx/c})}{(1 - \rho e^{2sx/c})} \qquad (3.124)$$

Consider the circuit shown in Figure 3.18. A transmission line of length l and characteristic impedance Z_c is terminated in a load impedance Z_L. Note that the origin

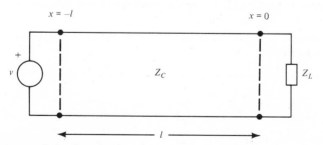

FIGURE 3.18 A transmission-line circuit.

of the coordinate system is at the load, another convention widely used in such problems.

We then have at $x = 0$:

$$Z(0,s) \equiv Z_L = Z_c(1 + \rho)/(1 - \rho) \tag{3.125}$$

Solving for ρ, we find that the voltage reflection coefficient is given by

$$\rho = \frac{Z_L - Z_c}{Z_L + Z_c} \tag{3.126}$$

Substituting this expression into Equation 3.124 yields

$$Z(x,s) = Z_c \frac{[Z_L(1 + e^{2sx/c}) + Z_c(1 - e^{2sx/c})]}{[Z_L(1 - e^{2sx/c}) + Z_c(1 + e^{2sx/c})]} \tag{3.127}$$

With the use of the hyperbolic tangent function, we write Equation 3.127 as

$$Z(x,s) = Z_c \frac{Z_L - Z_c \tanh (sx/c)}{Z_c - Z_L \tanh (sx/c)} \tag{3.128}$$

At $x = -l$, the input impedance of the line is given by

$$Z(-l,s) = Z_{in} = Z_c \frac{Z_L + Z_c \tanh (sl/c)}{Z_c + Z_L \tanh (sl/c)} \tag{3.129}$$

In Equation 3.129 we can now set $s = \sigma + j\omega$, a complex frequency. If Re $s \equiv 0$, we have the sinusoidal impedance

$$Z_{in}(j\omega) = Z_c \frac{(Z_L + jZ_c \tan (\omega l/c))}{Z_c + jZ_L \tan (\omega l/c)} \tag{3.130}$$

There are two cases of interest. If $\tan (\omega l/c) \to \infty$, i.e., if $\omega l/c = \pi/2$ is the "electrical length" of the line, then

$$Z_{in} Z_L = Z_c^2 \tag{3.131}$$

while if $\omega l/c = \pi$,

$$Z_{in} = Z_L \tag{3.132}$$

It is worthwhile noting that the expression for the impedance given in Equation 3.130 forms the basis for the construction of the Smith chart that is so useful in impedance (or admittance) matching calculations.

It is customary to define a normalized input impedance and a normalized load impedance by writing

$$\bar{Z}_{in} = \frac{Z_{in}}{Z_c} \tag{3.133}$$

and

$$\bar{Z}_L = \frac{Z_L}{Z_c} \tag{3.134}$$

so that Equation 3.130 becomes

$$\bar{Z}_{in} = \frac{\bar{Z}_L + j \tan (\omega l/c)}{1 + j\bar{Z}_L \tan (\omega l/c)} \tag{3.135}$$

Since $\overline{Z}_{in}$ is obviously complex, we may write

$$\overline{Z}_{in} = \overline{R} + j\overline{X} \tag{3.136}$$

where $\overline{R}$ is the normalized resistive part and $\overline{X}$ the normalized reactive part of the input impedance. This development is pursued further in a problem at the end of the chapter.

If R,G are not zero, we have a *lossy line*, and the voltage obeys the equation

$$\frac{\partial^2 v}{\partial x^2} = \frac{1}{c^2}\frac{\partial^2 v}{\partial t^2} + 2a\frac{\partial v}{\partial t} + bv \tag{3.137}$$

where $2a = (LG + RC)$ and $b = RG$.

The Laplace transform of this equation, with $v(x,0) = v'(x,0) = 0$ and with $V(x,s) = \mathcal{L}\{v(x,t)\}$, yields

$$\frac{d^2 V}{dx^2} - \beta^2(s)V = 0 \tag{3.138}$$

where

$$\beta^2(s) = \frac{s^2}{c^2} + 2as + b \tag{3.139}$$

A solution to Equation 3.138 is

$$V(x,s) = V_1 e^{-\beta(s)x} + V_2 e^{\beta(s)x} \tag{3.140}$$

where the first term is a forward traveling wave and the second term a backward traveling voltage wave, according to the convention adopted earlier. Then, since

$$-\frac{dV(x,s)}{dx} = (Ls + R)I(x,s) \tag{3.141}$$

we obtain

$$I(x,s) = \frac{\beta(s)}{Ls + R}(V_1 e^{-\beta(s)x} - V_2 e^{\beta(s)x}) \tag{3.142}$$

The ratio of $V(x,s)$ to $I(x,s)$ is, again, an impedance $Z(x,s)$. We have

$$Z(x,s) = Z_c(s)\frac{V_1 e^{-\beta(s)x} + V_2 e^{\beta(s)x}}{V_1 e^{-\beta(s)x} - V_2 e^{\beta(s)x}} \tag{3.143}$$

where the characteristic impedance here is a function of s,

$$Z_c(s) = \frac{Ls + R}{\beta(s)} = \sqrt{\frac{Ls + R}{Cs + G}} \tag{3.144}$$

as opposed to the lossless line discussed earlier. This leads to distortion of pulses on the lossy line. We now investigate the meaning of the last remark. The fact that s is a complex frequency means that each frequency will have its unique characteristic impedance $Z_c(s)$. If some frequencies are attenuated more rapidly than others on the lossy line, then time-dependent pulse will change its shape as it moves along the line. This phenomenon is called pulse distortion. From Equation 3.137, on setting

$$v(x,t) = e^{-\beta t} u(x,t) \tag{3.145}$$

and then choosing $\beta = ac^2$, we have

$$\frac{\partial^2 u}{\partial x^2} = \frac{1}{c^2} \frac{\partial^2 u}{\partial t^2} - (a^2 c^2 - b)u = 0 \tag{3.146}$$

Noting that $\beta = ac^2 > 0$, we see that there will be attenuation of the voltage as it travels along the lossy line. Now define a new independent variable

$$z \equiv \sqrt{c^2 t^2 - x^2} > 0 \tag{3.147}$$

Equation 3.142 then becomes a total differential equation in the variable z, namely,

$$\frac{d^2 u}{dz^2} + \frac{1}{z} \frac{du}{dz} - k^2 u = 0 \tag{3.148}$$

which is a standard form for a zero-order Bessel function of imaginary argument (see Appendix C).

We shall, however, take the Laplace transform of Equation 3.148 and solve for $u(z)$ by using the inversion theorem. Let $U(s) = \mathcal{L}\{u(z)\}$ and rewrite Equation 3.148 as follows:

$$z \frac{d^2 u}{dz^2} + \frac{du}{dz} - k^2 z u = 0 \tag{3.149}$$

Also, let $u(0_-) = 1$ and $u'(0_-) = 0$; these initial conditions follow from the series expansion of the Bessel function of order zero (see Appendix C).

The Laplace transform of Equation 3.149 becomes

$$-\frac{d}{ds}(s^2 U(s) - s) + sU(s) - 1 + k^2 \frac{dU(s)}{ds} = 0 \tag{3.150}$$

Simplification results in the first-order differential equation

$$\frac{dU}{ds} = \frac{sU(s)}{k^2 - s^2} \tag{3.151}$$

whose solution is, with u_0 a constant integration,

$$U(s) = \frac{u_0}{\sqrt{s^2 - k^2}} \tag{3.152}$$

Therefore, using the inversion theorem, we write

$$u(z) = \frac{u_0}{2\pi j} \int_{\gamma+j\infty}^{\gamma+j\infty} \frac{e^{sz}}{\sqrt{s^2 - k^2}} \, ds \tag{3.153}$$

We now want to evaluate the integral

$$I = \oint_C \frac{e^{sz}}{\sqrt{s^2 - k^2}} \, ds \tag{3.154}$$

about the contour shown in Figure 3.19, where the branch points at $s = \pm k$ must be avoided, in order to find $u(z)$.

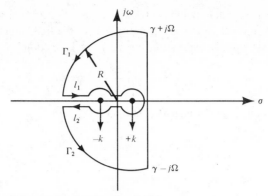

FIGURE 3.19   Contour of integration for Equation 3.153.

Since there are no singularities within the contour shown, we know that $I \equiv 0$. As $R, \Omega \to \infty$, the integrals along the arcs Γ_1 and Γ_2 vanish. The integrals along l_1 and l_2 cancel one another. On the small circles about the points $\pm k$, we set $s = \rho e^{j\phi} \pm k$, and as $\rho \to 0$, the integrals about these circles vanish. Consequently, we have, as R, $\Omega \to \infty$ and as $\rho \to 0$,

$$0 = \int_{\gamma - j\infty}^{\gamma + j\infty} \frac{e^{sz}}{\sqrt{s^2 - k^2}} \, ds + \int_{-k}^{k} \frac{e^{\sigma z}}{\sqrt{\sigma^2 - k^2}} \, d\sigma - \int_{k}^{-k} \frac{e^{\sigma z}}{\sqrt{\sigma^2 - k^2}} \, d\sigma \qquad (3.155)$$

Therefore,

$$\frac{1}{2\pi j} \int_{\gamma - j\infty}^{\gamma + j\infty} \frac{e^{sz}}{\sqrt{s^2 - k^2}} \, ds = -\frac{1}{\pi j} \int_{-k}^{k} \frac{e^{\sigma z}}{\sqrt{\sigma^2 - k^2}} \, d\sigma \qquad (3.156)$$

or, since $k \geq \sigma$,

$$\frac{1}{2\pi j} \int_{\gamma - j\infty}^{\gamma + j\infty} \frac{e^{sz}}{\sqrt{s^2 - k^2}} \, ds = -\frac{1}{\pi} \int_{-k}^{k} \frac{e^{\sigma z}}{\sqrt{k^2 - \sigma^2}} \, d\sigma \qquad (3.157)$$

Let $\sigma = k \cos \phi$ so that $d\sigma / \sqrt{k^2 - \sigma^2} = -d\phi$. We have, finally,

$$u(z) = \frac{u_0}{2\pi j} \int_{\gamma - j\infty}^{\gamma + j\infty} \frac{e^{sz}}{\sqrt{s^2 - k^2}} \, ds = \frac{u_0}{\pi} \int_{0}^{\pi} e^{kz \cos \phi} \, d\phi \qquad (3.158)$$

The right-hand side is an integral representation of the function $I_0(kz)$, a Bessel function of imaginary argument and order zero, as presented in Appendix C.

Inserting the expression

$$z = \sqrt{c^2 t^2 - x^2} > 0$$

we have

$$u(\sqrt{c^2 t^2 - x^2}) = u_0 I_0 (k\sqrt{c^2 t^2 - x^2}) \qquad (3.159)$$

so that the voltage $v(x,t)$ is

$$v(x,t) = \begin{cases} u_0 e^{-ac^2 t} I_0(k\sqrt{c^2 t^2 - x^2}) & |ct| > |x| \\ 0 & \text{otherwise} \end{cases} \qquad (3.160)$$

The voltage is not only attenuated on the lossy line, but its behavior is significantly altered as time progresses. For a given position x on the line, suppose that $|ct| >> |x|$. Then, using the asymptotic expression for the Bessel function,

$$\lim_{t \to \infty} I_0(kct\sqrt{1 - x^2/c^2t^2}) \sim \frac{e^{kct(1 - x^2/2c^2t^2)}}{\sqrt{t}} \qquad (3.161)$$

so that $v(x,t)$ becomes an attenuated Gaussian pulse, i.e.,

$$\lim_{t \to \infty} v(x,t) \sim u_0 e^{-\lambda t} \frac{e^{-kx^2/2ct}}{\sqrt{t}} \qquad (3.162)$$

where $\lambda = c(ac - k) > 0$.

3.12   THE DIFFUSION EQUATION

The diffusion equation is important in many applications in engineering, including probability theory, the propagation of electromagnetic waves in media whose conductivity is high, the flow of heat in material bodies, and the flow of charge carriers in solids. We derive the equation in a way that is standard in solid state engineering.

The continuity equation for charges and currents in the presence of sources is

$$\frac{\partial \rho}{\partial t} + \nabla \cdot \mathbf{j} = S \qquad (3.163)$$

where ρ is a charge per unit volume, $\mathbf{j}$ is a current density vector, and S is a function that characterizes the sources per unit time. With no electromagnetic fields present, the current density is given by Fick's law as

$$\mathbf{j} = - \lambda \nabla \rho \qquad (3.164)$$

i.e., the current density is proportional to the negative gradient of the charge density. Then

$$\frac{\partial \rho}{\partial t} - \lambda \nabla^2 \rho = S \qquad (3.165)$$

where the constant λ has dimensions of meters^2/second, and is often called the diffusion constant. We shall study Equation 3.165 for the case where $\rho = \rho(x,t)$.

Example 3.36   With sources absent, $\rho(x,t)$ satisfies the equation

$$\frac{1}{\lambda} \frac{\partial \rho}{\partial t} = \frac{\partial^2 \rho}{\partial x^2}$$

Let us assume, in this example, that $\rho(x,t)$ is defined in $0 \leq x \leq \infty$ and for $t \geq 0$, with $\rho(x,0) = 0$ and $\rho(0,t) = \rho_0$. Let the Laplace transform of $\rho(x,t)$ with respect to t be

$$\mathscr{L}\{\rho(x,t)\} \equiv R(x,s) = \int_{0_-}^{\infty} \rho(x,t)e^{-st}dt$$

The transformed equation is then

$$\frac{d^2 R(x,s)}{dx^2} - \frac{s}{\lambda} R(x,s) = 0$$

Since $\rho(o,t) = \rho_0$, $R(o,s) = \rho_0/s$. We require a solution to the transformed equation that is bounded as $x \to \infty$ and that reduces to ρ_0/s as $x \to 0$. Such a solution is

$$R(x,s) = \frac{\rho_0}{s} e^{-\sqrt{s/\lambda}\, x}$$

The inversion of this expression, which yields $\rho(x,t)$, was discussed in Example 3.32. We have, therefore,

$$\rho(x,t) = \rho_0 \text{erfc} \left(\frac{x}{2\sqrt{\lambda t}} \right) \qquad \blacksquare$$

With each change in initial and/or boundary conditions, there is a corresponding change in $\rho(x,t)$. This fact is illustrated by further examples.

Example 3.37   Let

$$\frac{1}{\lambda} \frac{\partial \rho}{\partial t} = \frac{\partial^2 \rho}{\partial x^2}$$

for $x\epsilon(0,\infty)$ and $t \geq 0$. Let $\rho(x, 0) = 0$ and let $\rho(0,t) = f(t)$. Then $R(x,s)$ is a solution to

$$\frac{d^2 R(x,s)}{dx^2} - \frac{s}{\lambda} R(x,s) = 0$$

which satisfies the condition $R(0,s) = F(s)$, where $F(s) = \mathcal{L}\{f(t)\}$. A bounded solution is

$$R(x,s) = F(s) e^{-\sqrt{s/\lambda}\, x}$$

Then, since $R(x,s)$ is the product of two Laplace transforms, $\rho(x,t)$ can be written as a convolution integral

$$\rho(x,t) = \int_{0_-}^{t} f(t,\tau) g(x,\tau) d\tau$$

where

$$g(x,t) = \mathcal{L}^{-1} \{ e^{-\sqrt{s/\lambda}\, x} \} = \frac{1}{2} \frac{x}{\sqrt{\lambda}} \frac{e^{-x^2/4\lambda t}}{t^{3/2}}$$

The integration can be carried out for a known $f(t)$. $\qquad \blacksquare$

3.13   MATRIX DIFFERENTIAL EQUATIONS

In this section we use Laplace transform methods to solve matrix differential equations. Typically, in problems involving linear systems with multiple inputs and multiple outputs, the system is characterized by a state vector $\mathbf{x} = (x_1, \ldots, x_n)^T$ and an output vector $\mathbf{y} = (y_1, \ldots, y_m)^T$. The state equation can be written as the first-order matrix differential equation[4]

$$\frac{d\mathbf{x}}{dt} = \mathbf{Ax} + \mathbf{Bu} \tag{3.166}$$

The homogeneous case of this equation, $\mathbf{u} = \mathbf{0}$, was considered in Chapter 1, Section 1.11. The output $\mathbf{y}(t)$ is related to $\mathbf{x}$ by the algebraic equation

$$\mathbf{y} = \mathbf{Cx} + \mathbf{Du} \tag{3.167}$$

Here, as noted, $\mathbf{x}$ and $\mathbf{y}$ are column vectors, and $\mathbf{A}$, $\mathbf{B}$, $\mathbf{C}$, $\mathbf{D}$ are constant matrices if the system is also time invariant. The vector $\mathbf{u}(t)$ is the input (forcing function).

A block diagram for Equations 3.166 and 3.167 is shown in Figure 3.20. It serves as a useful tool in simulating the system on an analog computer, as well as a visual aid for the relationships among the variables.

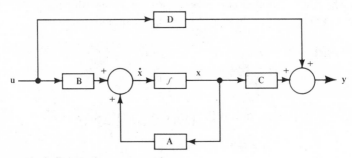

FIGURE 3.20   Block diagram for state equations.

Since Equation 3.167 is simply an algebraic relation linking $\mathbf{y}$ and $\mathbf{u}$ through the state vector $\mathbf{x}$, our main emphasis here is concentrated on Equation 3.166, and, in particular, on the use of the Laplace transform to find its solution, $\mathbf{x}(t)$.

It is convenient, at first, to consider, as was done in Chapter 1, the scalar form of Equation 3.166, namely,

$$\frac{dx}{dt} = ax + f(t) \quad f(t) = bu(t) \tag{3.168}$$

where a is a constant. Using the Laplace transform on Equation 3.168, we obtain

$$X(s) = \frac{1}{s - a} x(0_-) + \frac{1}{s - a} F(s) \tag{3.169}$$

By inversion, and using the convolution integral, we get

$$x(t) = e^{at}x(0_-) + \int_{0_-}^{t} e^{a(t - \tau)}f(\tau)d\tau \tag{3.170}$$

In complete analogy with Equation 3.170, we write the solution to Equation 3.166 as

$$\mathbf{x}(t) = e^{\mathbf{A}t}\mathbf{x}(0_-) + \int_{0_-}^{t} e^{\mathbf{A}(t - \tau)}\mathbf{B}(\tau)\mathbf{u}(\tau)d\tau \tag{3.171}$$

To prove that Equation 3.171 is indeed the solution, we use Laplace transform techniques. A typical component of Equation 3.166 is the scalar differential equation

$$\frac{dx_i}{dt} = \sum_k a_{ik}x_k + f_i(t) \tag{3.172}$$

where $f_i(t)$ is defined as the ith component of the vector **Bu**. Let $X_i(s) = \mathcal{L}\{x_i(t)\}$ and $F_i(s) = \mathcal{L}\{f_i(t)\}$. Then, transforming Equation 3.172, we get

$$sX_i(s) - x_i(0_-) = \sum_k a_{ik}X_k(s) + F_i(s) \tag{3.173}$$

or

$$\sum_k (s\delta_{ik} - a_{ik})X_k(s) = x_i(0_-) + F_i(s) \tag{3.174}$$

where δ_{ik} is the Kronecker delta symbol, defined as follows:

$$\delta_{ik} = \begin{cases} 1, & i = k \\ 0, & i \neq k \end{cases} \tag{3.175}$$

Equation 3.174 can be written for all the components as the single matrix equation

$$(s\mathbf{I} - \mathbf{A})\mathbf{X}(s) = \mathbf{x}(0_-) + \mathbf{F}(s) \tag{3.176}$$

where **I** is the unit matrix. Upon premultiplying both sides by the inverse of the matrix $(s\mathbf{I} - \mathbf{A})$, we have

$$\mathbf{X}(s) = (s\mathbf{I} - \mathbf{A})^{-1}\mathbf{x}(0_-) + (s\mathbf{U} - \mathbf{A})^{-1}\mathbf{F}(s) \tag{3.177}$$

Let the matrix exponential function be

$$e^{\mathbf{A}t} = \mathcal{L}^{-1}\{(s\mathbf{I} - \mathbf{A})^{-1}\} \tag{3.178}$$

Then, by inverting Equation 3.177 and making use of the convolution theorem, we get

$$\mathbf{x}(t) = e^{\mathbf{A}t}\mathbf{x}(0_-) + \int_{0_-}^{t} e^{\mathbf{A}(t-\tau)}\mathbf{Bu}(\tau)d\tau \tag{3.179}$$

where we have inserted $\mathbf{F}(\tau) = \mathbf{Bu}(\tau)$. See also Problems 3.19 and 3.20.

Example 3.38   Find a solution to the matrix differential equation

$$\frac{d\mathbf{x}}{dt} = \mathbf{Ax} + \mathbf{Bu}$$

if $\mathbf{A} = \begin{bmatrix} 3/2 & 1 \\ -1/4 & 1/2 \end{bmatrix}$, $\mathbf{B} = \begin{bmatrix} 1 \\ 1 \end{bmatrix}$, $u = e^{-t}$, and $\mathbf{x}(0_-) = \begin{bmatrix} 1 \\ 0 \end{bmatrix}$. We have the solution

$$\mathbf{x}(t) = e^{\mathbf{A}t}\begin{bmatrix} 1 \\ 0 \end{bmatrix} + \int_{0_-}^{t} e^{\mathbf{A}(t-\tau)}\begin{bmatrix} 1 \\ 1 \end{bmatrix}e^{-\tau}d\tau$$

It is necessary only to calculate

$$e^{\mathbf{A}t} = \mathcal{L}^{-1}\{(s\mathbf{I} - \mathbf{A})^{-1}\}$$

We have

$$(s\mathbf{I} - \mathbf{A}) = \begin{bmatrix} s - 3/2 & -1 \\ 1/4 & s - 1/2 \end{bmatrix}$$

Then the inverse matrix is the adjoint divided by the determinant of $(s\mathbf{I} - \mathbf{A})$:

$$(s\mathbf{I} - \mathbf{A})^{-1} = \begin{bmatrix} \dfrac{s - \frac{1}{2}}{(s-1)^2} + \dfrac{1}{(s-1)^2} \\[3mm] -\dfrac{\frac{1}{4}}{(s-1)^2} \qquad \dfrac{s - \frac{3}{2}}{(s-1)^2} \end{bmatrix}$$

We therefore have

$$e^{\mathbf{A}t} = \mathscr{L}^{-1}\{(s\mathbf{I} - \mathbf{A})^{-1}\} = \begin{bmatrix} e^t + \frac{1}{2} t e^t & t e^t \\ -t e^t/4 & e^t - \frac{1}{2} t e^t \end{bmatrix}$$

Then the expression for $\mathbf{x}(t)$ becomes

$$\mathbf{x}(t) = \begin{bmatrix} e^t + \frac{1}{2} t e^t & +t e^t \\ -t e^t/4 & e^t(1 - t/2) \end{bmatrix}\begin{bmatrix} 1 \\ 0 \end{bmatrix} + \int_0^t \begin{bmatrix} e^\lambda + \frac{1}{2} \lambda e^\lambda & \lambda e^\lambda \\ -\lambda e^\lambda/4 & e^\lambda(1 - \lambda/2) \end{bmatrix}\begin{bmatrix} e^{-\tau} \\ e^{-\tau} \end{bmatrix} d\tau$$

where $\lambda = (t - \tau)$.

Example 3.39 We now examine the circuit shown in Figure 3.21 in order to show the development of matrix differential equations. Let the voltage drop across capacitor C_1 be denoted by v_{c_1} and that across C_2 by v_{c_2}. Then, at node 1, Kirchhoff's current law equation reads

$$C_1 \frac{dv_{c_1}(t)}{dt} = \frac{v(t) - v_{c_1}(t)}{R_1} + \frac{v_{c_2}(t) - v_{c_1}(t)}{R_2}$$

and at node 2,

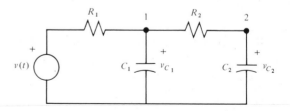

FIGURE 3.21 Example 3.39.

$$C_2 \frac{dv_{c_2}(t)}{dt} = -\frac{v_{c_2}(t) - v_{c_1}(t)}{R_2}$$

With $\tau^{-1} = \tau_{11}^{-1} + \tau_{12}^{-1}$, $\tau_{11} = R_1 C_1$, $\tau_{22} = R_2 C_2$, and $\tau_{12} = R_2 C_1$ as time constants, these equations can be written as

$$\frac{dv_{c_1}}{dt} = -\frac{1}{\tau} v_{c_1} + \frac{v(t)}{\tau_{11}} + \frac{1}{\tau_{12}} v_{c_2}(t)$$

and

$$\frac{dv_{c_2}}{dt} = \frac{v_{c_1}}{\tau_{22}} - \frac{v_{c_2}}{\tau_{22}}$$

Define a state vector $\mathbf{x}(t)$ as

$$\mathbf{x}(t) = \begin{bmatrix} v_{c_1}(t) \\ v_{c_2}(t) \end{bmatrix}$$

and the matrix $\mathbf{A}$ as

$$A = \begin{bmatrix} -\dfrac{1}{\tau} & \dfrac{1}{\tau_{12}} \\[2ex] \dfrac{1}{\tau_{22}} & -\dfrac{1}{\tau_{22}} \end{bmatrix}$$

Then the two current equations can be written here as

$$\frac{d\mathbf{x}}{dt} = \mathbf{A}\mathbf{x} + \mathbf{u}$$

where $\mathbf{u} = [v(t)]$. Note that the two initial conditions, $v_{c_1}(0_-)$ and $v_{c_2}(0_-)$ constitute, quite properly, the initial state vector

$$\mathbf{x}(0_-) = \begin{bmatrix} v_{c_1}(0_-) \\ v_{c_2}(0_-) \end{bmatrix}$$

This example also illustrates the justification for the term "state vector." Its components (here, the two capacitive voltages), together with the given input, determine uniquely the state of the network at every $t \geq 0$. In other words, by knowing $\mathbf{x}(t)$ at every instant, together with $\mathbf{u}(t)$, we can easily find $\mathbf{y}(t)$, at most by purely algebraic calculations.

A general method for the formulation of state matrix differential equations for circuits, based on topological considerations, is given in Problem 3-22. ∎

This brief introduction to the important topic of state vectors and their equations is certainly insufficient. It is included at this point to show that Laplace transform methods are useful in solving matrix differential equations. In Chapter 6, a more complete discussion is given, together with applications.

PROBLEMS

3-1 Establish whether or not the following functions $f(t)$ are of exponential order: (a) $e^{t \sin t}$; (b) e^{t^2}; (c) $e^{\cos t/t}$.

3-2 We have shown that $\mathscr{L}\{\sin \omega_0 t\} = \omega_0/(s^2 + \omega_0^2)$. From this fact, and by using properties of the Laplace transforms, find the transforms of the following functions:

(a) $t \sin \omega_0 t$

(b) $\dfrac{\sin \omega_0 t}{t}$

(c) $e^{-at} \sin \omega_0 t$ $(a > 0$ and real)

(d) $\sin \omega_0(t - \tau) \begin{cases} \text{for } t > \tau \\ 0 \text{ otherwise} \end{cases}$

(e) $(\sin \omega_0 t - \omega_0 t \cos \omega_0 t)/2\omega_0^2$

3-3 In Equations 3.149–3.151 we see the use of the Laplace transform methods in differential equations with time-varying coefficients. Such an approach may not be always fruitful: it may, at times, lead to a *differential* equation in the s-domain which is not easier to solve than the original equation. (This is in contrast with constant coefficients where the transformed equation is *algebraic*.) Try using the Laplace transform on[1]

(a) $\dfrac{d^2y}{dt^2} + \dfrac{1}{t}\dfrac{dy}{dt} + y = 0, \quad y(0_-) = 1, \quad y'(0_-) = 0$

(b) $(t^2 + 1)\dfrac{dy}{dt} + ty = 0, \quad y(0_-) = 0$

Note You can solve case (b) directly, by separating the variables. Do it and compare.

3-4 Given

$$F(s) = \frac{-3s^3 + 2s^2 + 10s + 2}{(s^2 + 2s + 10)^2}$$

without ever finding $f(t)$, calculate $f(0_-), f(\infty), f'(0_-), f'(\infty)$.

3-5 In the circuit shown, the capacitor C is uncharged prior to $t = 0$, i.e., $v_c(0_-) = 0$. At $t = 0$ the voltage input $v_i(t) = Au(t)$ is applied, where $u(t)$ is the unit step function and the output is the current $i_c(t)$.

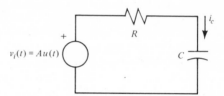

FIGURE 3.22 Problem 3-5.

(a) Show that the input–output differential equation, Equation 3.66a, here is

$$R\frac{di_c}{dt} + \frac{1}{C}i_c = \frac{dv_i}{dt}$$

and

$$\frac{dv_i}{dt} = A\delta(t)$$

(b) Verify that i_c is discontinuous at $t = 0$, $i_c(0_-) \neq i_c(0_+)$. Show that $i_c(0_+) = A/R$.

(c) Find the impulse response of this system.

(d) By convolution, find the zero-state response to a sinusoidal input $v_i(t) = V_m \sin \beta t$.

3-6 Let a system be described as in Equation 3.66a by

$$\frac{d^2y}{dt^2} + 2\frac{dy}{dt} + 10y = \frac{d^2p}{dt^2} - 3\frac{dp}{dt} + 5p$$

Find its impulse response. Explain physically the various terms appearing in this response.

3-7 An alternate derivation of the convolution integral for linear time-invariant systems, Equation 3.69, is given in the following steps. Here we use the notation

$$L\{\text{input}\} = \text{output}$$

designating the linear system operator L as operating on an input to produce the output.

In each step provide a one-sentence justification, involving linearity and time invariance, appropriately. The first step, being a definition, is written fully:

$L\{\delta(t)\} = h(t)$, the definition of the impulse response.

$L\{\delta(t - \tau)\} = h(t - \tau)$,   ?   ?

$L\{f(\tau)\delta(t - \tau)\} = f(\tau)h(t - \tau)$,   ?   ?

$L\{\int_{0_-}^{t} f(\tau)\delta(t - \tau)d\tau\} = \int_{0_-}^{t} f(\tau)h(t - \tau)d\tau$,   ?   ?

$L\{f(t)\} = \int_{0_-}^{t} f(\tau)h(t - \tau)d\tau$?   ?

$y(t) = \int_{0_-}^{t} f(\tau)h(t - \tau)d\tau$?   ?

3-8 In many cases, a geometrical interpretation is very useful when evaluating the convolution integral. In particular, consider the convolution of two functions, $g(t)$ and $h(t)$,

$$\int_{0_-}^{t} g(t - \tau)h(\tau)d\tau$$

where $g(t)$ and $h(t)$ have different forms over different ranges of t.
To be specific, consider[2]

$$g(t) = \begin{cases} 1 & 0 \le t \le 0.5 \\ 0 & \text{elsewhere} \end{cases}$$

and

$$h(t) = \begin{cases} t & 0 \le t \le 0.5 \\ 0.5 & 0.5 \le t \le 1.0 \\ 1.5 - t & 1.0 \le t \le 1.5 \\ 0 & \text{elsewhere} \end{cases}$$

as shown in Figure 3.23

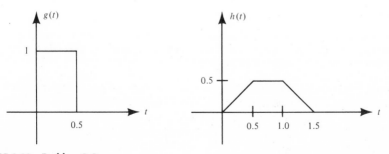

FIGURE 3.23 Problem 3-8.

We wish to obtain the analytic answers, particularly with regard to the appropriate limits and the integrands, and the proper ranges of the time axis involved. For these purposes, we plot on the (t, τ)-plane all the information needed. In our example, proceed as follows:

1. Write $h(\tau)$ from the given $h(t)$, i.e., in our case

$$h(\tau) = \begin{cases} \tau & 0 \le \tau \le 0.5 \\ 0.5 & 0.5 \le \tau \le 1.0 \\ 1.5 - \tau & 1.0 \le \tau \le 1.5 \\ 0 & \text{elsewhere} \end{cases}$$

2. Write $g(t - \tau)$ from the given $g(t)$, here

$$g(t - \tau) = \begin{cases} 1 & 0 \le t - \tau \le 0.5 \\ 0 & \text{elsewhere} \end{cases}$$

3. Rearrange the inequalities in $g(t - \tau)$ in terms of τ only, i.e.,

$$g(t - \tau) = \begin{cases} 1 & t - 0.5 \le \tau \le t \\ 0 & \text{elsewhere} \end{cases}$$

4. On the (t,τ)-plane, plot the inequalities of all the limits on τ in steps 1 and 3. Specifically, here we have the plots shown in Figure 3.24.

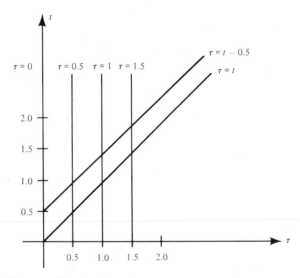

FIGURE 3.24   Problem 3-8: the (t,τ)-plane plots.

5. On this plot label corresponding areas that are nonzero with the corresponding products of $g(t - \tau)h(\tau)$. Each such product is an integrand.

6. Set up the convolution integrals with respect to τ, with the proper limits, integrands, and restrictions on τ as given in the (t,τ) plot.

   In our example, we have, therefore, as a final answer

$$\int_0^t 1 . \tau d\tau = \frac{t^2}{2} \qquad 0 \le t \le 0.5$$

$$\int_{t-0.5}^{0.5} \tau d\tau + \int_{0.5}^t 0.5 \, d\tau = 1/2[0.25 - (t - 0.5)^2 + (t - 0.5)] \qquad 0.5 \le t \le 1.0$$

and two additional integrals. Complete these. Plot the total answer versus t.

3-9 Use the method outlined in Problem 3-8 to convolve $g(t)$ with $h(t)$, where the two functions are given in Figure 3.25. The answer should be in analytical form for the appropriate ranges of t. Plot it.

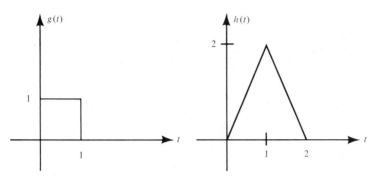

FIGURE 3.25   Problem 3-9.

3-10 Find the Laplace transforms of the following functions

(a) $\dfrac{1}{2\sqrt{\pi t^3}}\,(e^{-at} - e^{-bt})u(t)$

(b) $e^{-at}\mathrm{erf}(\lambda\sqrt{t})u(t)$

(c) $\dfrac{1}{\sqrt{t}}\cos 2\sqrt{kt}\;u(t)$

(d) $\dfrac{1}{\sqrt{\pi t}}\,e^{-\lambda^2/4t}u(t)$

3-11 Find the inverse Laplace transform of the following functions, by use of the Laplace inversion theorem:

(a) $\dfrac{1}{s(s^2 + a^2)}$

(b) $\dfrac{1}{s^2(s^2 + a^2)}$

(c) $\dfrac{1}{s^4 - a^4}$

(d) $\dfrac{1}{(s^2 + a^2)^n}\quad (n > 0)$

(e) $\dfrac{1}{s(e^{sT} - a)}$

(f) $\dfrac{1}{s\,\cosh sT}$

(g) $e^{-k\sqrt{s}}$

Note   In parts (e) and (f), T is the period of a periodic function $f(t)$.

3-12 In our discussion of the lossless transmission line, it is shown that a reflection coefficient at a load with impedance Z_L is

$$\rho = \frac{Z_L - Z_c}{Z_L + Z_c}$$

In terms of normalized load impedances, the expression for ρ is

$$\rho = \frac{\bar{Z}_L - 1}{\bar{Z}_L + 1}$$

If this is substituted into the normalized form of Equation 3.124, we have

$$\bar{Z}(x,s) = \frac{1 + \rho e^{2sx/c}}{1 - \rho e^{2sx/c}}$$

so that ρ can be written, at any point on the line, as

$$\rho = \frac{\bar{Z} - 1}{\bar{Z} + 1} e^{-2sx/c}$$

Let $\bar{Z} = \bar{R} + j\bar{X}$ be the normalized impedance as discussed in the text. Then the reflection coefficient, at $x = -l$,

$$\bar{\rho} = \frac{\bar{R} + j\bar{X} - 1}{\bar{R} + j\bar{X} + 1} = \rho e^{-2sl/c}$$

is *a complex quantity*. Set $\bar{\rho} = u + jv$ and show that

$$\left(u - \frac{\bar{R}}{\bar{R} + 1}\right)^2 + v^2 = \frac{1}{(\bar{R} + 1)^2}$$

Find the equation for another family of circles whose radius involves the reactance variable $\bar{X}$. Plots of these orthogonal families of circles are available as the useful Smith chart.

3-13 A concept of use in transmission-line analysis is that of a *voltage standing wave ratio* (VSWR). The voltage at any point on the line can be written as the Laplace transform expression

$$V(x,s) = V_1(e^{-sx} + \rho e^{sx})$$

where $\rho = V_2/V_1$ is the reflection coefficient. Let $s = j\omega$, so that an unattenuated sinusoidal wave is propagating. Then

$$V(x,\omega) = V_1(e^{-j\omega x} + \rho e^{j\omega x}) = V_1 e^{-j\omega x}(1 + \rho e^{2j\omega x})$$

At some point on the line this expression is a maximum, while at another point it will be a minimum. The ratio of the absolute values of the maximum to the minimum is known as the VSWR. Establish the result that

$$\text{VSWR} = \frac{1 + |\rho|}{1 - |\rho|}$$

where $|\rho|$ is the absolute value of the reflection coefficient.

3-14 Sections of transmission lines are often used as delay lines. We know that the speed of propagation of signals on a lossless transmission line is given by $c = (LC)^{-1/2}$. Design a line 2 meters long that will cause a signal to be delayed by a time of 2×10^{-8} seconds relative to a signal propagating in free space, for which $c_{vac} \cong 3 \times 10^8$ meter/second.

Note   There is an infinite number of solutions to the problem, depending on choices for L and C. Be realistic; choose commercially available values of inductance and capacitance.

3-15   The lossless diffusion equation is discussed in the text. If there is absorption of charge carriers, the continuity equation is

$$\frac{\partial \rho}{\partial t} + \nabla \cdot \mathbf{j} + \sigma_a \rho = 0$$

where σ_a is a reciprocal time.
     Fick's law reads, for no electromagnetic fields present,

$$\mathbf{j} = -\lambda \nabla \rho$$

For $\rho = \rho(x,t)$, the diffusion equation with losses becomes

$$\frac{\partial \rho}{\partial t} - \lambda \frac{\partial^2 \rho}{\partial x^2} + \sigma_a \rho = 0$$

Find a solution to this equation for $x, t \geq 0$ when $\rho(x,0) = 0$ and $\rho(0,t) = \rho_0$, a constant, using Laplace transform methods.

3-16   In case there is an electric field present in some region of space, Fick's law for the current density is, in that region,

$$\mathbf{j} = -(\lambda \nabla \rho + \mathbf{K}\rho)$$

where $\mathbf{K}$ is a vector proportional to the force exerted by the electric field on the charge density ρ. Under these conditions, and with no absorption of particles, the one-dimensional continuity equation, in the case of constant $\mathbf{K}$, reduces to

$$\frac{\partial \rho}{\partial t} - \lambda \frac{\partial^2 \rho}{\partial x^2} - K \frac{\partial \rho}{\partial x} = 0$$

where K is the magnitude of $\mathbf{K}$. Find, by Laplace transform methods, a solution for $\rho(x,t)$ for $x, t \geq 0$ if $\rho(x,0) = 0$ and $\rho(0,t) = \rho_0$, a constant. The Laplace transform $R(x,s)$ of $\rho(x,t)$ is a solution to the differential equation

$$\frac{d^2 R}{dx^2} + \beta \frac{dR}{dx} - \frac{s}{\lambda} R = 0$$

where $\beta = K/\lambda$.

Hint   You may first want to set

$$R(x,s) = T(x,s)e^{-\beta x/2}$$

This will yield an equation in $T(x,s)$ in which no first derivative appears. Then the solution to the equation for $T(x,s)$ can be written by inspection. The inversion integral will contain branch point singularities.

3-17   Stability is an important aspect in the analysis and design of systems. Consider the *impulse response stability* of a linear time-invariant system as follows: Let the transfer function be $H(s) = P(s)/Q(s)$, a rational function in s, without common factors between the two polynomials $P(s)$ and $Q(s)$. In most physical systems the degree of $P(s)$ is less than that of $Q(s)$.

The impulse response of the system is then

$$h(t) = \mathcal{L}^{-1} \frac{P(s)}{Q(s)}$$

(a) Write $h(t)$ explicitly in terms of the poles of $H(s)$, i.e., the characteristic roots of $Q(s) = 0$, for the following cases:

(1) All the poles are real, distinct, and in the left half of the s-plane.
(2) All the poles are real, some are repeated, and in the left half of the s-plane.
(3) In addition to cases 1 and 2, some poles are on the $j\omega$-axis and distinct.

In all these cases, write the expressions for $h(t)$ and show that $h(t)$ is bounded, i.e.,

$$\lim_{t \to \infty} h(t) = 0$$

or

$$\lim_{t \to \infty} h(t) \le M, \text{ a constant}$$

and the system is stable.

(b) For the remaining cases, i.e., when some poles are multiple on the $j\omega$-axis and/or in the right half of the s-plane, show that $h(t)$ is unbounded

$$\lim_{t \to \infty} h(t) \to \infty$$

and therefore the system is unstable.

3-18   An elementary linear feedback system is shown in Figure 3.26.

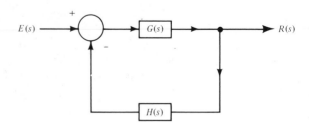

FIGURE 3.26   Problem 3-18.

(a) Show that the overall transfer function, $R(s)/E(s)$, with the feedback through $H(s)$, is given by

$$\frac{\mathcal{L}(\text{output})}{\mathcal{L}(\text{input})} = \frac{R(s)}{E(s)} = \frac{G(s)}{1 + G(s)H(s)}$$

(b) Consider a two-phase inductor motor, for which

$$G(s) = \frac{A}{s(s + \alpha)}, \quad \alpha > 0$$

and which has a feedback loop of unity, i.e.,

$$H(s) = 1$$

For this overall system, show that the transfer function can be written as

$$\frac{R(s)}{E(s)} = \frac{B}{s^2 + 2\zeta\omega_n s + \omega_n^2}$$

Investigate in full the response (output) to a unit step input for the following cases:
  (1) The damping coefficient is less than unity, $\zeta < 1$ (the *underdamped*, or oscillating, case).
  (2) The damping coefficient ζ is greater than unity, $\zeta > 1$ (the *overdamped* case).
  (3) The damping coefficient ζ is unity, $\zeta = 1$ (the *critically damped* case).

3-19 The time-domain solution of the matrix state equation

$$\dot{\mathbf{x}} = \mathbf{A}\mathbf{x} + \mathbf{B}\mathbf{u}$$

requires the definition of the exponential matrix function $e^{\mathbf{A}t}$. It is

$$e^{\mathbf{A}t} = \mathbf{I} + \mathbf{A}t + \mathbf{A}^2\frac{t^2}{2!} + \cdots = \sum_{k=0}^{\infty} \mathbf{A}^k \frac{t^k}{k!}$$

and is analogous to the scalar series of e^{At}. It can be shown that the series in $e^{\mathbf{A}t}$ converges for all $\mathbf{A}$ and for all finite t.
  To show that the solution of the matrix state equation is indeed given by Equation 3.171, i.e.,

$$\mathbf{x}(t) = e^{\mathbf{A}t}\mathbf{x}(0_-) + \int_{0_-}^{t} e^{\mathbf{A}(t-\tau)}\mathbf{B}\mathbf{u}(\tau)d\tau$$

carry out the following two steps:
  (a) Show that the initial state vector, $\mathbf{x}(0_-)$, is satisfied by the solution $\mathbf{x}(t)$ at $t = 0_-$.
  (b) Substitute the given solution into the differential equation to see if it is satisfied.

3-20 The exponential matrix function $e^{\mathbf{A}t}$ is often designated by $\boldsymbol{\phi}(t)$

$$\boldsymbol{\phi}(t) = e^{\mathbf{A}t}$$

and is called the *state transition matrix*. Thus the zero-input solution to the state equation is given by

$$\mathbf{x}(t) = \boldsymbol{\phi}(t)\mathbf{x}(0_-)$$

and the explanation of the term "transition" is clear: The initial state $\mathbf{x}(0_-)$ undergoes a transformation, or transition, to another state at time t. Write the complete solution to the matrix state equation using $\boldsymbol{\phi}(t)$. Using $\boldsymbol{\phi}(s) = \mathcal{L}\{\boldsymbol{\phi}(t)\}$, write its corresponding expression in the s-domain. Compare with Equations 3.177 and 3.178.

3-21 In evaluating $(s\mathbf{I} - \mathbf{A})^{-1}$, as in Equation 3.178, we use the determinant of $(s\mathbf{I} - \mathbf{A})$,

$$\Delta = \det(s\mathbf{I} - \mathbf{A})$$

The roots of the characteristic equation

$$\Delta = \det(s\mathbf{I} - \mathbf{A}) = 0$$

are the characteristic values.
  If the state vector is to be bounded, i.e.,

$$\lim_{t\to\infty} \|\mathbf{x}(t)\| = 0$$

establish restrictions on the location of the characteristic values in the complex s-plane. See also Problem 3.17.

3-22 The systematic formulation of the first-order matrix differential equation for circuits is done as follows:
(a) Draw the graph of the network, using a branch for every network element.
(b) Choose a tree containing all the voltage sources, a maximal number of capacitors, and a minimal number of inductors. Some resistors may be needed to complete this tree.
(c) Each capacitive voltage in this tree and each inductive current in the co-tree becomes a *state variable* in the state vector $\mathbf{x}(t)$,

$$\mathbf{x}(t) = [v_{c_1}(t) \quad v_{c_2}(t) \quad \ldots \quad i_{L_1}(t) \quad i_{L_2}(t) \quad \ldots]^T$$

(d) Write a fundamental cut-set equation for each capacitor in the tree and a fundamental loop equation for each inductor in the co-tree. These equations, in matrix form, become

$$\dot{\mathbf{x}} = \mathbf{Ax} + \mathbf{Bu}$$

Derive this state matrix equation for the network shown in Figure 3.27. Solve for $\mathbf{x}(t)$ if $R_1 = 1$ ohm, $R_2 = 2$ ohms, $L = 1$ henry, $C_1 = C_2 = 0.1$ farad, $v_1(t) = u(t)$, $i_1(t) = \delta(t)$. All initial conditions are zero.

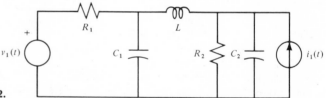

FIGURE 3.27 Problem 3-22.

3-23 Derive the state matrix equation, as in the previous problem, for the network shown in Figure 3.28. Solve it for the following values: $R_1 = R_2 = 1$ ohm, $C_1 = 1/2$ farad, $C_2 = 1/4$

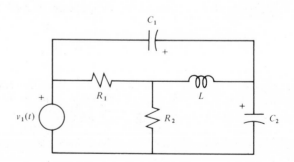

FIGURE 3.28 Problem 3-23.

farad, $L = 1$ henry, $v_1(t) = 2e^{-t}u(t)$. The capacitors are initially charged as shown, $q_{c_1}(0_-) = 2$ coulombs, $q_{c_2}(0_-) = 1$ coulomb.

3-24 For the op-amp circuit shown in Figure 3.29, derive the state matrix equation.
Hint Write Kirchhoff's current law at nodes A and B.

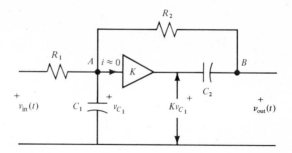

FIGURE 3.29   Problem 3-24.

Solve the state matrix equation for $R_1 = 10$ kΩ, $R_2 = 2$ ohms, $C_1 = 1$ μF, $C_2 = 0.1$ μF, $K = -10^5$. The capacitors are uncharged initially. Write the output equation ($\mathbf{y}(t) = v_{\text{out}}$) in terms of the state vector $\mathbf{x}(t)$ and the input. See Equation 3.167.

SELECTED BIBLIOGRAPHY

1. S. Karni, *Intermediate Network Analysis*. Boston: Allyn & Bacon, Inc., 1971.

2. D. E. Cartier, "Mirror Mirror on the Wall . . . Convolution Isn't Hard at All," *EDN*, pp. 55–59, March 1975.

3. S. Karni and D. Etter, "An Algebraic-Recursive Algorithm for Partial Fraction Expansion with Multiple Poles," *IEEE Transactions on Education,* vol. E-22, no. 1, pp. 25–27, February 1979.

4. L. S. Zadeh and C. A. Desoer, *Linear Systems Theory: The State Space Approach*. New York: McGraw-Hill Book Co., Inc., 1963.

5. T. Kailath, *Linear Systems*. Englewood Cliffs, N.J.: Prentice-Hall, Inc., 1980.

6. A. Erdelyi, *Operational Calculus and Generalized Functions*. New York: Holt, Rinehart & Winston, 1962.

7. G. Doetsch, *Guide to the Applications of the Laplace and Z-Transforms*. London: Van Nostrand Reinhold Company, 1971.

8. R. V. Churchill, *Operational Mathematics*. New York: McGraw-Hill Book Co., Inc., 1958.

9. P. K. Kuhfittig, *Introduction to the Laplace Transform*. New York: Plenum Press, 1978.

10. H. S. Carslaw and J. C. Jaeger, *Operational Methods in Applied Mathematics*. Cambridge, England: Oxford University Press, 1948. (Also available in paperback. New York: Dover Publications, 1963.)

CHAPTER 4

The Fourier Transform and Applications

4.1 INTRODUCTION

In this chapter we study Fourier transforms and a few of their applications. In Section 4.2 the exponential Fourier transform pair is defined and examples of the calculation of transform pairs given. Section 4.3 discusses Fourier cosine and sine transform pairs, with examples of their evaluation. A few theorems of use are given in Section 4.4. There are various discontinuous functions that are important idealizations of physically realistic functions; these, and their transforms, are covered in Section 4.5. The extension of the Fourier transform to multidimensional spaces is made in Section 4.6, where Fourier-Bessel integrals and Hankel transforms are introduced. The remainder of the chapter covers a few applications. These include solutions to the wave equation in one or more spatial dimensions, with a discussion of the Hertzian antenna (Section 4.7), remarks on filters (Section 4.8), and, finally, (Section 4.9), the application of Fourier transforms to amplitude- and frequency-modulated communications systems. We stress that it is our primary intention in this chapter to cover ways in which Fourier transforms are useful in system analysis, rather than to discuss at length the systems themselves.

4.2 THE EXPONENTIAL FOURIER TRANSFORM PAIR

By the sifting property of the delta function, the identity

$$f(t) = \int_{-\infty}^{\infty} f(\tau)\delta(t - \tau)\, d\tau \tag{4.1}$$

holds. On using the integral representation of the delta function (see Appendix A)

$$\delta(t - \tau) = \frac{1}{2\pi} \int_{-\infty}^{\infty} e^{j\omega(t-\tau)} \, d\omega \qquad (4.2)$$

$f(t)$ is written as

$$f(t) = \frac{1}{2\pi} \int_{-\infty}^{\infty} \int_{-\infty}^{\infty} f(\tau) e^{j\omega(t-\tau)} \, d\omega \, d\tau \qquad (4.3)$$

On defining the function

$$F(\omega) = \int_{-\infty}^{\infty} e^{-j\omega\tau} f(\tau) \, d\tau \qquad (4.4)$$

we see that Equation 4.3 reduces to

$$f(t) = \frac{1}{2\pi} \int_{-\infty}^{\infty} e^{j\omega t} F(\omega) \, d\omega \qquad (4.5)$$

Equations 4.4 and 4.5 define an exponential Fourier transform pair. Here t is a time and ω is a reciprocal time, or angular frequency. We have been a bit cavalier in our use of the delta function and its integral representation in order to reach the results embodied in Equations 4.4 and 4.5 quickly. A few comments on the conditions for the existence of $F(\omega)$ and $f(t)$ (because of the rather impressive symmetry exhibited by the transform pair) are now made. If in Equation 4.4 we set $\omega = 0$, then

$$F(0) = \int_{-\infty}^{\infty} f(t) \, dt \qquad (4.6)$$

In order for $F(0)$ to exist, it follows that $f(t)$ must be a function such that the integral on the right-hand side of Equation 4.6 exists. If, in addition, we now require that

$$\int_{-\infty}^{\infty} |f(t)| \, dt$$

is bounded for a piecewise continuous function $f(t)$, and if, at a point of discontinuity $t = t_0$, $f(t)$ is defined by

$$f(t_0) = \lim_{\epsilon \to 0} \frac{1}{2} \{ f(t_0 - \epsilon) + f(t_0 + \epsilon) \}$$

then the Fourier transform $F(\omega)$ of the function $f(t)$ will exist.

We now give several examples of the calculation of either $F(\omega)$ or $f(t)$ where one of the two is prescribed.

Example 4.1   Let $f(t) = e^{-at}$ $(a > 0)$ for $t \geq 0$, and zero elsewhere. Then

$$F(\omega) = \int_{0}^{\infty} e^{-(a+j\omega)t} \, dt = \frac{1}{a + j\omega}$$

or

$$F(\omega) = F_R(\omega) + jF_I(\omega) = \frac{a}{a^2 + \omega^2} - \frac{j\omega}{a^2 + \omega^2}$$

where the real and imaginary parts of $F(\omega)$ are shown.   ∎

Example 4.2   Let $f(t) = e^{-a|t|}$ $(a > 0)$ for $t\epsilon[-\infty,\infty]$. Since the function $f(t)$ given here is even, we find that

$$F(\omega) = \int_{-\infty}^{\infty} e^{-a|t|} e^{j\omega t} \, dt = \int_{-\infty}^{\infty} e^{-a|t|} \cos \omega t \, dt$$

from which

$$F(\omega) = 2 \int_{0}^{\infty} e^{-at} \cos \omega t \, dt$$

Since $F(\omega)$ is, formally, twice the value of the Laplace transform of a cosine, then

$$F(\omega) = \frac{2a}{\omega^2 + a^2}$$ ∎

Example 4.3   Let $f(t) = \sin \omega_0 t$ in $t\epsilon(-\infty,\infty)$. Then, on inserting the exponential representation of the sine function, $F(\omega)$ is expressed as

$$F(\omega) = \frac{1}{2j} \int_{-\infty}^{\infty} [e^{j(\omega + \omega_0)t} - e^{j(\omega - \omega_0)t}] \, dt$$

or, alternatively, as

$$F(\omega) = -j\pi[\delta(\omega + \omega_0) - \delta(\omega - \omega_0)]$$

by definition of the integral representation of a delta function.   ∎

Suppose now that we are given the quantity $F(\omega)$ and want to determine the function $f(t)$ by inversion. This usually requires integration in the complex plane.

Example 4.4   Given

$$F(\omega) = \frac{\omega}{(\omega + \omega_0)(\omega - \omega_1)}$$

find $f(t)$. The function $f(t)$ will be the value of the integral

$$f(t) = \frac{1}{2\pi} \int_{-\infty}^{\infty} e^{j\omega t} \frac{\omega}{(\omega + \omega_0)(\omega - \omega_1)} \, d\omega$$

To find $f(t)$ we consider the integral

$$I = \oint \frac{e^{jzt} z}{(z + \omega_0)(z - \omega_1)} \, dz$$

about the contour shown in Figure 4.1. Since there are no singularities within the contour, we have

$$I = 0 = \sum_{i=1}^{6} I_i$$

where the contributions to I from separate parts of the contour are labeled in the figure. From

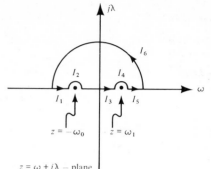

FIGURE 4.1 Contour for use in Example 4.4. $z = \omega + j\lambda$ – plane

previous studies,* $\lim_{\Omega \to \infty} I_6 \equiv 0$. On the semicircles surrounding $z = -\omega_0$ and $z = \omega_1$, for which $z = -\omega_0 + \rho e^{j\phi}$ and $z = \omega_1 + \rho e^{j}$, we find, as $\rho \to 0$, that

$$\lim_{\rho \to 0} I_2 = \frac{-\pi j \omega_0 e^{-j\omega_0 t}}{(\omega_0 + \omega_1)}$$

and that

$$\lim_{\rho \to 0} I_4 = \frac{-\pi j \omega_1 e^{j\omega_1 t}}{\omega_0 + \omega_1}$$

Now, as $\Omega \to \infty$ and as $\rho \to 0$, the remaining three integrals become

$$I_1 + I_3 + I_5 = \int_{-\infty}^{\infty} \frac{e^{j\omega t} \omega}{(\omega + \omega_0)(\omega - \omega_1)} \, d\omega = 2\pi f(t)$$

Thus,

$$f(t) = \frac{j(\omega_0 e^{-j\omega_0 t} + \omega_1 e^{+j\omega_1 t})}{2(\omega_0 + \omega_1)}$$ ∎

Example 4.5 Given an unnormalized Gaussian curve, $F(\omega) = e^{-(\omega/\omega_0)^2}$, find $f(t)$. In this example we see that explicit use of contour integration is unnecessary and we show that "the Fourier transform of a Gaussian is a Gaussian." The expression for $f(t)$ is

$$f(t) = \frac{1}{2\pi} \int_{-\infty}^{\infty} e^{-(\omega/\omega_0)^2} e^{j\omega t} \, d\omega$$

Now

$$\left(\frac{\omega}{\omega_0}\right)^2 - j\omega t = \frac{1}{\omega_0^2}(\omega - \alpha)^2 + \frac{\alpha^2}{\omega_0^2}$$

where $\alpha = j\omega_0^2 t/2$. Thus,

$$f(t) = \frac{1}{2\pi} e^{-\omega_0^2 t^2/4} \int_{-\infty}^{\infty} e^{-(\omega - \alpha)^2/\omega_0^2} \, d\omega$$

With a new variable $x = (\omega - \alpha)/\omega_0$, $d\omega = \omega_0 \, dx$, so that

*Integrals such as the one denoted by I_6, for which $z = \Omega e^{j\phi}$, were discussed at length in Chapter 2.

$$f(t) = \frac{\omega_0}{2\pi} e^{-\omega_0^2 t^2/4} \int_{-\infty-j\gamma}^{\infty-j\gamma} e^{-x^2} dx$$

where $\gamma = \omega_0 t/2$.

We previously encountered the remaining integral whose value is $\sqrt{\pi}$, so that

$$f(t) = \frac{\omega_0}{2\sqrt{\pi}} e^{-\omega_0^2 t^2/4} \qquad \blacksquare$$

4.3 FOURIER COSINE AND SINE TRANSFORMS

To find expressions for Fourier cosine and sine transform pairs, it is convenient to start by writing Equation 4.3 once again. We have

$$f(t) = \frac{1}{2\pi} \int_{-\infty}^{\infty} \int_{-\infty}^{\infty} f(\tau) e^{j\omega(t-\tau)} d\omega \, d\tau \qquad (4.3)$$

Suppose that $f(t)$ is real. Then Equation 4.3 becomes

$$f(t) = \frac{1}{2\pi} \int_{-\infty}^{\infty} \int_{-\infty}^{\infty} f(\tau) \cos \omega(t - \tau) \, d\omega \, d\tau \qquad (4.7)$$

On using the identity $\cos(a - b) = \cos a \cos b + \sin a \sin b$, Equation 4.7 becomes

$$f(t) = \frac{1}{2\pi} \int_{-\infty}^{\infty} \int_{-\infty}^{\infty} f(\tau)\{\cos \omega t \cos \omega \tau + \sin \omega t \sin \omega \tau\} \, d\omega \, d\tau \qquad (4.8)$$

Fourier cosine and sine transform pairs are now found in a straightforward manner from Equation 4.8 by further restrictions placed on the function $f(t)$. If $f(t)$ is even, $f(t) = f(-t)$, then it can be represented in terms of even functions, namely, those containing the term $\cos \omega t$, whereas if it is odd, $f(t) = -f(-t)$, the choice of $\sin \omega t$ is appropriate. Suppose that $f(t)$ is even. Then, from Equation 4.8 a valid representation of $f(t)$ is

$$f(t) = \frac{1}{2\pi} \int_{-\infty}^{\infty} \int_{-\infty}^{\infty} f(\tau) \cos \omega t \cos \omega \tau \, d\omega \, d\tau \qquad (4.9)$$

On defining

$$F_c(\omega) = \frac{1}{2} \int_{-\infty}^{\infty} f(\tau) \cos \omega \tau \, d\tau$$

we have

$$f(t) = \frac{1}{\pi} \int_{-\infty}^{\infty} F_c(\omega) \cos \omega t \, d\omega \qquad (4.10)$$

But because $f(\tau)$ is also even,

$$F_c(\omega) = \int_{0}^{\infty} f(\tau) \cos \omega \tau \, d\tau \qquad (4.11)$$

Equations 4.10 and 4.11 are a Fourier cosine transform pair.

If $f(t) = -f(-t)$, then a representation of $f(t)$ is

$$f(t) = \frac{1}{2\pi} \int_{-\infty}^{\infty} \int_{-\infty}^{\infty} f(\tau) \sin \omega t \sin \omega \tau \, d\omega \, d\tau$$

and on defining

$$F_s(\omega) = \int_{0}^{\infty} f(\tau) \sin \omega \tau \, d\tau \tag{4.12}$$

we have

$$f(t) = \frac{1}{\pi} \int_{-\infty}^{\infty} F_s(\omega) \sin \omega t \, d\omega \tag{4.13}$$

These last two relations are a Fourier sine transform pair, holding, as noted, for $f(t)$ odd and real.

We illustrate the calculation of these transform pairs with additional examples.

Example 4.6   If $f(t) = e^{-at}$, then

$$F_c(\omega) = \int_{0}^{\infty} e^{-at} \cos \omega t \, dt = \frac{a}{\omega^2 + a^2}$$ ∎

Example 4.7   Given that $F_c(\omega) = e^{-|\omega|/\omega_0}$, $f(t)$ will be even and given by

$$f(t) = \frac{1}{\pi} \int_{-\infty}^{\infty} e^{-|\omega|/\omega_0} \cos \omega t \, d\omega = \frac{2}{\pi} \int_{0}^{\infty} e^{-\omega/\omega_0} \cos \omega t \, d\omega$$

We find that

$$f(t) = \frac{2}{\pi} \frac{\omega_0}{\omega_0^2 t^2 + 1}$$

an even function of t. ∎

Both of the foregoing examples have been simplified by our choice of the functions $f(t)$ and $F_c(\omega)$, since the resulting integrations are, essentially, in the form of Laplace transforms.

Example 4.8   Let $f(t) = \cos \omega_0 t$ in $-\pi/2\omega_0 \leq t \leq \pi/2\omega_0$ and let $f(t) \equiv 0$ otherwise. Then, since $f(t)$ is an even function,

$$F_c(\omega) = \int_{-\pi/2\omega_0}^{\pi/2\omega_0} \cos \omega_0 t \cos \omega t \, dt$$

Now $\cos a \cos b = \frac{1}{2}[\cos (a - b) + \cos (a + b)]$, so that

$$F_c(\omega) = \frac{1}{2} \int_{-\pi/2\omega_0}^{\pi/2\omega_0} [\cos (\omega_0 - \omega)t + \cos (\omega + \omega_0)t] \, dt$$

which is easily integrable with the result

$$F_c(\omega) = \frac{\sin\left[(\omega_0 - \omega)\pi/2\omega_0\right]}{\omega_0 - \omega} + \frac{\sin\left[(\omega_0 + \omega)\pi/2\omega_0\right]}{\omega_0 + \omega} \qquad \blacksquare$$

Example 4.9   Let $f(t) = \sin \omega_0 t$ in $-\pi/2\omega_0 \le t \le \pi/2\omega_0$ and let $f(t) \equiv 0$ otherwise. Since $f(t)$ is odd over the interval for which it is defined, we calculate

$$F_s(\omega) = \int_{-\pi/2\omega_0}^{\pi/2\omega_0} \sin \omega_0 t \, \sin \omega t \, dt$$

The trigonometric identity $\sin a \sin b = \frac{1}{2}[\cos (a - b) - \cos (a + b)]$, when used in the expression for $F_s(\omega)$, produces the result

$$F_s(\omega) = \frac{\sin\left[(\omega_0 - \omega)\pi/2\omega_0\right]}{\omega_0 - \omega} - \frac{\sin\left[(\omega_0 + \omega)\pi/2\omega_0\right]}{\omega_0 + \omega} \qquad \blacksquare$$

Example 4.10   Let $F_s(\omega) = \omega/(\omega^2 + \omega_0^2)$. We are to find

$$f(t) = \frac{1}{\pi} \int_{-\infty}^{\infty} \frac{\omega \sin \omega t}{\omega^2 + \omega_0^2} \, d\omega$$

Now, as was done in Chapter 2, we can write

$$f(t) = \frac{1}{\pi} \operatorname{Im} \int_{-\infty}^{\infty} \frac{\omega e^{j\omega t}}{\omega^2 + \omega_0^2} \, d\omega$$

A contour consisting of the ω-axis and closed in the upper half-plane, when used in evaluating the integral

$$I = \oint_C \frac{z e^{jzt}}{z^2 + \omega_0^2} \, dz$$

will contain only a single pole at $z = j\omega_0$. The residue theorem then gives

$$I = \frac{j\omega_0 e^{-\omega_0 t}}{2j\omega_0} (2\pi j) = j\pi e^{-\omega_0 t}$$

Then, as the radius of the semicircle in the upper half-plane tends toward infinity, the contribution over the arc will vanish, so that, with $z = \omega$ along the horizontal axis,

$$I = \int_{-\infty}^{\infty} \frac{\omega e^{j\omega t}}{\omega^2 + \omega_0^2} \, d\omega$$

Since $f(t) = \pi^{-1} \operatorname{Im} I$, we have that

$$f(t) = e^{-\omega_0 t}$$

This result may appear rather alarming, since it seems to say that as $t \to -\infty$, $f(t) \to \infty$. But, according to Equation 4.12 and its equivalent (Equation 4.11) for cosine transforms, $f(t)$ is defined only for $t > 0$. $\qquad \blacksquare$

4.4   THEOREMS FOR FOURIER TRANSFORM PAIRS

Because of the high degree of symmetry exhibited by an exponential Fourier transform pair, theorems relating to $f(t)$, for example, will also hold for $F(\omega) = \mathcal{F}\{f(t)\}$, the

Fourier transform of $f(t)$. For that reason, we prove theorems for $f(t)$ and quote those holding for $F(\omega)$.

Theorem 4.1

Given that $F(\omega) = \mathcal{F}\{f(t)\}$, then $j\omega F(\omega) = \mathcal{F}\{df/dt\}$. This theorem on the Fourier transform of the first derivative of $f(t)$ is proved in the following way. By the definition of $f(t)$, its derivative is

$$\frac{df}{dt} = \frac{1}{2\pi} \int_{-\infty}^{\infty} j\omega e^{j\omega t} F(\omega)\, d\omega \tag{4.14}$$

Then we have

$$\int_{-\infty}^{\infty} e^{-j\lambda t} \frac{df}{dt}\, dt = \frac{1}{2\pi} \int_{-\infty}^{\infty}\int_{-\infty}^{\infty} j\omega F(\omega) e^{j(\omega - \lambda)t}\, d\omega\, dt \tag{4.15}$$

By the integral representation of the delta function, the right-hand side of Equation 4.15 becomes

$$\int_{-\infty}^{\infty} j\omega F(\omega)\delta(\omega - \lambda)\, d\omega = j\lambda F(\lambda). \tag{4.16}$$

Thus, on substituting ω for λ, we have

$$j\omega F(\omega) = \int_{-\infty}^{\infty} e^{-j\omega t} \frac{df}{dt}\, dt$$

or

$$j\omega F(\omega) = \mathcal{F}\left\{\frac{df}{dt}\right\} \tag{4.17}$$

A corollary to the theorem is as follows: Given that

$$g(t) = \int_{0}^{t} f(\tau)\, d\tau$$

then

$$\frac{dg}{dt} = f(t)$$

We find that

$$j\omega G(\omega) = F(\omega) = \int_{-\infty}^{\infty} f(\tau) e^{-j\omega\tau}\, d\tau$$

That is,

$$G(\omega) = \frac{1}{j\omega} F(\omega) \tag{4.17a}$$

The statement is often made that integration of $f(t)$ with respect to t corresponds to division of $F(\omega)$ by $j\omega$.

The corresponding theorem for the derivative of $F(\omega)$ is as follows: Given that

$$F(\omega) = \int_{-\infty}^{\infty} e^{-j\omega t} f(t) \, dt$$

then

$$\frac{dF}{d\omega} = \int_{-\infty}^{\infty} -jt e^{-j\omega t} f(t) \, dt$$

so that the Fourier transform pair is

$$-jt f(t) = \mathcal{F}^{-1}\left\{\frac{dF}{d\omega}\right\} \qquad (4.18)$$

where the notation $\mathcal{F}^{-1}$ is read as the inverse Fourier transform.

Theorem 4.2

With $\mathcal{F}\{f(t)\} = F(\omega)$, then

$$(j\omega)^n F(\omega) = \mathcal{F}\left\{\frac{d^n f}{dt^n}\right\} \qquad (4.19)$$

This theorem is proved in the same way as was the last. With

$$f(t) = \frac{1}{2\pi} \int_{-\infty}^{\infty} e^{j\omega t} F(\omega) \, d\omega$$

each differentiation of $f(t)$ "brings down" a factor $j\omega$, so that

$$\frac{d^n f}{dt^n} = \frac{1}{2\pi} \int_{-\infty}^{\infty} (j\omega)^n F(\omega) e^{j\omega t} \, d\omega \qquad (4.20)$$

That is, differentiation with respect to t corresponds to multiplication by $j\omega$. The inversion of this last relation yields the statement of the theorem, i.e.,

$$(j\omega)^n F(\omega) = \int_{-\infty}^{\infty} e^{-j\omega t} \frac{d^n f}{dt^n} \, dt$$

or

$$(j\omega)^n F(\omega) = \mathcal{F}\left\{\frac{d^n f}{dt^n}\right\} \qquad (4.21)$$

Similarly, the companion theorem is

$$(-jt)^n f(t) = \mathcal{F}^{-1}\left\{\frac{d^n F}{d\omega^n}\right\} \qquad (4.22)$$

Theorem 4.3

With $F(\omega) = \mathcal{F}\{f(t)\}$,

$$\frac{1}{2}\{F(\omega + \omega_0) + F(\omega - \omega_0)\} = \mathcal{F}\{f(t) \cos \omega_0 t\} \tag{4.23}$$

This shifting theorem is of importance in a discussion of amplitude-modulated (AM) and frequency-modulated (FM) signals. To prove the theorem, we define, provisionally, a quantity

$$G(\omega) = \int_{-\infty}^{\infty} e^{-j\omega t} f(t) \cos \omega_0 t \, dt \tag{4.24}$$

Then on inserting the exponential representation of the cosine function, we express $G(\omega)$ as

$$G(\omega) = \frac{1}{2} \int_{-\infty}^{\infty} (e^{-j(\omega-\omega_0)t} + e^{-j(\omega+\omega_0)t}) f(t) \, dt \tag{4.25}$$

But this last equation can be written as

$$G(\omega) = \frac{1}{2}\{F(\omega - \omega_0) + F(\omega + \omega_0)\} \tag{4.26}$$

from which the statement of the theorem follows.

The companion theorem is written as follows: With $f(t) = \mathcal{F}^{-1}\{F(\omega)\}$,

$$\frac{1}{2}\{f(t + t_0) + f(t - t_0)\} = \mathcal{F}^{-1}\{F(\omega) \cos \omega t_0\} \tag{4.27}$$

We now turn to the convolution theorem for Fourier transforms.

Theorem 4.4

With $F(\omega) = \mathcal{F}\{f(t)\}$,

$$F_1(\omega)F_2(\omega) = \int_{-\infty}^{\infty} f_1(\tau)f_2(t - \tau) \, d\tau \tag{4.28}$$

The proof of this important convolution theorem is now given. Let

$$f(t) = \int_{-\infty}^{\infty} f_1(\tau)f_2(t - \tau) \, d\tau \tag{4.29}$$

Then the Fourier transform of $f(t)$ is given, once again, by

$$F(\omega) = \int_{-\infty}^{\infty} e^{-j\omega t} f(t) \, dt \tag{4.5}$$

and becomes, on inserting the expression for $f(t)$,

$$F(\omega) = \int_{-\infty}^{\infty} \int_{-\infty}^{\infty} e^{-j\omega t} f_1(\tau)f_2(t - \tau) \, d\tau \, dt \tag{4.30}$$

Consider the integral

$$g(\tau) = \int_{-\infty}^{\infty} e^{-j\omega t} f_2(t - \tau) \, dt \tag{4.31}$$

and let $t - \tau = u$. Then

$$g(\tau) = \int_{-\infty}^{\infty} e^{-j\omega(u + \tau)} f_2(u) \, du \tag{4.32}$$

as a consequence of which

$$F(\omega) = \int_{-\infty}^{\infty} e^{-j\omega\tau} f_1(\tau) \, d\tau \int_{-\infty}^{\infty} e^{-j\omega u} f_2(u) \, du \tag{4.33}$$

But this means, by definition of the product of two Fourier transforms, that

$$F(\omega) = F_1(\omega)F_2(\omega) \tag{4.34}$$

Thus,

$$F_1(\omega)F_2(\omega) = \int_{-\infty}^{\infty} f_1(\tau)f_2(t - \tau) \, d\tau \tag{4.35}$$

The corresponding convolution theorem in the frequency domain is

$$f_1(t)f_2(t) = \mathscr{F}^{-1}\left\{ \frac{1}{2\pi} \int_{-\infty}^{\infty} F_1(\omega')F_2(\omega - \omega') \, d\omega' \right\} \tag{4.36}$$

Theorem 4.5

Given that $f(t)$ is represented by a uniformly convergent Fourier series

$$f(t) = \sum_{n=-\infty}^{\infty} f(t_n)e^{j\omega_n t} \tag{4.37}$$

then

$$\mathscr{F}\{f(t)\} = 2\pi \sum_{n=-\infty}^{\infty} f(t_n)\delta(\omega - \omega_n) \tag{4.38}$$

The proof of the theorem depends on the interchange of the order of integration and summation. Because we have stated that $f(t)$ is uniformly convergent, we have

$$\mathscr{F}\{f(t)\} = \sum_{n=-\infty}^{\infty} f(t_n) \int_{-\infty}^{\infty} e^{-j(\omega - \omega_n)t} \, dt \tag{4.39}$$

The relation given in Equation 4.37 then follows from the integral representation of the delta function.

The representation of a given function $f(t)$ as a Fourier series is commonplace, provided, of course, that $f(t)$ satisfies the necessary requirements to be expandable. A function

$$H(\omega) = \sum_{n=-\infty}^{\infty} a_n \delta(\omega - \omega_n) \tag{4.40}$$

containing delta functions of amplitude a_n at points $\omega = \omega_n$ can be thought of as a sample of a continuous function $a(\omega)$, taken at points $\omega = \omega_n$. We shall have occasion to use such representations frequently in the remainder of this chapter and in the next.

Theorem 4.6 (Parseval's Theorem)

Let us assume that $f(t)$ is a complex voltage. Then the quantity ff^*, where f^* is the complex conjugate of f, is real and is proportional to power. Indeed, if a signal $P(t) = ff^*$ were fed through a resistor R, ff^*/R would be an instantaneous power. The above remarks serve to introduce a theorem concerning power, called Parseval's theorem. Its statement is:

Given that $F(\omega) = \mathscr{F}\{f(t)\}$, then

$$\int_{-\infty}^{\infty} f(t)f^*(t)\, dt = \frac{1}{2\pi} \int_{-\infty}^{\infty} F(\omega)F^*(\omega)\, d\omega \tag{4.41}$$

To prove the theorem, write the usual expression for $f(t)$, i.e.,

$$f(t) = \frac{1}{2\pi} \int_{-\infty}^{\infty} e^{j\omega t} F(\omega)\, d\omega$$

so that

$$f^*(t) = \frac{1}{2\pi} \int_{-\infty}^{\infty} e^{-j\lambda t} F^*(\lambda)\, d\lambda$$

Then

$$\int_{-\infty}^{\infty} f(t)f^*(t)\, dt = \frac{1}{4\pi^2} \int_{-\infty}^{\infty} \int_{-\infty}^{\infty} \int_{-\infty}^{\infty} F(\omega)F^*(\lambda)e^{j(\omega-\lambda)t}\, d\omega\, d\lambda\, dt$$

Using the integral representation of the delta function, the right-hand side becomes, on integrating over t,

$$\frac{1}{2\pi} \int_{-\infty}^{\infty} \int_{-\infty}^{\infty} F(\omega)F^*(\lambda)\delta(\omega - \lambda)\, d\omega\, d\lambda$$

The sifting property of the delta function then gives us

$$\int_{-\infty}^{\infty} f(t)f^*(t)\, dt = \frac{1}{2\pi} \int_{-\infty}^{\infty} F(\omega)F^*(\omega)\, d\omega$$

On introducing absolute value notation, Parseval's theorem is written as

$$\int_{-\infty}^{\infty} |f(t)|^2\, dt = \frac{1}{2\pi} \int_{-\infty}^{\infty} |F(\omega)|^2\, d\omega$$

where the notation $|f(t)|^2$, for example, is read as the square of the absolute value of $f(t)$.

4.5   FOURIER TRANSFORMS OF DISCONTINUOUS FUNCTIONS

Various functions that appear frequently in problems in electrical engineering are important when idealized models of physical systems are considered. Several of these functions were introduced in Chapter 3, and we study their Fourier transforms in this section.

The Delta Function

Given $f(t) = \delta(t - t_0)$, then $F(\omega) = \mathcal{F}\{f(t)\}$ is

$$F(\omega) = \int_{-\infty}^{\infty} e^{-j\omega t}\delta(t - t_0)\, dt \tag{4.42}$$

By the sifting property of the delta function, we find

$$F(\omega) = e^{-j\omega t_0} \tag{4.43}$$

The Unit Step Function

Previously we showed that the Laplace transform of the step function $u(t)$ is

$$\mathcal{L}\{u(t)\} = \int_{0_-}^{\infty} e^{-st}u(t)\, dt = \frac{1}{s} \tag{4.44}$$

There is a difficulty associated with finding the Fourier transform of the unit step function that arises because of the fact that $F(\omega) = \mathcal{F}\{u(t)\}$ involves an integration over time in $t\epsilon(-\infty,\infty)$, with $u(t)$ discontinuous at $t = 0$. This discontinuity is the source of the problem. We circumvent the difficulty by defining a continuous function,

$$u_c(t) = \begin{cases} 1 & t > \epsilon \\ \dfrac{1}{2} & t = 0 \\ 0 & t < -\epsilon \end{cases}$$

and define the unit step function as

$$u(t) = \lim_{\epsilon \to 0} u_c(t)$$

The continuous function $u_c(t)$ is shown in Figure 4.2.

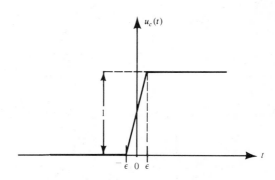

FIGURE 4.2   The continuous function $u_c(t)$.

The Fourier transform of $u_c(t)$ is given by

$$\mathcal{F}\{u_c(t)\} = \frac{1}{2}\int_{-\epsilon}^{\epsilon}\left(1 + \frac{t}{\epsilon}\right)e^{-j\omega t}\, dt + \int_{\epsilon}^{\infty} e^{-j\omega t}\, dt \tag{4.45}$$

The value of the first integral on the right-hand side of Equation 4.45 is, as $\epsilon \to 0$, $(j\omega)^{-1}$, while, as $\epsilon \to 0$ and from the fact that the delta function is even,

$$\int_0^\infty e^{-j\omega t} \, dt = \frac{1}{2} \int_{-\infty}^\infty e^{-j\omega t} \, dt = \pi\delta(\omega)$$

Thus

$$\mathcal{F}\{u(t)\} = \frac{1}{j\omega} + \pi\delta(\omega) \qquad (4.46)$$

$t_o = 1$

The Gate Function

$\frac{\sin t}{t}$

The gate function is defined by the equation

$$g(t) = \begin{cases} 1 & t\epsilon\left(-\frac{t_0}{2}, \frac{t_0}{2}\right) \\ 0 & \text{otherwise} \end{cases} \qquad (4.47)$$

In this text, the Fourier transform of the gate function is always denoted by $G(x)$. That is,

$$G(x) = \int_{-t_0/2}^{t_0/2} e^{-j\omega t} \, dt = t_0 \frac{\sin x}{x} \qquad (4.48)$$

where $x = \omega t_0/2$.

The corresponding inverse Fourier transform is a function $f(t)$, defined by

will cover

$$f(t) = \frac{1}{2\pi} \int_{-\omega_0/2}^{\omega_0/2} e^{j\omega t} \, d\omega \qquad \text{Laurent Series} \qquad (4.49)$$

Room for final

or

$$f(x) = \frac{\omega_0}{2\pi} \frac{\sin x}{x}, \qquad x = \frac{\omega_0 t}{2} \qquad \boxed{\begin{array}{c} 421\epsilon \\ 9{:}00 \end{array}} \qquad (4.50)$$

In Figure 4.3(a,b), the functions $g(t)$ and $G(x)$ are shown. For $F(\omega) = 1$

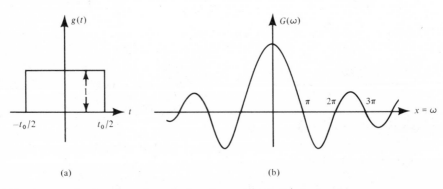

(a)   (b)

FIGURE 4.3 (a) The time-dependent gate function and (b) its Fourier transform.

in $-\omega_0/2 < \omega < \omega_0/2$, so that $f(x) = (\omega_0/2)(\sin x /x)$, there is the interesting interpretation that $F(\omega)$ is the frequency characteristic of an *ideal filter*—i.e., a device
whose frequency response is such as to reject all frequencies $\omega > |\omega_0/2|$ and pass any
within the band $-(\omega_0/2) < \omega < \omega_0/2$.

The periodic gate function is a generalization of the square wave in which the
width of the pulses is, in general, different from a period or a fraction thereof. Consider
Figure 4.4, where the gate function $f(t)$ is shown. We want to find the Fourier trans-

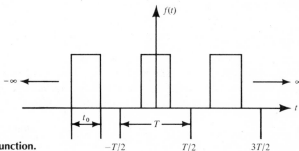

FIGURE 4.4 The periodic gate function.

form of the periodic gate function. One of the easier methods of doing this is to expand
$f(t)$ in a (convergent) Fourier series and then find the transform of the result. We write

$$f(t) = \sum_{n=-\infty}^{\infty} F_n e^{j\omega_n t} \qquad (4.51)$$

where $\omega_n = n\omega_0$, with n an integer and $\omega_0 = 2\pi/T$, and where T is the period of $f(t)$.
We must find the F_n. We have

$$\int_{-T/2}^{T/2} f(t)e^{-j\omega_k t}\, dt = \sum_{n=-\infty}^{\infty} F_n \int_{-T/2}^{T/2} e^{j(\omega_n - \omega_k)t}\, dt \qquad (4.52)$$

Since the integral on the right-hand side is zero unless $\omega_n = \omega_k$, we find that

$$F_k = \frac{1}{T} \int_{-T/2}^{T/2} f(t)e^{-j\omega_k t}\, dt \qquad (4.53)$$

or, since $f(t) = 1$ in $-t_0/2 < t < t_0/2$ and is zero otherwise,

$$F_k = \frac{1}{T} \cdot \int_{-t_0/2}^{t_0/2} e^{-j\omega_k t}\, dt$$

The result is

$$F_k = \frac{t_0}{T} \frac{\sin x_k}{x_k} = \frac{1}{T} G_k(x) \qquad (4.54)$$

where $x_k = \omega_k t_0/2$, or $x_n = n\omega_0 t_0/2$.

We now have $f(t)$ expressed in the form

$$f(t) = \frac{1}{T} \sum_{n=-\infty}^{\infty} G_n(x)e^{j\omega_n t} \qquad (4.55)$$

The Fourier transform of the periodic gate function is, by definition,

$$F(\omega) = \int_{-\infty}^{\infty} e^{-j\omega t} f(t)\, dt$$

and becomes, on interchanging the order of summation and integration,

$$F(\omega) = \frac{1}{T} \sum_{n=-\infty}^{\infty} G_n(x) \int_{-\infty}^{\infty} e^{-j(\omega-\omega_n)t}\, dt \tag{4.56}$$

or

$$F(\omega) = \frac{2\pi}{T} \sum_{n=-\infty}^{\infty} G_n(x)\delta(\omega - \omega_n) \tag{4.57}$$

The Fourier transform of the periodic gate function contains a series of delta functions at points $\omega = \omega_n = n\omega_0$; i.e., at all of the harmonics of the fundamental frequency $\omega_0 = 2\pi/T$. Each of these delta functions is multiplied by its characteristic amplitude

$$2\pi T^{-1} G_n(x) = \frac{2\pi t_0}{T} \frac{\sin(n\omega_0 t_0/2)}{(n\omega_0 t_0/2)} \tag{4.58}$$

As $n \to \infty$,

$$\lim_{n\to\infty} T^{-1} G_n(x) \to 0$$

so that the amplitudes of the higher order harmonics vanish. The importance of the periodic gate function, with a Fourier spectrum given by Equation 4.56, is that it represents an archetypal function in sampled data systems, as discussed in Chapter 5; in addition, functions allied to it occur in filter theory and in the analysis of FM systems. The above remarks show, once again, as in Theorem 4.5, the importance of Fourier transforms consisting of a series of delta functions.

4.6   FOURIER-BESSEL INTEGRALS: TWO-DIMENSIONAL FOURIER TRANSFORMS

We show, in what follows, that a function $f(r)$ can be expanded in the following way:

$$f(r) = \int_0^{\infty} \int_0^{\infty} f(\rho) J_n(kr) J_n(k\rho) k\, dk\, \rho\, d\rho \tag{4.59}$$

with the expansion in terms of Bessel functions of order n and the arguments shown. To show that Equation 4.59 is valid, we show that it reduces to a two-dimensional Fourier transform in rectangular coordinates. For this reason, Equation 4.59 is frequently called a Fourier-Bessel integral. In the particular case for which $n = 0$, if we write

$$f(r) = \int_0^{\infty} F(k) J_0(kr) k\, dk \tag{4.60}$$

then

$$F(k) = \int_0^\infty f(r) J_0(kr) r \, dr \tag{4.61}$$

The remarkable symmetry exhibited by Equations 4.60 and 4.61 is immediately evident. These relations are called a *Hankel transform* pair, and are, as observed, self-reciprocal. We use the Hankel transform formalism in a later section of this chapter to discuss the Hertzian antenna.

We now proceed with the proof that Equation 4.59 represents, under a coordinate transformation, a two-dimensional Fourier integral. According to Appendix C, an integral representation of a Bessel function of order n can be found from the identity

$$e^{jx \sin \phi} = \sum_{n=-\infty}^{\infty} J_n(x) e^{jn\phi} \tag{4.62}$$

On multiplying both sides of Equation 4.62 by $e^{-jl\phi}$, with l an integer, and integrating over ϕ, we find that

$$J_l(x) = \frac{1}{2\pi} \int_0^{2\pi} e^{jx \sin \phi} e^{-jl\phi} \, d\phi \tag{4.63}$$

We use this integral representation in Equation 4.59 to express $f(r)$ as

$$f(r) = \frac{1}{(2\pi)^2} \int_0^\infty \int_0^\infty \int_0^{2\pi} \int_0^{2\pi} f(\rho) e^{jkr \sin \phi} e^{-jn\phi} e^{jk\rho \sin \psi} e^{-jm\psi} \, k \, dk \, \rho \, d\rho \, d\phi \, d\psi \tag{4.64}$$

We now make a coordinate transformation to Cartesian variables. Observing that the entire two-dimensional space is covered, we infer that the limits of integration on the Cartesian coordinates will be $(-\infty, \infty)$. To accomplish the transformation mentioned, consider the expression $kr \sin \phi$. Set $\phi = (\theta - \chi + \pi/2)$. Then

$$kr \sin \phi \equiv kr \cos (\theta - \chi)$$

If we now define

$$k_x = k \cos \theta$$
$$k_y = k \sin \theta$$
$$x = r \cos \chi$$

and

$$y = r \sin \chi$$

then

$$kr \cos (\theta - \chi) = k_x x + k_y y$$

Also,

$$e^{jkr \sin \phi} e^{-jn\phi} = e^{(jk_x x + k_y y)} e^{-jn(\theta - \chi + \pi/2)}$$

A similar transformation involving the term

$$e^{jk\rho \sin \psi} e^{-jm\psi}$$

is made by setting $\psi = (\lambda - \theta - \pi/2)$. Then,

$$e^{jk\rho \sin \psi} e^{-jm\psi} = e^{-jk\rho \cos(\lambda - \theta)} e^{-jn(\lambda - \theta - \pi/2)}$$

With $\xi = \rho \cos \lambda$ and $\eta = \rho \sin \lambda$, and k_x, k_y defined as before, the exponential terms appearing in the integrand of Equation 4.64 are now in the form

$$e^{jk_x(x-\xi)} e^{jk_y(y-\eta)} e^{-jn(\lambda - \chi)}$$

With the variables of integration being k_x, k_y, ξ, and η, we have, since all of space is the region of integration,

$$f(r) = \frac{1}{(2\pi)^2} \int\int_{-\infty}^{\infty} \int\int_{-\infty}^{\infty} f(\rho) e^{jk_x(x-\xi)} e^{-jn(\lambda - \chi)} e^{jk_y(y-\eta)} \, dk_x \, dk_y \, d\xi \, d\eta$$

We now define the quantities

$$f(r) e^{-jn\chi} \equiv g(x,y)$$

and   (4.65)

$$f(\rho) e^{-jn\lambda} \equiv g(\xi,\eta)$$

where, for example $\chi = \tan^{-1}(y/x)$ and $r = \sqrt{x^2 + y^2}$. Then

$$g(x,y) = \frac{1}{(2\pi)^2} \int\int_{-\infty}^{\infty} \int\int_{-\infty}^{\infty} g(\xi,\eta) e^{jk_x(x-\xi)} e^{jk_y(y-\eta)} \, dk_x \, dk_y \, d\xi \, d\eta \qquad (4.66)$$

Equation 4.66 is an identity. To establish this fact, we integrate first over k_x and k_y and use the integral representation of the delta function to find that

$$g(x,y) = \int\int_{-\infty}^{\infty} g(\xi,\eta) \delta(x - \xi) \delta(y - \eta) \, d\xi \, d\eta$$

from which the identity $g(x,y) \equiv g(x,y)$ follows. If we define

$$G(k_x,k_y) = \int\int_{-\infty}^{\infty} e^{-jk_x\xi} e^{-jk_y\eta} g(\xi,\eta) \, d\xi \, d\eta \qquad (4.67)$$

then

$$g(x,y) = \frac{1}{(2\pi)^2} \int\int_{-\infty}^{\infty} e^{jk_x x} e^{jk_y y} G(k_x,k_y) \, dk_x \, dk_y \qquad (4.68)$$

Equations 4.67 and 4.68 are a two-dimensional exponential Fourier transform pair. Note that the particular choices made in Equation 4.65 for $g(x,y)$ are valid for the integer $n = 0$ and that there is no loss in generality in expressing $g(x,y)$ as a complex quantity.

There are problems for which it is convenient to take Fourier transforms in three (or more) spatial dimensions. We can write a Fourier transform pair in an n-dimensional space as

$$g(\mathbf{r}) = \frac{1}{(2\pi)^n} \int_{V_n(\mathbf{k})} e^{j\mathbf{k}\cdot\mathbf{r}} G(\mathbf{k}) \, d\mathbf{k} \tag{4.69}$$

with

$$G(\mathbf{k}) = \int_{V_n(\mathbf{r})} e^{-j\mathbf{k}\cdot\mathbf{r}} g(\mathbf{r}) \, d\mathbf{r} \tag{4.70}$$

where, for example, $V_n(\mathbf{r})$ is an n-dimensional volume whose volume element $d\mathbf{r} \equiv dx_1 \, dx_2 \cdots dx_n$ and

$$\mathbf{k} \cdot \mathbf{r} = \sum_{i=1}^{n} k_i x_i$$

is the usual expression for the dot product of two vectors.

4.7   THE WAVE EQUATION

In this section we find a function $v(x,t)$ which is a solution to the wave equation

$$\frac{\partial^2 v}{\partial x^2} - \frac{1}{c^2} \frac{\partial^2 v}{\partial t^2} = 0 \tag{4.71}$$

by using Fourier transform methods. We set

$$v(0,t) = f(t) \qquad \text{and} \qquad \frac{\partial v}{\partial x}\bigg]_{x=0} = g(t) \tag{4.72}$$

where both $f(t)$ and $g(t)$ are known functions on the boundary $x = 0$. Define the Fourier transform of $v(x,t)$ as

$$V(x,\omega) = \int_{-\infty}^{\infty} e^{-j\omega t} v(x,t) \, dt \tag{4.73}$$

so that, by inversion, we obtain $v(x,t)$ as

$$v(x,t) = \frac{1}{2\pi} \int_{-\infty}^{\infty} e^{j\omega t} V(x,\omega) \, d\omega \tag{4.74}$$

The wave equation for $v(x,t)$ becomes a total differential equation for $V(x,\omega)$, namely,

$$\frac{d^2 V}{dx^2} + \frac{\omega^2}{c^2} V = 0 \tag{4.75}$$

with a solution

$$V(x,\omega) = A(\omega) e^{j\omega x/c} + B(\omega) e^{-j\omega x/c} \tag{4.76}$$

Here, the constants can be, as indicated, functions of ω. Then, from Equation 4.74, we have for $v(x,t)$

$$v(x,t) = \frac{1}{2\pi} \int_{-\infty}^{\infty} \{A(\omega) e^{j\omega(t+x/c)} + B(\omega) e^{j\omega(t-x/c)}\} \, d\omega \tag{4.77}$$

The boundary conditions now give

$$f(t) = \frac{1}{2\pi} \int_{-\infty}^{\infty} (A(\omega) + B(\omega))e^{j\omega t} \, d\omega \tag{4.78a}$$

and

$$g(t) = \frac{1}{2\pi} \int_{-\infty}^{\infty} \frac{j\omega}{c} (A(\omega) - B(\omega))e^{j\omega t} \, d\omega \tag{4.78b}$$

With $f(t)$ and $g(t)$ known, we can determine the two constants $A(\omega)$ and $B(\omega)$. These become, on inverting Equations 4.78(a) and (b), and then solving for $A(\omega)$ and $B(\omega)$,

$$A(\omega) = \frac{1}{2} \int_{-\infty}^{\infty} e^{-j\omega\tau}\{f(\tau) + \frac{c}{j\omega}g(\tau)\} \, d\tau \tag{4.79a}$$

and

$$B(\omega) = \frac{1}{2} \int_{-\infty}^{\infty} e^{-j\omega\tau}\{f(\tau) - \frac{c}{j\omega}g(\tau)\} \, d\tau \tag{4.79b}$$

These, when placed in Equation 4.77 for $v(x,t)$ enable us to write

$$v(x,t) = v_1(x,t) + v_2(x,t) \tag{4.80}$$

where

$$v_1(x,t) = \frac{1}{4\pi} \int_{-\infty}^{\infty} \int_{-\infty}^{\infty} f(\tau)\{e^{j\omega(t+x/c-\tau)} + e^{j\omega(t-x/c-\tau)}\} \, d\tau \, d\omega \tag{4.81a}$$

and

$$v_2(x,t) = \frac{c}{4\pi} \int_{-\infty}^{\infty} \int_{-\infty}^{\infty} \frac{1}{j\omega} g(\tau)\{e^{j\omega(t+x/c-\tau)} - e^{j\omega(t-x/c-\tau)}\} \, d\tau \, d\omega \tag{4.81b}$$

We find $v_1(x,t)$ first and then use the corollary to Theorem 4.1 to write the answer for $v_2(x,t)$. Use of the integral representation of the delta function on integration over ω in Equation 4.81a gives us

$$v_1(x,t) = \frac{1}{2} \int_{-\infty}^{\infty} f(\tau)\left\{\delta\left(t + \frac{x}{c} - \tau\right) + \delta\left(t - \frac{x}{c} - \tau\right)\right\} \, d\tau \tag{4.82}$$

The sifting property of the delta functions then produces

$$v_1(x,t) = \frac{1}{2}\left\{f\left(t + \frac{x}{c}\right) + f\left(t - \frac{x}{c}\right)\right\} \tag{4.83}$$

The evaluation of $v_2(x,t)$ proceeds as follows: The integration over ω yields the integrals of delta functions, i.e., step functions of arguments $(t \pm x/c - \tau)$. The integration over τ then gives

$$v_2(x,t) = \frac{c}{2} \int_{t-x/c}^{t+x/c} g(\tau) \, d\tau \tag{4.84}$$

Consequently, the quantity $v(x,t)$ is given by

$$v(x,t) = \frac{1}{2}\left\{ f\left(t + \frac{x}{c}\right) + f\left(t - \frac{x}{c}\right) + c \int_{t-x/c}^{t+x/c} g(\tau)\, d\tau \right\} \tag{4.85}$$

and represents a solution to the wave equation in terms of two arbitrary functions whose values at $x = 0$ are $f(t)$ and $g(t)$, and which take on the values shown at any later time. Because of sign conventions used in electrical engineering, we say that $f(t - x/c)$ represents a wave traveling in the positive x-direction with a speed c, while $f(t + x/c)$ is a backward traveling wave. The remaining term represents the contribution to $v(x,t)$ from the integral of $\partial v/\partial x$ with proper account taken of the causal nature of the solution.

The wave equation in a three-dimensional space is now considered. Let a potential $v(\mathbf{r},t)$, with $\mathbf{r}$ a position vector, satisfy the wave equation

$$\nabla^2 v - \frac{1}{c^2}\frac{\partial^2 v}{\partial t^2} = f(\mathbf{r},t) \tag{4.86}$$

With $v(\mathbf{r},t)$ expressed in volts, the source $f(\mathbf{r},t)$ has the dimensions of volts per unit area. Let the Fourier transform of $v(\mathbf{r},t)$ with respect to t be $V(\mathbf{r},\omega)$. Then, with $k = \omega/c$ and $F(\mathbf{r},\omega) = \mathscr{F}\{f(\mathbf{r},t)\}$, we find that $V(\mathbf{r},\omega)$ will be a solution to the partial differential equation

$$\nabla^2 V + k^2 V = F \tag{4.87}$$

Define a linear operator M as

$$M \equiv \nabla^2 + k^2 \tag{4.88}$$

Following the discussion in Chapter 3, Section 3.7, we can express the solution to the equation

$$MV = F \tag{4.89}$$

as a convolution integral of F with the unit impulse response $G(|\mathbf{r} - \mathbf{r}'|;\omega)$, which is a solution to

$$MG = \delta(\mathbf{r} - \mathbf{r}') \tag{4.90}$$

That is, we can write*

$$V(\mathbf{r},\omega) = \int_{V_0} F(\mathbf{r}',\omega)G(|\mathbf{r} - \mathbf{r}'|;\omega)\, d\mathbf{r}' \tag{4.91}$$

where the integral is over a volume V_0 containing the source F. To prove this statement, we can write

$$MV = \int_{V_0} F(\mathbf{r}',\omega)MG\, d\mathbf{r}' \tag{4.92}$$

since M, by definition, operates only on the coordinates $\mathbf{r}$. But, from Equation 4.90 we have

---

*There are, frequently, additional contributions to $V(\mathbf{r},\omega)$ arising from distributions of potential or charge on surfaces. We are not concerned with such problems here.

$$MV = \int_{V_0} F(\mathbf{r}',\omega)\delta(\mathbf{r} - \mathbf{r}')\, d\mathbf{r}' \tag{4.93}$$

or, by the sifting property of the delta function,

$$MV = F \tag{4.94}$$

We need the solution for the unit impulse response, or, as it is frequently called, the Green's function, $G(|\mathbf{r} - \mathbf{r}'|;\omega)$. In general, the form of $G(|\mathbf{r} - \mathbf{r}'|;\omega)$ depends on the boundary conditions imposed on the function; each time these are changed, the form of $G(|\mathbf{r} - \mathbf{r}'|;\omega)$ changes. We shall find the free space unit impulse, or Green's function, subject to the condition that

$$\lim_{|\mathbf{r}|\to\infty} G(|\mathbf{r} - \mathbf{r}'|;\omega) \to 0$$

Since the delta function is a reciprocal volume (dimensionally), the Green's function must be a reciprocal length. Since G is a scalar, and the length under consideration is $|\mathbf{r} - \mathbf{r}'|$, we infer that G must be proportional to $|\mathbf{r} - \mathbf{r}'|^{-1}$. We now establish this fact. If $|\mathbf{r} - \mathbf{r}'| \neq 0$, then

$$(\nabla^2 + k^2)G = 0 \tag{4.95}$$

We write this equation in a spherically symmetric coordinate system by changing to the variable $R = |\mathbf{r} - \mathbf{r}'|$ where $R = 0$ is the origin. Then, for $R \neq 0$,

$$\nabla^2 G + k^2 G = 0 \tag{4.96}$$

becomes

$$\frac{1}{R^2}\frac{d}{dR}\left(R^2\frac{dG}{dR}\right) + k^2 G = 0 \tag{4.97}$$

The identity

$$\frac{1}{R^2}\frac{d}{dR}\left(R^2\frac{dG}{dR}\right) = \frac{1}{R}\frac{d^2}{dR^2}(RG) \tag{4.98}$$

and the change of dependent variable to $u = RG$ yields the equation

$$\frac{d^2u}{dR^2} + k^2 u = 0 \tag{4.99}$$

with a solution

$$u = Ce^{\pm jkR} \tag{4.100}$$

Then

$$G(|\mathbf{r} - \mathbf{r}'|;\omega) = \frac{Ce^{\pm jk|\mathbf{r}-\mathbf{r}'|}}{|\mathbf{r} - \mathbf{r}'|} \tag{4.101a}$$

when k is parallel with $R = |\mathbf{r} - \mathbf{r}'|$. The constant C can be evaluated. Without discussing details, $C = (4\pi)^{-1}$, so that the free space unit impulse function is

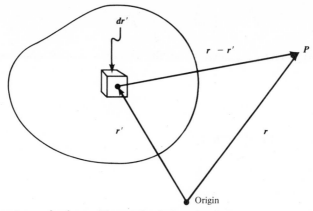

FIGURE 4.5 The vectors and volume of integration in Equation 4.102.

$$G(|\mathbf{r} - \mathbf{r}'|;\omega) = \frac{e^{\pm jk|\mathbf{r} - \mathbf{r}'|}}{4\pi|\mathbf{r} - \mathbf{r}'|} \qquad (4.101b)$$

As noted earlier, the impulse response is, dimensionally, a reciprocal length. The quantity $V(\mathbf{r},\omega)$ is found by evaluating

$$V(\mathbf{r},\omega) = \frac{1}{4\pi} \int_{V_0} F(\mathbf{r}',\omega)\frac{e^{\pm jkR}}{R} \, d\mathbf{r}' \qquad (4.102)$$

where we have set, once again, $R = |\mathbf{r} - \mathbf{r}'|$. The physical significance of this result is made more apparent by considering Figure 4.5.

Within the volume element $d\mathbf{r}'$, there is a total source $F(\mathbf{r}',\omega)\, d\mathbf{r}'$. At the point P whose coordinates are given by the vector $\mathbf{r}$, we find $V(\mathbf{r},\omega)$ by multiplying the total source $F(\mathbf{r}',\omega)\, d\mathbf{r}$ by the Green's function and integrating over the volume V_0. The significance of the Green's function is that it accounts for the influence of geometry on the voltage reaching the point P from within V_0. There is a propagating wave whose spatial character is $e^{\pm jkR}/R$, with the factor R^{-1} accounting for spherical spreading from the point (delta) source and the consequent loss of amplitude.

A special case of importance is now discussed. If

$$F(\mathbf{r}',\omega) = A\delta(\mathbf{r}') \qquad (4.103a)$$

which means that

$$f(\mathbf{r}',t) = A\delta(\mathbf{r}')\delta(t) \qquad (4.103b)$$

then

$$V(\mathbf{r},\omega) = A\frac{e^{\pm jkr}}{4\pi r} \qquad (4.104)$$

with $r = |\mathbf{r}| = \sqrt{x^2 + y^2 + z^2}$ in Cartesian coordinates. This last expression plays a role in the theory of short linear antennas.

In the more general case, consider the expression for $v(\mathbf{r},t)$, the voltage, given by the Fourier integral

$$v(\mathbf{r},t) = \frac{1}{2\pi} \int_{-\infty}^{\infty} e^{j\omega t} V(\mathbf{r},\omega) \, d\omega \tag{4.105}$$

With $V(\mathbf{r},\omega)$ given by Equation 4.102, the definition of the Fourier transform gives us the result

$$v(\mathbf{r},t) = \frac{1}{4\pi} \int_{V_0} \frac{f(\mathbf{r}',t - R/c)}{R} \, d\mathbf{r}' \tag{4.106}$$

Note that if $f(\mathbf{r}',t) = A\delta(\mathbf{r}')\delta(t)$,

$$v(\mathbf{r},t) = \frac{A}{4\pi} \frac{\delta(t - r/c)}{r} \tag{4.107}$$

As a final example of the use of multidimensional transforms in the analysis of propagating waves, we discuss the radiation pattern from a simple Hertzian dipole antenna. A cylindrical coordinate system will be used, so that Fourier-Bessel or Hankel transforms will appear. For the purposes of our discussion we can define a Hertzian dipole antenna as one that carries a current density whose magnitude is given by

$$j(\mathbf{r},t) = A\delta(\mathbf{r})\delta(t) \tag{4.108}$$

The current density has the units of amperes per square meter in the SI system. Keeping in mind the discussions of the delta function, it then follows that the constant A has the dimensions of QL, where Q is a charge and L a length. Thus A is defined as a dipole moment. In this case the expression

$$V(\mathbf{r},\omega) = \frac{Ae^{-jkr}}{4\pi\epsilon_0 r} \tag{4.109}$$

is a valid solution for the function V, which will have the dimensions of volts if the constant ϵ_0 has the dimensions of farads per meter. The negative sign in the exponent is taken so that an outgoing wave is represented. In cylindrical coordinates ρ, ϕ, z,

$$x = \rho \cos \phi$$
$$y = \rho \sin \phi$$

so that

$$r = \sqrt{\rho^2 + z^2}$$

We now want to show that the scalar quantity

$$\psi(r) = \frac{e^{-jkr}}{r} \tag{4.110}$$

can be expressed as an integral containing a Bessel function of order zero. Since we know that $\psi(r)$ is a solution to

$$\nabla^2\psi + k^2\psi = 0, \quad r \neq 0 \tag{4.111}$$

where $r = r(\rho,z)$ is, as shown, a function of both ρ and z, we can write in cylindrical coordinates, independent of the azimuth angle ϕ,

$$\frac{1}{\rho}\frac{\partial}{\partial\rho}\left(\rho\frac{\partial\psi}{\partial\rho}\right) + \frac{\partial^2\psi}{\partial z^2} + k^2\psi = 0 \tag{4.112}$$

Now, let $\psi = e^{-j\beta z}u(\rho)$, so that

$$\frac{1}{\rho}\frac{d}{d\rho}\left(\rho\frac{du}{d\rho}\right) + \lambda^2 u = 0 \tag{4.113}$$

where $\lambda^2 = k^2 - \beta^2$. The solution that is finite for $\rho\epsilon(0, \infty)$ is

$$u(\rho) = J_0(\lambda\rho) \tag{4.114}$$

i.e., a Bessel function of order zero. Thus we have that a solution to Equation 4.111 is

$$\psi(\rho,z) = J_0(\lambda\rho)e^{-j\beta z} \tag{4.115}$$

If this expression is a solution, then the function

$$\chi(\rho,z) = \int_0^\infty J_0(\lambda\rho)e^{-j\beta(\lambda)z}g(\lambda)\lambda \ d\lambda \tag{4.116}$$

is also a solution. Further, we now see that for a particular function $g(\lambda)$, the identity

$$\frac{e^{-jkr}}{r} \equiv \int_0^\infty J_0(\lambda\rho)e^{-j\beta(\lambda)z}g(\lambda)\lambda \ d\lambda \tag{4.117}$$

must hold. This follows since both functions are solutions of the same differential equation. To find $g(\lambda)$, we first set $z = 0$, obtaining

$$\frac{e^{-jk\rho}}{\rho} = \int_0^\infty J_0(\lambda\rho)g(\lambda)\lambda \ d\lambda \tag{4.118}$$

But this is just the Hankel transform introduced in Section 4.6 of this chapter. We have immediately, because of the self-reciprocal nature of such transforms,

$$g(\lambda) = \int_0^\infty e^{-jk\rho}J_0(\lambda\rho) \ d\rho \tag{4.119}$$

i.e., the Fourier transform of a function

$$f(\rho) = \begin{cases} J_0(\lambda), & \rho \geq 0 \\ 0, & \rho < 0 \end{cases} \tag{4.120}$$

Evaluation of this integral gives us the result

$$g(\lambda) = \frac{1}{\sqrt{\lambda^2 - k^2}} \tag{4.121}$$

Our identity is, therefore,

$$\frac{e^{-jkr}}{r} \equiv \int_0^\infty \frac{J_0(\lambda\rho)}{\sqrt{\lambda^2 - k^2}}e^{-j\sqrt{k^2-\lambda^2}z}\lambda \ d\lambda \tag{4.122}$$

Consequently, the voltage $V(r,\omega)$ is given by the expression

$$V(\rho,z,\omega) = \frac{A}{4\pi\epsilon_0} \int_0^\infty \frac{J_0(\lambda\rho)}{\sqrt{\lambda^2 - k^2}} e^{-\sqrt{\lambda^2 - k^2}z}\lambda \; d\lambda \qquad (4.123)$$

It is hard to overstate the importance of transforms such as the one just discussed in the development of antenna theory. Starting with A. Sommerfeld's work on the Hertzian dipole in the early days of this century, through the publication of such works as those given in the bibliography[1,9,10] at the end of this chapter, and even to this date, an impressive number of scientists and engineers contributed to the theory of radio-wave propagation. When boundaries such as an earth–air interface are included, the problem of matching boundary conditions brings in additional constants to be evaluated. But the fundamental terms that contribute to the radiated voltage (or potential) are integrals over some parameter λ, where both poles and branch points are found to occur, and consequently to contribute to the radiated signal. In this way, surface waves that are important for low-frequency long-range radio communication were predicted. With $z = 0$ defining the earth's surface, surface waves fall off with distance as $\rho^{-1/2}$, and arise, mathematically, from an asymptotic expansion of the Bessel function.

4.8   REMARKS ON FILTERS

A filter is defined as a device that will selectively pass some frequencies within a spectrum and tends to reject others. We study filters and some of their properties by starting with a few examples of increasing complexity and then formalizing our results in the form of a theorem regarding filters of various types and their design.

Example 4.11   Let a voltage source in a series LC circuit be a step function $v_0 u(t)$. The equation governing the behavior of the current is

$$\frac{d^2 i}{dt^2} + \omega_0^2 i = \frac{i_0 \delta(t)}{\tau}$$

where $\omega_0^2 = (LC)^{-1}$ is the square of the natural frequency of the circuit and $i_0 \tau^{-1}$ is the strength of the impulse. Let $I(\omega) = \mathcal{F}\{i(t)\}$. Then the transform of this equation is

$$I(\omega) = \frac{i_0}{\tau} \frac{1}{\omega_0^2 - \omega^2}$$

Inversion of $I(\omega)$ yields the current $i(t)$:

$$i(t) = \frac{i_0}{2\pi\tau} \int_{-\infty}^\infty \frac{e^{j\omega t}}{\omega_0^2 - \omega^2} \; d\omega$$

Evaluation of the integral results in

$$i(t) = \frac{i_0}{\omega_0\tau} \sin \omega_0 t \qquad (t \geq 0)$$

Now, the delta function that drives the above system has a flat frequency spectrum, i.e.,

$$\mathcal{F}\{\delta(t)\} = 1$$

But only the frequency $\omega = \omega_0$ appears in the current. The LC circuit has acted as a filter and rejected all but the single frequency at which it is resonant.

In practice, ideal inductors and capacitors cannot be made, in the sense that some resistance will be present in the circuit. But the ordinary LC circuit will have a filter characteristic that is sharply peaked about $\omega = \omega_0$ in its "passband" characteristics.   ∎

Example 4.12   Consider the time response of a series RC circuit such that the current $i(t)$ is given by a solution to the equation

$$\frac{di}{dt} + \frac{i}{\tau} = i_0 \delta(t)$$

where $\tau = RC$ is the time constant. If $i(0) = 0$, the response is, by the convolution theorem,

$$i(t) = i_0 \int_{-\infty}^{\infty} \delta(\xi) e^{-(t-\xi)/\tau} \, d\xi$$

or

$$i(t) = i_0 e^{-t/\tau}$$

The exponentially decaying current in the circuit arises because of the discharge of the capacitor through the resistor.

The smaller the time constant τ, the more quickly $i(t)$ is attenuated. The question becomes: How is this attenuation related to the frequency response of the circuit? Take the Fourier transform of the differential equation for the current to answer this question. On defining $I(\omega) = \mathscr{F}\{i(t)\}$, we find that

$$I(\omega) = \frac{i_0 \tau}{j\omega \tau + 1}$$

Thus, when $|\omega\tau| \gg 1$, $|I| \to 0$ and when $|\omega\tau| \ll 1$, $|I| \to i_0\tau$. The conclusion is that the RC network acts as a low-pass filter, preferentially attenuating higher frequencies. We can define the low-frequency region as a passband of frequencies and the high-frequency range of ω as a stopband. The transition between the two is a gradual one.   ∎

We now turn to a more complicated case. We want to establish conditions under which a filter will have both stop- and passbands. In this connection, Floquet's theorem, applied to the behavior of the solutions to second-order differential equations with periodic coefficients, is of importance. We shall establish Floquet's result by considering a function $\psi(x)$ which is a solution to the differential equation

$$\frac{d^2\psi}{dx^2} + k^2(x)\psi = 0 \tag{4.124}$$

where $k^2(x) = k^2(x + na)$, with n an integer and a a fundamental length if x is a length. Thus $k^2(x)$ has a spatial periodicity of a.

There are only two linearly independent solutions to any second-order differential equation. Denote these by $\psi_1(x)$ and $\psi_2(x)$. Then the general solution to Equation 4.124 is

$$\psi(x) = A\psi_1(x) + B\psi_2(x) \tag{4.125}$$

where A and B are arbitrary constants. From Equation 4.125 we also have that

$$\psi(x + a) = A\psi_1(x + a) + B\psi_2(x + a)$$

But both $\psi_1(x + a)$ and $\psi_2(x + a)$ can be written as linear combinations of the two fundamental solutions, i.e.,

$$\psi_1(x + a) = \alpha\psi_1(x) + \beta\psi_2(x)$$

and   (4.126)

$$\psi_2(x + a) = \gamma\psi_1(x) + \delta\psi_2(x)$$

Here, α, β, γ, and δ are constants. We now have

$$\psi(x + a) = A(\alpha\psi_1(x) + \beta\psi_2(x)) + B(\gamma\psi_1(x) + \delta\psi_2(x)) \quad (4.127)$$

We now find solutions to Equation 4.124 that satisfy the additional requirement

$$\psi(x + a) = \lambda\psi(x) \quad (4.128)$$

for certain eigenvalues of the parameter λ. We have, on equating the expressions for $\psi(x + a)$ from Equations 4.127 and 4.128, that the coefficients of $\psi_1(x)$ and $\psi_2(x)$ must satisfy the following equations:

$$\begin{aligned} A(\lambda - \alpha) - B\gamma &= 0 \\ -A\beta + B(\lambda - \delta) &= 0 \end{aligned} \quad (4.129)$$

Equation 4.129 can be written as the matrix relation

$$T\begin{pmatrix} A \\ B \end{pmatrix} = \mathbf{0} \quad (4.130)$$

where $\mathbf{T}$ is the matrix

$$T = \begin{bmatrix} \lambda - \alpha & -\gamma \\ -\beta & \lambda - \delta \end{bmatrix} \quad (4.131)$$

In order for Equation 4.130 to have a nontrivial solution, we require that the determinant of $\mathbf{T}$ vanish; i.e., that

$$\lambda^2 - (\alpha + \delta)\lambda + (\alpha\delta - \beta\gamma) = 0 \quad (4.132)$$

Define a matrix

$$\Omega = \begin{bmatrix} \alpha & \beta \\ \gamma & \delta \end{bmatrix} \quad (4.133)$$

Then $\alpha + \delta \equiv \text{Tr }\Omega$ is the trace of Ω, and $\alpha\delta - \gamma\beta = \Delta(\Omega)$, the determinant of Ω. We have that

$$\lambda = \frac{1}{2}\text{Tr }\Omega \pm \frac{1}{2}\sqrt{(\text{Tr }\Omega)^2 - 4\Delta} \quad (4.134)$$

Now if $x\epsilon(0,\infty)$ or if $x\epsilon(-\infty,\infty)$, λ cannot be greater than unity in absolute value. If this were so, the use of the recursive statement

$$\psi(x + a) = \lambda\psi(x) = \lambda^2\psi(x - a) = \lambda^3\psi(x - 2a) = \cdots \quad (4.135)$$

means that as $|n| \to \infty$, $\psi \to \infty$ for $\lambda > 1$. This would mean, physically, that we could insert a signal at some point and extract more energy at large $|x_n| = |x + na|$ than was put into the device, which is obviously impossible. The value $\lambda = 1$ is certainly allowable, since we then have

$$\psi(x + na) = \psi(x) \tag{4.136}$$

for all integers n. The conclusion is this: We have, as a condition for the existence of eigenvalues λ, that

$$|\text{Tr } \boldsymbol{\Omega}| \leq 2|\Delta|^{1/2} \tag{4.137}$$

If the inequality of Equation 4.137 holds, the two roots of λ are a complex conjugate pair. Physically, it is also seen that if there are no losses in the system, so that $|\psi(x + na)| = |\psi(x)|$ for all n, then the complex quantity representing λ is of modulus unity; i.e., only a phase change occurs in $\psi(x)$ as x changes to $x + na$ for positive or negative n. We can thus write

$$\lambda = e^{j\phi} \tag{4.138}$$

Therefore we have, in the lossless case, for a semi-infinite or infinite structure,

$$e^{j\phi} = \frac{1}{2} \text{Tr } \boldsymbol{\Omega} \pm \frac{1}{2} \sqrt{(\text{Tr } \boldsymbol{\Omega})^2 - 4\Delta} \tag{4.139}$$

as the condition for the existence of eigenvalues of the phase ϕ. We have also shown that

$$\psi(x + a) = e^{j\phi(a)}\psi(x) \tag{4.140}$$

which is a statement of Floquet's theorem; namely, that if a differential equation has a periodic coefficient, then bounded solutions must also be periodic with the periodicity of the coefficient when x becomes unbounded.

Example 4.13 The above analysis is now applied to a discussion of a filter having pass- and stopbands. If a lossless transmission line is periodically loaded with capacitors at points $x = x_n$, where $x_n = na$, then the capacitors have a spacing a along the line, and there is, at each of these points, a delta function discontinuity in the characteristic impedance $Z_c = \sqrt{L/C}$ of the lossless line. The spatial behavior of a voltage wave on such a line can be modeled by requiring solutions to the equation

$$\frac{d^2v(x)}{dx^2} + k^2v(x) = \beta \sum_{n=-\infty}^{\infty} \delta(x - x_n)v(x)$$

for a line of infinite length. Here $k^2 = \omega^2 LC$, and β is, for dimensional reasons, a reciprocal length. On taking the Fourier transform of the above equation, letting $V(\lambda) \equiv \mathcal{F}\{v(x)\}$, and noting the identity $\delta(x - x_n)v(x) \equiv \delta(x - x_n)v(x_n)$, we find that

$$V(\lambda) = \frac{\beta}{k^2 - \lambda^2} \sum_{n=-\infty}^{\infty} e^{-j\lambda x_n}v(x_n)$$

Inversion gives us $v(x)$ in the form

$$v(x) = \frac{\beta}{k} \sum_{n=-\infty}^{\infty} v(x_n) \sin k(x - x_n) u(x - x_n)$$

where $u(x - x_n)$ is the unit step function. The derivative of $v(x)$ is

$$\frac{dv}{dx} \equiv v'(x) = \beta \sum_{n=-\infty}^{\infty} v(x_n) \cos k(x - x_n) u(x - x_n)$$

We pick a point $x = x_p$ and write

$$v(x_p) \equiv v_p = \frac{\beta}{k} \sum_{n=-\infty}^{p-1} v_n \sin k(x_p - x_n)$$

and

$$v_p' = \beta \sum_{n=-\infty}^{p} v_n \cos k(x_p - x_n)$$

On setting $x = x_{p+1} = x_p + a$, the voltage and its derivative are, at x_{p+1},

$$v_{p+1} = \frac{\beta}{k} \sum_{n=-\infty}^{p} v_n \sin k(x_p - x_n + a)$$

and

$$v_{p+1}' = \beta \sum_{n=-\infty}^{p+1} v_n \cos k(x_p - x_n + a)$$

We now want to express v_{p+1} and v_{p+1}' in terms of their values at point p. Using a well-known trigonometric identity, the result for v_{p+1} becomes

$$v_{p+1} = \cos ka \left(\frac{\beta}{k} \sum_{n=-\infty}^{p-1} v_n \sin k(x_p - x_n) \right) + \frac{\sin ka}{k} \left(\beta \sum_{n=-\infty}^{p} v_n \cos k(x_p - x_n) \right)$$

We immediately find that v_{p+1} can be expressed as

$$v_{p+1} = \cos ka v_p + \frac{\sin ka}{k} v_p'$$

The quantity v_{p+1}' can be written in the form

$$v'_{p+1} = \beta v_{p+1} + \beta \sum_{n=-\infty}^{p} v_n \cos k(x_p - x_n + a)$$

On expanding the term $\cos k(x_p - x_n + a)$, we have

$$v_{p+1}' = \beta v_{p+1} + \cos ka v_p' - k \sin ka v_p$$

Insertion of the expression for v_{p+1} and collection of terms produce an alternative equation for v_{p+1}'; it is

$$v_{p+1}' = (\beta \cos ka - k \sin ka) v_p + \left(\cos ka + \frac{\beta}{k} \sin ka \right) v_p'$$

Define a vector

$$\mathbf{v}_R = \begin{bmatrix} v_R \\ v_R' \end{bmatrix}$$

and a matrix

$$\Lambda = \begin{bmatrix} \cos ka & \sin ka/k \\ \beta \cos ka - k \sin ka & \cos ka + (\beta/k) \sin ka \end{bmatrix}$$

Note that the determinant of Λ, defined as $\Delta(\Lambda)$, is equal to unity. The relation between $\mathbf{v}_{p+1}$ and $\mathbf{v}_p$ is then the concise matrix equation

$$\mathbf{v}_{p+1} = \Lambda \mathbf{v}_p$$

According to the Floquet theorem, we must have

$$\mathbf{v}_{p+1} = e^{j\phi} \mathbf{v}_p$$

so that

$$\Delta(e^{j\phi}\mathbf{I} - \Lambda) = 0$$

is the condition for the existence of eigenvalues. We find that

$$\begin{vmatrix} e^{j\phi} - \cos ka & -(\sin ka/k) \\ -\beta \cos ka + k \sin ka & e^{j\phi} - \cos ka - \beta/k \sin ka \end{vmatrix} = 0$$

from which, because $\Delta(\Lambda) \equiv 1$, we obtain

$$e^{2j\phi} - e^{j\phi}\left(2 \cos ka + \frac{\beta}{k} \sin ka\right) + 1 = 0$$

Noting that both the trace of Λ and its determinant are real, we may separately equate both real and imaginary parts of the eigenvalue equation to zero. While both will give, as they must, identical results for eigenvalues, it is more direct to deal with the imaginary part of the equation. We immediately find that

$$\sin 2\phi - \sin \phi\left(2 \cos ka + \frac{\beta}{k} \sin ka\right) = 0$$

The two roots of this equation are

$$\sin \phi = 0$$

and

$$\cos \phi = \cos ka + \frac{\beta}{2k} \sin ka$$

Now, we can always set $\phi \doteq \kappa a$, where a is the spacing of capacitors and κ is equal to $2\pi/\gamma$, where γ is a wavelength. Further, since β is a reciprocal length, we shall set $\beta = 2l/a$, where l is some number. Then either

$$\sin \kappa a = 0$$

or

$$\cos \kappa a = \cos ka + \frac{l}{ka} \sin ka$$

From the first of these equations, we conclude that

$$\kappa = \frac{m\pi}{a}$$

where m is an integer. In this case the wavelength $\gamma = 2a/m$. The second of the equations for the eigenvalues contains far more information and also contains the eigenvalues $\kappa = m\pi/a$ as a limiting case. Its left-hand side has a value somewhere in the interval $-1 \leq \cos \kappa a \leq 1$, so that only those values of k for which

$$\left| \cos ka + \frac{l}{ka} \sin ka \right| \leq 1$$

are eigenvalues.*

A plot of $f(ka) \equiv \cos ka + (l/ka) \sin ka$, with the dotted lines equal to the maximum and minimum of $\cos \kappa a$, is shown in Figure 4.6 for $ka > 0$. Since $f(ka)$ is even, the plot for $ka < 0$ is unnecessary. Stopbands are defined as intervals along the ka-axis for which $|f(ka)| > 1$. Passbands are intervals for which $|f(ka)| < 1$. Band edges occur at points for which $|f(ka)| = 1$. Consider these latter points. If $|\cos \kappa a| = 1$, then $\kappa a = m\pi$. Thus the values of $\kappa = m\pi/a$ at band edges are also values of κ for which $\sin \kappa a = 0$. The latter condition, then, is identically satisfied at band edges.

The above analysis of a periodically loaded filter carries over into solid-state physics and engineering. The time-independent, one-dimensional Schroedinger equation of quantum mechanics can be written as

$$\frac{d^2\psi}{dx^2} + (k^2 - U(x))\psi = 0$$

where $k^2 = 2mE\hbar^2$, and E the energy of a (charged) particle whose wave function is ψ, and with $U(x)$ an interaction energy between the charged particle and the potential in which it moves. In a one-dimensional crystal, where the atomic spacing is a, we may set

$$U(x) = \beta \sum \delta(x - x_n)$$

a periodic potential with spatial period a. The energy levels E then split into allowed (pass) and forbidden (stop) bands in a crystal.

There are various additional applications of differential equations with periodic coefficients. The behavior of a parametric amplifier is discussed in the problems at the end of this chapter. ∎

As a further application of the use of Fourier transforms in discussing filters, we study the problems of designing such devices with various bandpass characteristics. Let $f(t)$ be nonzero in the interval $|t| \leq T/2$ and equal to zero for $|t| > T/2$. Then, as in the case of the gate function, the Fourier transform of $f(t)$ is given by

$$F(\omega) = \int_{-T/2}^{T/2} e^{-j\omega t} f(t) \, dt \tag{4.141}$$

---

*In the Floquet theorem this corresponds to the condition that $\text{Tr } \Omega \leq 2\Delta^{1/2}$, which, in our case, since $\Delta^{1/2} \equiv \pm 1$, means that $|\text{Tr } \Omega| \leq 2$.

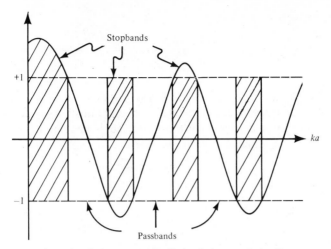

FIGURE 4.6   Stop- and passbands for a periodically loaded transmission line.

We shall assume that $f(t)$ is real and that it can be approximated by a convergent, truncated Fourier series of the form

$$f(t) = \sum_{n=-L}^{L} f_n e^{j\omega_n t} \tag{4.142}$$

where $\omega_n = n\omega_0 = 2\pi n/T$. Then

$$F(\omega) = \sum_{n=-L}^{L} f_n \int_{-T/2}^{T/2} e^{-j(\omega-\omega_n)t} \, dt \tag{4.143}$$

when integrated is given by

$$F(\omega) = 2 \sum_{n=-L}^{L} f_n \frac{\sin(\omega - \omega_n)T/2}{\omega - \omega_n} \tag{4.144}$$

We now discretize the frequency ω by setting $\omega = \omega_k = k\omega_0$ where $\omega_0 = 2\pi/T$. Then

$$F(\omega_k) = \frac{T}{\pi} \sum_{n=-L}^{L} f_n \frac{\sin(k-n)\pi}{k-n} \tag{4.145}$$

The Fourier coefficients, f_n, can now be evaluated by noticing that for $k \neq n$, $\sin(k-n)\pi = 0$, while

$$\lim_{k \to n} \frac{\sin(k-n)\pi}{(k-n)\pi} = 1 \tag{4.146}$$

The expression for the Fourier coefficients, f_k, consequently is

$$f_k = F(\omega_k)/T \tag{4.147}$$

Thus the discrete frequency spectrum $F(\omega_k)$ is

$$F(\omega_k) = \frac{1}{\pi} \sum_{n=-L}^{L} F(\omega_n) \frac{\sin(k-n)\pi}{(k-n)} \tag{4.148}$$

Since $\sin (k - n)\pi = (-1)^n \sin k\pi$

$$F(\omega_k) = \frac{\sin k\pi}{k\pi} \sum_{n=-L}^{L} F(\omega_n)(-1)^n \frac{k}{k - n} \tag{4.149}$$

The characteristic frequency spectrum of the gate function $\sin k\pi/k\pi$ is modified, in the present case, by the appearance of the summation in Equation 4.149. We now want to transform $F(\omega_k)$ into an alternative form that shows the way in which bandpass characteristics can be tailored. We write first that

$$\frac{k}{k - n} = -\frac{k/n}{1 - k/n} \tag{4.150}$$

Because $f(t)$ is assumed to be real, $F(\omega_n) = F^*(\omega_{-n})$. If we now let $L \to \infty$,

$$F(\omega_k) = D \frac{\sin k\pi}{k\pi} \frac{P(k/n)}{\displaystyle\prod_{n=1}^{\infty} (1 - k^2/n^2)} \tag{4.151}$$

where D is a constant, $P(k/n)$ is a polynomial in k/n, and the product in the denominator of Equation 4.151 is a consequence of the sum over n as $L \to \infty$. The product expansion of $\sin k\pi/k\pi$, which we write without proof, is

$$\frac{\sin k\pi}{k\pi} = \prod_{n=1}^{\infty} (1 - k^2/n^2) \tag{4.152}$$

Thus we find the remarkably simple result that

$$F(\omega_k) = DP(k/n) \tag{4.153}$$

In practice, this polynomial can be of finite degree. This follows directly from the Weirstrass approximation theorem, which states that any continuous curve defined on a finite interval can be approximated as closely as is needed by a polynomial of finite degree. Thus, if we want a bandpass characteristic on a part of the ω-axis, we can pass a curve through several desired points $\omega = \omega_k$ and fit that curve with a polynomial approximation. Filters based on Chebyshev polynomials are discussed in a problem at the end of this chapter.

   ·We summarize our work on filters as follows: Since the reactance of an inductor L is $j\omega L$ and that of a capacitor is $(j\omega C)^{-1}$, it follows that as $\omega \to \infty$, a capacitance presents a low impedance to high frequencies and an inductor is a high-impedance element for high frequencies. Then, for example, the filters shown in Figure 4.7(a) and 4.7(b) are low- and high-pass filters, respectively. Finally, in our work leading to the expression given in Equation 4.153, we found this simple result only because we were dealing with a modified gate function.

   We wish to generalize further. Let $H(\omega)$ be given as[6]

$$H(\omega) = \frac{\omega(1 - \lambda_2^2)(1 - \lambda_4^2)(1 - \lambda_6^2) \cdots}{(1 - \lambda_1^2)(1 - \lambda_3^2)(1 - \lambda_5^2) \cdots} \tag{4.154}$$

where $\lambda_i = \omega/\omega_i$ with the ω_i fixed values. We restrict $H(\omega)$ further by requiring that $|H(\omega)| \le 1$. This is in complete analogy to the requirement placed on the function

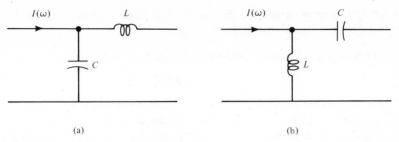

FIGURE 4.7 (a) Low pass and (b) high pass.

$$f(ka) = \cos ka + \frac{l}{\kappa a} \sin ka \qquad (4.155)$$

which appears in our previous discussion of the periodically loaded transmission line. A plot of $H(\omega)$ versus ω is shown in Figure 4.8, where stop- and passbands are shown. The passbands are the regions of the ω-axis for which $|H(\omega)| < 1$. Thus three pass-bands are shown in Figure 4.8, with stopbands defined as regions for which $|H(\omega)| > 1$. Band edges occur at points for which $|H(\omega)| = 1$. In this sense, Figure 4.8 can be considered a pictorial representation of a more general case than the one given in Example 4.13.

4.9 APPLICATIONS OF FOURIER TRANSFORMS TO AMPLITUDE- AND FREQUENCY-MODULATED SIGNALS

Introduction

In this section our main emphasis is on applying Fourier transform methods to the study of amplitude- and frequency-modulated (AM and FM) signals. Several texts cover

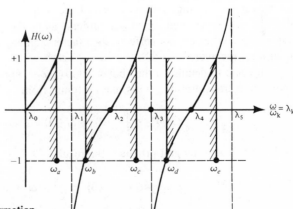

FIGURE 4.8 A frequency transformation.

these subjects in great detail. We discuss the two systems in order to show the importance of Fourier transforms in their analysis.

A general expression for a time-varying signal, $g(t)$, is given by

$$g(t) = f(t) \sin (\omega_c t + \phi(t)) \qquad (4.156)$$

We refer to $g(t)$ as a transmitted signal in what follows. Both the amplitude, $f(t)$, and the phase angle, $\phi(t)$, are time dependent, with the quantity ω_c defined as an angular carrier frequency. Our intention is to study two special cases of the foregoing expression for $g(t)$. For constant $\phi(t)$ and a particular choice of $f(t)$, the resulting expression is called a large carrier AM signal. With $f(t)$ independent of time and $\phi(t)$ varying, the signal is phase modulated (PM). One particular type of phase modulation is called FM. We start by examining AM signals.

Amplitude Modulation (AM)   It is convenient to set $\phi(t)$ equal to a constant whose value for all time is

$$\phi(t) = \pi/2$$

Then, with $f(t)$ real, if we write

$$f(t) = A + \lambda f_i(t) \qquad (4.157)$$

the resulting expression for the transmitted signal $g(t)$ is the real quantity

$$g(t) = (A + \lambda f_i(t)) \cos \omega_c t \qquad (4.158)$$

This relation is defined as a large carrier AM signal when $A > \lambda f_i(t)$. It is important to note that information is contained *only* in the term $f_i(t)$, the input signal, with the transmitted signal given by $g(t)$. The carrier is said to be *amplitude modulated* by the input signal.

The basic idea behind a communications system is to convey information accurately. Ideally, we want a receiver that yields an output signal, $f_0(t)$, such that

$$f_i(t) = f_0(t) \qquad (4.159)$$

This ideal can never be realized in practice. Between a transmitter and a receiver there is frequently an atmospheric path where noise is added to $g(t)$. If we attempt to filter out such noise, we may remove some of the frequency components of $g(t)$, thereby distorting the transmitted signal. Amplifiers can be designed with excellent frequency responses, but they are not perfect. Such factors, among others, prevent the realization of an ideal receiver.

To come to details on the above, let $G(\omega) \equiv \mathscr{F}\{g(t)\}$ and let $F_i(\omega) = \mathscr{F}\{f_i(t)\}$. The Fourier transform of $g(t)$ is readily found from

$$G(\omega) = \int_{-\infty}^{\infty} (A + \lambda f_i(t)) \cos \omega_c t e^{-j\omega t} dt \qquad (4.160)$$

Evaluation of this integral produces the result

$$G(\omega) = A\pi\{\delta(\omega + \omega_c) + \delta(\omega - \omega_c)\} + \frac{\lambda}{2}\{F_i(\omega + \omega_c) + F_i(\omega - \omega_c)\} \qquad (4.161)$$

That is, the Fourier transform of the transmitted signal consists of delta functions at the points $\omega = \pm \omega_c$ and the shifted Fourier spectrum of $f_i(t)$, with the shift in frequency being from ω to $\omega \pm \omega_c$.

A receiver will detect $g(t)$ and, from it, recover a signal proportional to $f_i(t)$ in various ways. A common method is to employ a local oscillator in the receiver that multiplies the transmitted signal by the term $\cos \omega_c t$, thereby forming the quantity

$$h(t) = g(t) \cos \omega_c t \tag{4.162}$$

On inserting the expression for $g(t)$ and simplifying the result, we find that

$$h(t) = \frac{1}{2}(A + \lambda f_i(t))(1 + \cos 2\omega_c t) \tag{4.163}$$

The Fourier transform of $h(t)$, called $H(\omega)$, is

$$H(\omega) = \frac{1}{2} \int_{-\infty}^{\infty} (A + \lambda f_i(t))(1 + \cos 2\omega_c t)e^{-j\omega t} \, dt \tag{4.164}$$

The integral, when evaluated, yields $H(\omega)$ as

$$H(\omega) = \pi A\{\delta(\omega) + \delta(\omega + 2\omega_c) + \delta(\omega - 2\omega_c)\} + \lambda\{F_i(\omega) + \frac{1}{2}F_i(\omega + 2\omega_c)$$

$$+ F_i(\omega - 2\omega_c)\} \tag{4.165}$$

Suppose that the function $H(\omega)$ is now passed through an ideal filter whose characteristics are given by

$$P(\omega) = \begin{cases} 1 & -\omega_0 \leq \omega \leq \omega_0 \\ 0 & \text{otherwise} \end{cases} \tag{4.166}$$

We shall assume, additionally, that $|\omega_0| < |\omega_c|$. The output signal, $f_0(t)$, which is passed by the filter, is then of the form

$$f_0(t) = \frac{1}{2\pi} \int_{-\infty}^{\infty} e^{j\omega t} H(\omega)P(\omega) \, d\omega \tag{4.167}$$

which becomes

$$f_0(t) = \frac{1}{2\pi} \int_{-\omega_0}^{\omega_0} (\lambda F_i(\omega) + \pi A\delta(\omega))e^{j\omega t} \, d\omega \tag{4.168}$$

Suppose that $F_i(\omega) \equiv \mathcal{F}\{f_i(t)\}$ is Gaussian with essentially zero amplitude outside the range $-\omega_0 \leq \omega \leq \omega_0$. Then

$$f_0(t) = \lambda f_i(t) + \pi A \tag{4.169}$$

The output signal is, apart from a constant, a mirror of the information carried by the modulating signal $\lambda f_i(t)$.

Figure 4.9 is helpful in understanding the assumptions made regarding the nature of $\lambda F_i(\omega)$ and the spectrum $H(\omega)$.

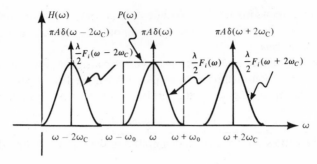

FIGURE 4.9   Fourier transform, $H(\omega)$, of the modulated transmitted signal. The dotted line is the ideal filter (gate) characteristic, $P(\omega)$.

In the preceding discussion, the assumption made is that the carrier frequency remains at exactly $\omega = \omega_c$, both in the transmitter and in the receiver. Now, AM receivers are not notoriously expensive, and for that reason the electronic circuitry is sometimes not overly designed. Consequently, the local oscillator in an AM receiver may drift from a value ω_c to $\omega_c + \Delta\omega$. We want to investigate the effect of such a change. For $\phi(t) = \phi_0 = \pi/2$, and a local oscillator frequency $\omega_c + \Delta\omega$,

$$\sin\left[(\omega_c + \Delta\omega)t + \pi/2\right] = \cos\left[(\omega_c + \Delta\omega)t\right] \tag{4.170}$$

Thus the received signal $h(t)$ is now given by

$$h(t) = (A + \lambda f_i(t)) \cos(\omega_c t) \cos\left[(\omega_c + \Delta\omega)t\right] \tag{4.171}$$

or

$$h(t) = \frac{1}{2}(A + \lambda f_i(t))\{\cos(2\omega_c + \Delta\omega)t + \cos(\Delta\omega t)\}$$

The change in the received signal, after filtering, is contained in the term

$$h_c(t) = \frac{1}{2}(A + \lambda f_i(t)) \cos \Delta\omega t \tag{4.172}$$

As t increases, there will be instants of time for which

$$\cos \Delta\omega t_k = 0 \tag{4.173}$$

This leads to the phenomenon of fading in AM reception.

We now investigate the power in the signal

$$g(t) = (A + \lambda f_i(t)) \cos \omega_c t \tag{4.174}$$

The average power delivered to a resistive load R is, if $g(t)$ is a voltage,*

$$\langle P \rangle = \frac{\langle g^2(t) \rangle}{R} = \frac{1}{R} \langle [(A + \lambda f_i(t)) \cos(\omega_c t)]^2 \rangle \tag{4.175}$$

If the input signal $f_i(t)$ is such that $\langle f_i(t) \rangle \equiv 0$, then

---

*We use the brackets $\langle \ \rangle$ to indicate time averaging.

$$\langle P \rangle = \frac{1}{2R}\left(A^2 + \frac{\lambda^2}{2}\langle f_i^2(t)\rangle 2\right) \tag{4.176}$$

One of the peculiarities associated with AM signals is put into evidence by this expression for the power. No information is transmitted by the carrier wave, but, since $A > \lambda f_i(t)$ by assumption, more power is expended in transmitting the carrier than in sending the signal $\lambda f_i(t)$.

In this brief discussion of amplitude modulation we have stressed only the role of Fourier transforms in analyzing such a system. There are far more comprehensive discussions of AM systems in various texts, some of which are mentioned in the bibliography at the end of this chapter. Topics such as suppressed carrier AM, sidebands, the effects of noise, and methods of detection, as well as AM circuits themselves, are not covered here because of our primary interest in applications of the Fourier transform. We now turn to frequency modulation.

Frequency Modulation (FM)   Let a sinusoidal signal be given by

$$g(t) = \sin(\omega_c t + \phi(t)) \tag{4.177}$$

where the amplitude has been normalized to unity. The phase, $\phi(t)$, is assumed to vary with time according to

$$\phi(t) = \lambda \int_0^t f_i(\tau)\, d\tau + \pi/2 \tag{4.178}$$

so that

$$g(t) = \cos\left(\omega_c t + \lambda \int_0^t f_i(\tau)\, d\tau\right) \tag{4.179}$$

Note that if $f_i(t)$ is a voltage, then λ has the dimensions of $(\text{volt-sec})^{-1}$. Now, at any instant of time, there exists an angle $\theta(t)$, defined as

$$\theta(t) = \omega_c t + \lambda \int_0^t f_i(\tau)\, d\tau \tag{4.180}$$

with an associated instantaneous frequency

$$\omega_i(t) = \frac{d\phi}{dt} = \omega_c + \lambda f_i(t) \tag{4.181}$$

That is, the frequency now varies with time, with the variation due to an input signal $\lambda f_i(t)$. The signal $g(t)$ is frequency modulated.

For the case of an arbitrary time variation of the signal $f_i(t)$, the analysis of FM signals is complex. If, however, we imagine that $f_i(t)$ can be represented by a Fourier series, then we can discuss FM by examining one of the components of $f_i(t)$. To that purpose, we suppose that

$$f_i(t) = \cos \omega_0 t \tag{4.182}$$

where ω_0 is a fundamental modulating frequency and the amplitude of $f_i(t)$ is 1 volt for $f_i(t)$ a voltage. Then

$$\theta(t) = \omega_c t + \frac{\lambda}{\omega_0} \sin \omega_0 t \qquad (4.183)$$

or, for convenience, with $\lambda / \omega_0 \equiv k$ (k is dimensionless),

$$\theta(t) = \omega_c t + k \sin \omega_0 t \qquad (4.184)$$

Then $g(t)$, the transmitted signal, is represented by

$$g(t) = \cos(\omega_c t + k \sin \omega_0 t) = \cos \theta(t) \qquad (4.185)$$

or, alternatively, as

$$g(t) = \text{Re}\{e^{j(\omega_c t + k \sin \omega_0 t)}\} \qquad (4.186)$$

From Appendix C, we have the identity

$$e^{jk \sin \omega_0 t} = \sum_{n=-\infty}^{\infty} J_n(k) e^{jn\omega_0 t} \qquad (4.187)$$

where $J_n(k)$ is a Bessel function of order n and argument k. Consequently,

$$g(t) = \text{Re}\left\{ e^{j\omega_c t} \sum_{n=-\infty}^{\infty} J_n(k) e^{jn\omega_0 t} \right\} \qquad (4.188)$$

The Fourier transform, $G(\omega)$, of this signal is then

$$(2\pi)^{-1} G(\omega) = \sum_{n=-\infty}^{\infty} J_n(k) \delta(\omega - \omega_c - n\omega_0) \qquad (4.189)$$

That is, the Fourier spectrum is composed of an infinite number of delta functions, at points $\omega = \omega_c + n\omega_0$, each of which has an amplitude $J_n(k)$. Such a signal is labeled a wide-band FM signal because there is now an infinite number of sidebands. However, only a few of the $J_n(k)$ are of numerical importance if $k = \lambda/\omega_0$ is small. To present this more clearly, table 4.1 gives values of $J_n(k)$ for a few fixed values of k and various integers n. If the value $|J_n(k)| < 0.005$, there is a blank in the appropriate tabular entry.

TABLE 4.1   Values of Bessel functions of various orders for the arguments shown

	$k = 1$	$k = 2$	$k = 3$	$k = 4$	$k = 5$
$J_0(k)$	0.765198	0.223891	−0.260052	−0.397150	−0.177596
$J_1(k)$	0.440051	0.557937	0.339060	−0.066043	−0.327579
$J_2(k)$	0.114903	0.352834	0.486091	0.364128	0.046565
$J_3(k)$	0.019563	0.128940	0.30906	0.43017	0.36483
$J_4(k)$		0.033996	0.13203	0.28113	0.39123
$J_5(k)$			0.04303	0.13209	0.26114
$J_6(k)$			0.011394	0.04909	0.13105
$J_7(k)$				0.015176	0.053376
$J_8(k)$					0.018405
$J_9(k)$					0.0055203

From table 4.1, if $\lambda/\omega_0 = 1$, then only the terms for which $|n| \leq 3$ contribute significantly to either $g(t)$ or its transform $G(\omega)$.

The average power in an FM signal is, for unit amplitude of $g(t)$, given by

$$\langle P \rangle = \frac{\langle g(t)^2 \rangle}{R} = \frac{\langle \cos^2 \theta(t) \rangle}{R} = \frac{1}{2R} \tag{4.190}$$

There is no power expended in transmitting a carrier wave, as in the case of an AM system. The frequency range of FM, being far higher than that of AM, means that "line-of-sight" communications is the general mode of FM broadcasting.* For such reasons, FM stations require less power than do their AM counterparts.

Finally, with regard to AM and FM systems, we have seen that if the local oscillator frequency in an AM receiver drifts, fading will result. In FM communication, information is contained in a time-varying phase angle $\theta(t) = \omega_c t + k \sin \omega_0 t$. In either case, it is necessary that a frequency be tightly controlled. We concentrate on FM in what follows, and examine a feedback method for "locking" the phase angle.

Linearized Phase-Locked Loop

The study of a linearized phase-locked loop provides a good example of the use of Fourier transforms in studying the control of a system.

Let two sinusoidal voltages be denoted by

$$g(t) = A \cos(\omega_c t + \theta_i(t)) \tag{4.191}$$

and

$$h(t) = B \sin(\omega_c t + \theta_0(t)) \tag{4.192}$$

If these signals are multiplied together, their product, $v(t)$, is given by

$$v(t) = k\frac{AB}{2} \{\sin(2\omega_c t + \theta_i + \theta_0) + \sin(\theta_i - \theta_0)\} \tag{4.193}$$

if k, the multiplier gain, has the dimensions of reciprocal volts. When $v(t)$ is passed through a low-pass filter, the output is a signal

$$v_0(t) = k\frac{AB}{2} \sin(\theta_i - \theta_0) \tag{4.194}$$

If the difference between $\theta_i(t)$ and $\theta_0(t)$ is small, then the linearized approximation for $v_0(t)$ is

$$v_0(t) \approx k\frac{AB}{2} \{\theta_i(t) - \theta_0(t)\} \tag{4.195}$$

Let $\theta_i(t)$ and $\theta_0(t)$ be input and output phase angles of FM signals; i.e., let

$$\theta_i(t) = \lambda_i \int_0^t v_i(\tau) \, d\tau$$

and
$$\tag{4.196}$$

---

*The AM broadcast band is approximately 550–1500 kHz; FM covers 88–108 MHz.

$$\theta_0(t) = \lambda_0 \int_0^t v_0(\tau) \, d\tau$$

where $v_i(t)$ and $v_0(t)$ are input and output modulating voltages. Then both λ_i and λ_0 have the dimensions of (volt-sec)$^{-1}$. The phase error $\theta_e(t)$ is then

$$\theta_e(t) = \lambda_i \int_0^t v_i(\tau) \, d\tau - \lambda_0 \int_0^t v_0(\tau) \, d\tau \tag{4.197}$$

and this quantity must be minimized.

A first-order minimization is readily available. From the expression given in Equation 4.194 we find by differentiation

$$\frac{dv_0}{dt} + \frac{1}{\tau_0} v_0(t) = \frac{1}{\tau_i} v_i \tag{4.198}$$

where the input and output time constants are, with $kAB/2 = \gamma$, a constant,

$$\tau_0 = (\gamma\lambda_0)^{-1}$$

and $\tag{4.199}$

$$\tau_i = (\gamma\lambda_i)^{-1}$$

The Fourier transform of Equation 4.198 is

$$V_0(\omega) = H(\omega)V_i(\omega) \tag{4.200}$$

where

$$H(\omega) = \frac{\tau_0}{\tau_i} \frac{1}{(j\omega\tau_0 + 1)} \tag{4.201}$$

This transfer function is that of an RC network, leading to exponential decay of the voltage. It is typical of a first-order phase-locked loop.

The time-dependent voltage $v_0(t)$ is, as a result of Equation 4.200, given by the convolution integral

$$v_0(t) = \int_0^t h(t - \tau)v_i(\tau) \, d\tau \tag{4.202}$$

Depending on the nature of the signal $v_i(t)$, there are various outputs $v_0(t)$. With

$$h(t) = \frac{\tau_0}{\tau_i} e^{-t/\tau_0} \tag{4.203}$$

$$v_0(t) = \frac{1}{\tau_i} \int_0^t e^{-(t-\tau)/\tau_0} v_i(\tau) \, d\tau \tag{4.204}$$

Let $v_i(\tau)$ be a step function of magnitude v_1. Then

$$v_0(t) = \frac{v_1\tau_0}{\tau_1}(1 - e^{-t/\tau_0}) \tag{4.205}$$

As $t \rightarrow \infty$, the output signal is

$$v_0(t) = \frac{v_1 \tau_0}{\tau_1} = K v_i(t) \tag{4.206}$$

If τ_0 is small, this limiting value of $v_0(t)$ is reached quickly. The difference in the phases will be proportional to the constant K, which is small if τ_0/τ_i is small.

More can be done, however, to lock the phase. Let the phase error $\theta_e(t)$ be fed through a network such that the output voltage, $v_0(t)$, is the convolution integral

$$v_0(t) = \beta \int_{-\infty}^{\infty} \theta_e(\tau) h(t - \tau) \, d\tau \tag{4.207}$$

Since θ_e is dimensionless and the transfer function can be made dimensionless, β has the dimensions of volts. The Fourier transform of Equation 4.207 is

$$V_0(\omega) = \beta \Theta_e(\omega) H(\omega) \tag{4.208}$$

From Equation 4.197 the Fourier transform of $\theta_e(t)$ is

$$j\omega \Theta_e(\omega) = \lambda_i (V_i(\omega) - V_0(\omega)) \tag{4.209}$$

Combining these last two equations produces

$$V_0(\omega) = \frac{\lambda_i \beta H(\omega) V_i(\omega)}{j\omega \left(1 + \dfrac{\beta \lambda_0}{j\omega} H(\omega)\right)} \tag{4.210}$$

If $|H(\omega)| \gg \omega/\beta\lambda_0$, then

$$|V_0(\omega)| = \frac{\lambda_i}{\lambda_0} |V_i(\omega)| \tag{4.211}$$

We have at our disposal, for design purposes, a network transfer function. It is standard to use a lead–lag filter in a second-order phase-locked loop, which is characterized by the function

$$H(\omega) = a + \frac{b}{j\omega} \tag{4.212}$$

where a and b are adjustable constants. Note that a is dimensionless and that b has the dimensions of ω. When this expression for $H(\omega)$ is substituted into Equation 4.210 and the result simplified, we find that $V_0(\omega)$ is given by

$$V_0(\omega) = G(\omega) V_i(\omega) \tag{4.213}$$

where

$$G(\omega) = \frac{\lambda_i \beta (j\omega a + b)}{-\omega^2 + j\omega \beta \lambda_0 a + \beta \lambda_0 b} \tag{4.214a}$$

Noting that $\beta\lambda_0 b$ has the dimensions of the square of a frequency and that $\beta\lambda_0$ is a frequency, we can write

$$G(\omega) = \frac{\lambda_i \beta (j\omega a + b)}{\bar{\omega}^2 - \omega^2 + j\omega\omega_0 a} \qquad (4.214b)$$

where $\bar{\omega}^2 = \beta\lambda_0 b$ and $\omega_0 = \beta\lambda_0$. Thus, $V_0(\omega)$, the frequency spectrum of the output, is the product of two Fourier transforms, so that the time-dependent output signal is the convolution integral

$$v_0(t) = \int_{-\infty}^{\infty} g(t - \tau)v_i(\tau) \, d\tau \qquad (4.215)$$

The output phase is, from its definition,

$$\theta_0(t) = \lambda_0 \int_0^t v_0(\tau) \, d\tau \qquad (4.216)$$

Several comments can now be made without further analysis. The form of $G(\omega)$ given in Equation 4.214b is typical of the Fourier transform of an *RLC* circuit. Such a circuit has a response that approaches zero as $t \to \infty$. If $v_i(t)$ is a delta function, then $v_0(t) = g(t)$ and will approach zero as $t \to \infty$. Thus the integral for $\theta_0(t)$ is bounded and will, as $t \to \infty$, approach a constant. A problem at the end of this chapter requires more detailed analysis.

PROBLEMS

4-1   Find the exponential Fourier transforms of the following functions $f(t)$:

(a) $e^{-at}u(t) - e^{at}u(-t) \qquad a > 0$

(b) $t^{n-1}e^{-at} \qquad t > 0$
     $\quad 0 \qquad\qquad t < 0$

(c) $e^{jat}/(t^2 + \tau^2) \qquad \tau > 0, a$ real

4-2   Find the Fourier cosine transforms of the following functions $f(t)$:

(a) $t \qquad\quad 0 < t < 1$
    $\quad 2 - t \quad 1 < t < 2$
    $\quad 0 \qquad\quad 2 < t < \infty$

(b) $t^{-1/2}$

(c) $t^{-1/2}e^{-at} \qquad (\text{Re } a > 0)$

(d) $e^{-\lambda t} \sin \omega_0 t \qquad (\text{Re } \lambda > 0; \omega_0 > 0)$

4-3   Given $F_c(\omega)$, a Fourier cosine transform, find $f(t)$ for the following functions:

(a) $\pi(\omega_0 - \omega)^{-1}$

(b) $\omega^{-1/2}e^{-a\omega} \qquad (\text{Re } a > 0; \omega > 0)$

(c) $e^{-a|\omega|}e^{-\beta\omega^2} \qquad (\text{Re } \beta > 0)$

4-4   Find the Fourier sine transform of the following functions $f(t)$:

(a) t^{-1}

(b) $t^{-1/2}$

(c) $t/(t^2 + \tau^2)$, where τ is a constant.

4-5   Find the inverse Fourier sine transforms of the following functions $F_s(\omega)$:

(a) $(2\pi\omega)^{-1/2}$

(b) $\pi e^{-\omega t_0} \cos(\omega t)$ $(t_0 > 0, \omega > 0)$

(c) $(1 - e^{-\omega t_0})$ $(t_0 > 0, \omega > 0)$

(d) $[(\omega_0^2 + \omega^2)^{1/2} - \lambda]^{1/2}$ $(\omega_0 > 0, \lambda > 0)$

4-6   Find the exponential Fourier transform of the triangular pulse shown in Figure 4.10.

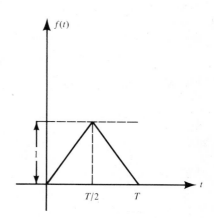

FIGURE 4.10   Problem 4-6: a triangular pulse.

4-7   Find the exponential Fourier transform of the sawtooth pulse shown in Figure 4.11.

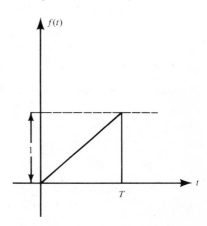

FIGURE 4.11   Problem 4-7: a sawtooth pulse.

4-8   By using the theorems relating to derivatives and convolution in Section 4.4, differential equations can be solved by Fourier transform techniques. The results are integral representations of a function $f(t)$. Find such expressions for $f(t)$ when it obeys the following differential equations:

(a) $\dfrac{df}{dt} + \lambda f = g(t) \qquad \lambda > 0$

(b) $\dfrac{d^2 f}{dt^2} + \lambda \dfrac{df}{dt} + \omega_0^2 f = \begin{Bmatrix} e^{-2t} & t > 0 \\ 0 & t < 0 \end{Bmatrix}$

The solution to wave equations in a lossless medium is discussed in the text. A natural generalization is the wave equation in a lossy medium, which can be written as

$$\frac{\partial^2 \psi}{\partial x^2} - \lambda \frac{\partial \psi}{\partial t} - \frac{1}{c^2} \frac{\partial^2 \psi}{\partial t^2} = 0 \qquad (\lambda > 0)$$

If $\psi(x,t)$ is such that $\psi(0,t) = f(t)$ and $(\partial \psi / \partial x)_{x=0} = 0$, find the Fourier transform $\Psi(x,\omega)$ of $\psi(x,t)$. Note that the inversion integral will involve branch points in the complex plane. Find $\psi(x,t)$ by inverting $\Psi(x,\omega)$.

4-9   Find a solution to the equation

$$(\nabla^2 + k^2)\psi = A\delta(x)\delta(y)\delta(z - z_0)\delta(t)$$

in terms of Hankel transforms such that $\psi(x,y,0,t) \equiv 0$. Here $\psi(\mathbf{r},t)$ represents the potential attributable to a Hertzian dipole located at $x = y = 0$ and at a height z_0 above the surface of the earth ($z = 0$). The boundary condition given means that the earth is treated as an infinitely conducting medium, which is a good approximation if the antenna is located over sea water, for example.

Hint   See reference 9 especially Section 32, pages 246 ff.

4-10   The Chebyshev polynomials used in filter design are defined as follows:

$$C_n(\omega) = \cos (n \cos^{-1} \omega)$$

Here C_n is the Chebyshev polynomial of order n. Thus we have

$$C_0 = \cos (0) = 1$$
$$C_1 = \cos (\cos^{-1} \omega) = \omega$$
$$C_2 = \cos (2 \cos^{-1} \omega) = 2\omega^2 - 1$$

etc.

(a)   Derive a recursion formula among C_{n-1}, C_n, and C_{n+1}. Hence, provide the listing of C_n for $n \leq 10$.

(b)   In the design of low-pass filters, the following approximation is used:

$$|H(\omega)|^2 = \frac{1}{1 + \epsilon^2 C_n^2(\omega)}$$

where $H(\omega)$ is the transfer function of the desired filter and $\epsilon < 1$ is a "ripple factor." Plot $|H(\omega)|$ versus ω for $\epsilon^2 = 0.1$ and for $n = 1,2,3$. Compare with the Butterworth filters in Problem 2.5.

4-11   Several of the principal features of a parmetric amplifier can be found by investigating current flow in the circuit shown in Figure 4.12. Let $C = C(t) = C_0 + C_1 f(t)$, with $f(t) =$

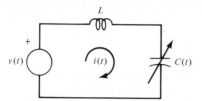

FIGURE 4.12   Problem 4-11: an LC circuit with a time-varying capacitor.

$f(t + T)$ a periodic function, and where $C_1 << C_0$ and $|f(t)| \le 1$. Then, on applying Kirchhoff's voltage law to the circuit, show that the current $i(t)$ satisfies, approximately,

$$\frac{d^2 i}{dt^2} + (\omega_0^2 - \omega_1^2 f(t))i = \frac{1}{L}\frac{dv}{dt}$$

where $\omega_0^2 = (LC_0)^{-1}$ and $\omega_1^2 = C_1/LC_0^2 << \omega_0^2$. Since $i(t)$ is a solution to a second-order differential equation with a periodic coefficient, it is clear that the Floquet theorem will hold.

Investigate the behavior of $i(t)$ when

$$f(t) = \sum_n a_n \cos \omega_n t$$

The resulting equation is known as Hill's equation.[2] In particular, show that there are regions of stability and instability of the solutions. When operated near the transition between a stable and an unstable mode, amplification of signals results.

4-12   The network shown in Figure 4.13 is a filter.

(a) Calculate its voltage-transfer function

$$G(\omega) = \frac{V_0(\omega)}{V_{in}(\omega)}$$

where, for convenience, you should use $\omega_0^2 = 1/LC$.

(b) Plot $|G(\omega)|$ versus ω and characterize this filter as low pass, high pass, etc.

(c) What are the natural frequencies of this network?

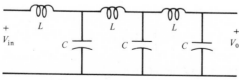

FIGURE 4.13   Problem 4-12: an LC filter circuit.

4-13   In the text Fourier transforms of purely sinusoidal FM signals are considered. We now consider an extension of this case. Let a signal be given by

$$y(t) = \cos\left[\omega_c t + \gamma(t)\right] \qquad (t \geq 0)$$

where

$$\gamma(t) = \lambda \int_0^t f_i(\tau)\, d\tau$$

with $f_i(t)$ the input signal. Then the Fourier transform of $y(t)$, denoted by $Y(\omega)$, is

$$Y(\omega) = \int_0^\infty \cos\left[\omega_c t + \gamma(t)\right] e^{-j\omega t}\, dt$$

(a) By using the identity $\cos\,(a + b) = \cos a \cos b - \sin a \sin b$, and then writing the cosine and sine terms as exponentials, show that $Y(\omega)$ can be reduced to a sum of integrals, each one of the general form

$$I = \int_0^\infty e^{-j(\omega \,\pm\, \omega_c)t} e^{\pm j\gamma(t)}\, dt$$

(b) A specific form of $\gamma(t)$ may permit evaluation of an integral such as I. Let $\gamma(t) = \epsilon(1 - e^{-at})$, with $a > 0$, $t > 0$, and ϵ a positive dimensionless constant. By setting $e^{-at} = u$, find a representation for I valid in the interval $0 \leq u \leq 1$. What difficulties would be encountered in evaluating this integral numerically?

4-14   Verify Parseval's theorem for the following signals $f(t)$:

(a) $f(t) = \dfrac{t}{T} \qquad (0 \leq t \leq T)$

$\quad = 0 \qquad$ otherwise

(b) $f(t) = e^{-at} \qquad (t > 0;\ a > 0)$

(c) $f(t) = e^{-at} \sin \omega_0 t \qquad (t > 0;\ a > 0)$

That is, find the Fourier transforms of each of the $f(t)$ and then show that

$$\int_{-\infty}^\infty |f(t)|^2\, dt = \frac{1}{2\pi} \int_{-\infty}^\infty |F(\omega)|^2\, d\omega$$

4-15   Find the total energy contents of the signal

$$f(t) = 2\,\frac{\sin t}{t}$$

using Parseval's theorem

4-16   Using Parseval's theorem, express

$$\int_{-\infty}^\infty t^2 |f(t)|^2\, dt$$

in terms of the Fourier transform $F(\omega)$ of $f(t)$.

Hint   Write $F(\omega)$ in its polar form $F(\omega) = A(\omega)e^{j\theta(\omega)}$

4-17   A set of functions $\{\phi_i(t)\}$ is *orthonormal* over the range $[a,b]$ if

$$\int_a^b \phi_i(t)\phi_j(t)\, dt = \begin{cases} 1 & i = j \\ 0 & i \neq j \end{cases}$$

The sine and cosine are examples of such functions. An arbitrary function $f(t)$ may be expanded in a "generalized Fourier series" as follows:

$$f(t) = \sum_i c_i \phi_i(t)$$

with

$$c_i = \int_a^b f(t)\phi_i(t)\, dt$$

Show that

$$\int_a^b |f(t)|^2\, dt = \sum_i |c_i|^2$$

This result is an extension of Parseval's theorem.

4-18   Equation 4.214b gives the transfer function of a second-order phase-locked loop system. Invert the expression to find the impulse response of the system. From this expression, find the output phase error. Draw a block diagram of the feedback loop circuit.

SELECTED BIBLIOGRAPHY

1.   A. Baños, *Dipole Radiation in the Presence of a Conducting Half Plane*. New York: Pergamon Press, Inc., 1966.

2.   L. Brillouin, *Wave Propagation in Periodic Structures*. New York: Dover Publications, Inc., 1953.

3.   J. D. Gaskill, *Linear Systems, Fourier Transforms and Optics*. New York: John Wiley & Sons, Inc., 1978.

4.   S. Haykin, *Communication Systems*. New York: John Wiley & Sons, Inc., 1978.

5.   W. Kaplan, *Operational Methods for Linear Systems*. Reading, Mass.: Addison-Wesley Publishing Co., Inc., 1962.

6.   S. Karni, *Network Theory-Analysis and Synthesis*. Boston: Allyn & Bacon, Inc., 1966.

7.   C. D. McGillem and G. R. Cooper, *Continuous and Discrete Signal and System Analysis*. New York: Holt, Rinehart & Winston, Inc., 1974.

8.   A. Papoulis, *The Fourier Integral and Its Applications*. New York: McGraw-Hill Book Company, Inc., 1965.

9.   A. Sommerfeld, *Partial Differential Equations of Mathematical Physics*. New York: Academic Press, Inc., 1949.

10.   C. T. Tai, *Dyadic Green's Functions in Electromagnetic Theory*. Scranton, Pa.: Intext Educational Publishers, 1971.

CHAPTER 5

Discrete
Transforms

5.1 INTRODUCTION: DISCRETE SIGNALS, DIFFERENCE EQUATIONS

Our discussions thus far have been related to functions of the continuous time variable t. Other situations exist where a signal is given, or is represented, as a sequence of values for the discrete time variable. A digital computer processes discrete signals. By sampling a continuous function $f(t)$ at every T seconds, as shown in Figure 5.1, we obtain the discrete function $f_d(t)$.

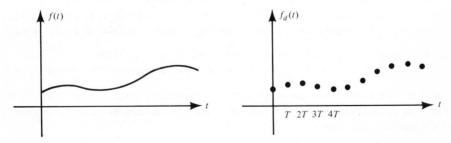

FIGURE 5.1 Continuous function $f(t)$ and (b) discrete function $f_d(t)$ obtained by sampling $f(t)$.

A convenient representation for $f_d(t)$ can be written in terms of the unit impulse function

$$\delta(t - nT) = \begin{cases} 1 & \text{for } t = nT \\ 0 & \text{for } t \neq nT \end{cases} \tag{5.1}$$

in the following way:

$$f_d(t) = \sum_{n=0}^{\infty} f(nT)\delta(t - nT) \tag{5.2}$$

i.e., as a sum of impulse functions, each of strength $f(nT)$.

A moment of reflection will convince us that this representation is correct and that, in fact, even the continuous function $f(t)$ can be thought of as a sum (an integral) of impulse functions, as given in a previous chapter, namely,

$$f(t) = \int_0^\infty f(\tau)\delta(t - \tau)d\tau \tag{5.3}$$

In Equations 5.2 and 5.3 we have taken the lower limit to be zero for functions $f(t) = 0$ for $t < 0$.

In our subsequent discussion we use the notation $f(n)$ or, equivalently, $f(nT)$ to designate functions of the discrete time variable. A powerful transform technique, known as the Z-transform, is discussed in connection with such functions.

Another important class of these functions is the one where $f(n)$ has only a finite number of nonzero values and is, therefore, of finite duration. For such functions, a special transform has been developed—the discrete Fourier transform (DFT).

These two transforms are considered in the present chapter.

Ordinary differential equations describe dynamic systems where input and output are functions of the continuous variable t. A general form for such an equation, relating the output $y(t)$ to the input $x(t)$, is (see also Chapter 3, Section 3.7)

$$a_n \frac{d^n y}{dt^n} + a_{n-1} \frac{d^{n-1}y}{dt^{n-1}} + \cdots + a_1 \frac{dy}{dt} + a_0 y =$$
$$= b_m \frac{d^m x}{dt^m} + b_{m-1} \frac{d^{m-1}x}{dt^{m-1}} + \cdots + b_1 \frac{dx}{dt} + b_0 \tag{5.4}$$

where, for a time-invariant system, the a's and b's are constants.

In a discrete-time system the description of input–output relations is through a *difference* equation. Let x be the discrete input defined only at $t = 0, T, 2T, \ldots, kT$, being, therefore, a function of the interger k, $x = x(k)$. Similarly, the discrete output is $y = y(k)$. The general form of the difference equation relating $x(k)$ and $y(k)$ is

$$a_n y(k + n) + a_{n-1}y(k + n - 1) + \cdots + a_1 y(k + 1) + a_0 y(k) =$$
$$= b_m x(k + m) + b_{m-1}x(k + m - 1) + \cdots + b_1 x(k + 1) + b_0 x(k) \tag{5.5}$$

where the a's and b's are constants for a time-invariant system. The *order* of the difference equation is n, the difference between the largest and the smallest arguments of the unknown function y.

Example 5.1   In the network shown in Figure 5.2 the input–output relation for the continuous $v_1(t)$ and $v_2(t)$ is the differential equation (verify it!)

$$\frac{L}{R}\frac{dv_2}{dt} + v_2 = v_1$$

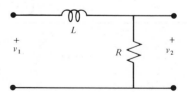

FIGURE 5.2   Example 5.1.

The equivalent difference equation for discrete $v_1(k)$ and $v_2(k)$ can be obtained by writing

$$\frac{L}{R}\left[\frac{v_2(k+1) - v_2(k)}{\Delta t}\right] + v_2(k) = v_1(k)$$

that is,

$$v_2(k+1) + \left(\frac{R\,\Delta t}{L} - 1\right) v_2(k) = \frac{R\,\Delta t}{L} v_1(k)$$

a first-order difference equation in $v_2(k)$. ∎

Example 5.2 Certain resistive networks also obey difference equations. Consider the ladder network shown in Figure 5.3. All the resistors, except the last one, are 1 ohm each. The node equation for $v(k+1)$ reads[1]

$$3v(k+1) - v(k) - v(k+2) = 0$$

or

$$v(k+2) - 3v(k+1) + v(k) = 0$$

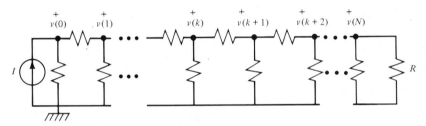

FIGURE 5.3 A ladder network.

a second-order homogeneous difference equation, valid for all k except $k = 0$ and $k = N$, where we have the two "boundary" conditions

$$v(1) = 2v(0) - I$$

and

$$v(N) = \frac{R}{R+1} v(N-1)$$ ∎

Example 5.3 A digital filter can be defined as a system that processes an input $x(k)$ in a prescribed manner and produces an output $y(k)$. For example, the first-order difference equation

$$y(k) = 2y(k-1) + 4x(k)$$

describes an input–output relation of a digital filter. Here a typical output $y(k)$ is obtained by multiplying the immediate previous output $y(k-1)$ by 2 and adding to it $4x(k)$. A block diagram depicting this filter is shown in Figure 5.4, where the input and output nodes are labeled. The branch labeled "4" symbolically multiplies its input, $x(k)$, by four and adds it to the summing node (the small circle). The output $y(k)$ is passed through a unit delay to produce $y(k-1)$. Then $y(k-1)$ is multiplied by two and added to the summing node. Consequently, at the summing node we obtain the difference equation describing this filter. ∎

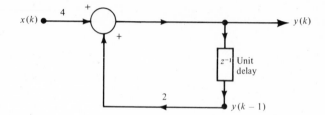

FIGURE 5.4 Example 5.3.

5.2 THE Z-TRANSFORM

The discrete-time function $f_d(t)$ in Equation 5.2 has for its Laplace transform

$$\mathcal{L}\{f_d(t)\} = F_d(s) = \sum_{n=0}^{\infty} f(nT)e^{-nTs} \tag{5.6}$$

With a new complex variable z defined by

$$z = e^{sT} \tag{5.7}$$

we have the definition of the *one-sided Z-transform* of a discrete-time function $f(nT)$:

$$\mathcal{Z}\{f(nT)\} = \sum_{n=0}^{\infty} f(nT)z^{-n} = F(z) \tag{5.8}$$

If the sequence $f(nT)$ includes negative values of n, then the *two-sided Z-transform* is similarly defined as

$$\mathcal{Z}\{f(nT)\} = \sum_{n=-\infty}^{\infty} f(nT)z^{-n} \tag{5.9}$$

Unless specifically stated otherwise, we shall be concerned henceforth with the one-sided transform.

Example 5.4 The discrete-time unit step function is defined as

$$u(n) = \begin{cases} 1 & n \geq 0 \\ 0 & n < 0 \end{cases}$$

Therefore its Z-transform is

$$\mathcal{Z}\{u(n)\} = \sum_{n=0}^{\infty} z^{-n} = 1 + z^{-1} + z^{-2} + \cdots = \frac{z}{z-1} = \frac{1}{1-z^{-1}} \qquad \blacksquare$$

Example 5.5 Find the Z-transform of the function

$$f(n) = \begin{cases} a^n & n \geq 0 \\ 0 & n < 0 \end{cases}$$

$$\mathcal{Z}\{a^n\} = \sum_{n=0}^{\infty} a^n z^{-n} = 1 + az^{-1} + a^2 z^{-2} + \cdots = \frac{z}{z-a} = \frac{1}{1-az^{-1}} \qquad \blacksquare$$

Example 5.6 The discrete-time unit impulse is

$$\delta(n) = \begin{cases} 1 & n = 0 \\ 0 & n \neq 0 \end{cases}$$

Its Z-transform is therefore

$$\mathcal{Z}\{\delta(n)\} = 1$$ ∎

Example 5.7   Find the Z-transform of the exponential function

$$f(n) = \begin{cases} e^{-kn} & n \geq 0 \\ 0 & n < 0 \end{cases}$$

We have

$$\mathcal{Z}\{e^{-kn}\} = \sum_{n=0}^{\infty} e^{-kn}z^{-n} = 1 + e^{-k}z^{-1} + e^{-2k}z^{-2} + \cdots = \frac{1}{1 - e^{-k}z^{-1}}$$ ∎

Example 5.8   Find the Z-transform of the ramp function

$$f(n) = r(n) = \begin{cases} n & n \geq 0 \\ 0 & n < 0 \end{cases}$$

We write

$$\mathcal{Z}\{r(n)\} = \sum_{n=0}^{\infty} nz^{-n} = z^{-1} + 2z^{-2} + 3z^{-3} + \cdots = \frac{z}{(z - 1)^2}$$ ∎

Other Z-transforms can be obtained in a similar way. A short table of these is given in Appendix D.

Since the Z-transform, Equation 5.8, is a power series in the complex variable z, we must concern ourselves with its convergence, just as we did for the integral defining the Laplace transform. Let us apply the *ratio test* for the convergence of the series on the right-hand side of Equation 5.8. This test can be stated as follows: If the limit of two successive terms of a power series satisfies the inequality

$$\lim_{n \to \infty} \left| \frac{a_{n+1}}{a_n} \right| < 1 \tag{5.10}$$

then the series converges absolutely.
In our series, Equation 5.8, we have

$$\lim_{n \to \infty} \left| \frac{f(n+1)z^{-(n+1)}}{f(n)z^{-n}} \right| = \lim_{n \to \infty} \left| \frac{f(n+1)}{f(n)} \right| |z^{-1}| \tag{5.11}$$

and therefore the series converges in the region

$$|z| > R = \lim_{n \to \infty} \left| \frac{f(n+1)}{f(n)} \right| \tag{5.12}$$

Example 5.9   For $u(n)$ we have

$$R = \lim_{n \to \infty} \left| \frac{1}{1} \right| = 1$$

and therefore $F(z) = z/(z - 1)$ converges for $|z| > 1$.   ∎

Example 5.10   For a^n we find

$$R = \lim_{n \to \infty} \left| \frac{a^{n+1}}{a^n} \right| = |a|$$

and therefore $F(z) = z/(z - a)$ converges for $|z| > |a|$.   ∎

Example 5.11   For the ramp function $r(n)$

$$R = \lim_{n \to \infty} \left| \frac{n + 1}{n} \right| = 1$$

and therefore $F(z) = z/(z - 1)^2$ converges for $|z| > 1$.   ∎

Example 5.12   Consider the causal sinusoidal function

$$f(n) = \sin n\omega_0 \cdot u(n)$$

Its Z-transform is

$$F(z) = \mathscr{Z}\{\sin n\omega_0 \, u(n)\} = \sum_{n=0}^{\infty} \frac{e^{jn\omega_0} - e^{-jn\omega_0}}{2j} \cdot z^{-n} =$$

$$= \frac{1}{2j} \left\{ \frac{z}{z - e^{j\omega_0}} - \frac{z}{z - e^{-j\omega_0}} \right\} = \frac{z \sin \omega_0}{z^2 - 2z \cos \omega_0 + 1}$$

where the result of Example 5.5 has been used with $a = e^{-j\omega_0}$. Here

$$\lim_{n \to \infty} \left| \frac{e^{\pm j(n+1)\omega_0}}{e^{\pm jn\omega_0}} \right| = 1$$

and so $F(z)$ converges for $|z| > 1$.   ∎

5.3   PROPERTIES OF THE Z-TRANSFORM

In a parallel manner to the Laplace transform, we outline several of the properties of the Z-transform.

Linearity

With a_1 and a_2 constant, we have

$$\mathscr{Z}\{a_1 f_1(n) + a_2 f_2(n)\} = a_1 F_1(z) + a_2 F_2(z) \tag{5.13}$$

The proof is obtained directly from the defining expression for the Z-transform of $a_1 f_1(n) + a_2 f_2(n)$.

Shifting

If $F(z)$ is the Z-transform of $f(n)$, then

$$\mathcal{Z}\{f(n-1)\} = z^{-1}F(z) \tag{5.14}$$

To prove this property, we write

$$\mathcal{Z}\{f(n-1)\} = \sum_{n=-\infty}^{\infty} f(n-1)z^{-n} = z^{-1}\sum_{n=-\infty}^{\infty} f(n-1)z^{-(n-1)} =$$

$$= z^{-1}\sum_{k=-\infty}^{\infty} f(k)z^{-k} = z^{-1}F(z) \tag{5.15}$$

The interpretation of $f(n-1)$ is the sequence $f(n)$ shifted to the right, i.e., *delayed*, by one sampling interval. We call the multiplier z^{-1} the *unit delay* (see Example 5.3)*
More generally, for a delay of m sampling intervals ($m = 1, 2, 3, \ldots$) we have

$$\mathcal{Z}\{f(n-m)\} = z^{-m}F(z) \tag{5.16}$$

The shifting to the *left* is derived as follows:

$$\mathcal{Z}\{f(n+1)\} = \sum_{n=0}^{\infty} f(n+1)z^{-n} = z\sum_{n=0}^{\infty} f(n+1)z^{-(n+1)} =$$

$$= z\sum_{k=1}^{\infty} f(k)z^{-k} \tag{5.17}$$

with a new summation variable $k = n + 1$. If we add and subtract $f(0)$ on the right-hand side of Equation (5.17) we get a summation from $k = 0$

$$\mathcal{Z}\{f(n+1)\} = z\sum_{k=0}^{\infty} f(k)z^{-k} - f(0) = zF(z) - f(0) \tag{5.18}$$

Generalizing this approach, we get for $m = 1, 2, 3, \ldots$

$$\mathcal{Z}\{f(n+m)\} = z^m\left[F(z) - \sum_{k=0}^{m-1} f(k)z^{-k}\right] \tag{5.19}$$

The similarities between Equations 5.18, 5.19 and their counterparts in the Laplace transform are obvious.

Example 5.13 Consider the difference equation in Example 5.2, i.e.,

$$v(k+2) - 3v(k+1) + v(k) = 0$$

Transforming this equation, we get

$$z^2V(z) - z^2v(0) - zv(1) - 3[zV(z) - zv(0)] + V(z) = 0$$

$$\therefore V(z) = \frac{z[zv(0) - 3v(0) + v(1)]}{z^2 - 3z + 1}$$

*By comparison, s^{-1} can be considered as an *integrator* in the Laplace transform.

The completion of this example is given as Problem 5-7.   ∎

Multiplication by n

If $\mathcal{Z}\{f(n)\} = F(z)$, then

$$\mathcal{Z}\{nf(n)\} = -z \frac{d}{dz} F(z) \tag{5.20}$$

The proof is left as a problem (see Problem 5-9).

Scaling the Variable z

If $\mathcal{Z}\{f(n)\} = F(z)$, then

$$\mathcal{Z}\{a^{-n}f(n)\} = \sum_{n=0}^{\infty} a^{-n}f(n)z^{-n} =$$

$$= \sum_{n=0}^{\infty} f(n)(az)^{-n} = F(az) \tag{5.21}$$

The Initial Value f(0)

We write, by definition,

$$F(z) = f(0) + f(1)z^{-1} + f(2)z^{-2} + \cdots \tag{5.22}$$

and take the limit as $z \to \infty$. Thus,

$$f(0) = \lim_{z \to \infty} F(z) \tag{5.23}$$

provided this limit exists.

Successive values of $f(n)$ can be obtained in a similar way. Specifically,

$$f(1) = \lim_{z \to \infty} z[F(z) - f(0)] \tag{5.24}$$

$$f(2) = \lim_{z \to \infty} z^2[F(z) - f(0) - f(1)z^{-1}] \tag{5.25}$$

This method provides a convenient way to find the inverse Z-transform, as shown in the following example.

Example 5.14   Given $F(z) = z/(z + 1)$, find $f(n)$. From Equations 5.22 through 5.25 we have

$$f(0) = \lim_{z \to \infty} \frac{z}{z + 1} = 1$$

$$f(1) = \lim_{z \to \infty} z\left(\frac{z}{z + 1} - 1\right) = -1$$

$$f(2) = \lim_{z \to \infty} z^2\left(\frac{z}{z + 1} - 1 + \frac{1}{z}\right) = 1$$

Continuing in this fashion, we obtain

$$f(n) = (-1)^n$$

■

The Final Value $f(\infty)$

First write

$$\mathcal{Z}\{f(n + 1) - f(n)\} = \lim_{n \to \infty} \sum_{p=0}^{n} [f(p + 1) - f(p)]z^{-p} \qquad (5.26)$$

Then apply Equation 5.18 to the left-hand side:

$$zF(z) - zf(0) - F(z) = \lim_{n \to \infty} \sum_{p=0}^{n} [f(p + 1) - f(p)]z^{-p} \qquad (5.27)$$

New let $z \to 1$ in Equation 5.27. Since n and z are independent, letting $z \to 1$ can be done under the summation sign:

$$\lim_{z \to 1} (z - 1)F(z) - f(0) = \lim_{n \to \infty} \sum_{p=0}^{n} [f(p + 1) - f(p)] =$$

$$= \lim_{n \to \infty} \{[f(1) - f(0)] + [f(2) - f(1)] + \cdots + [f(n + 1) - f(n)]\}$$

$$= \lim_{n \to \infty} [-f(0) + f(n + 1)] = -f(0) + f(\infty) \qquad (5.28)$$

Therefore,

$$f(\infty) = \lim_{z \to 1} (z - 1)F(z) \qquad (5.29)$$

if this limit exists.

Example 5.15 For $F(z) = z/(z - 1)$ we have

$$f(\infty) = \lim_{z \to 1} (z - 1) \frac{z}{z - 1} = 1$$

which is correct, since $f(n) = u(n)$ and $u(\infty) = 1$.

■

Example 5.16 Consider the function in Example 5.14. There $F(z) = z/(z + 1)$, and hence

$$\lim_{z \to 1} (z - 1)F(z) = 0$$

But we know that $f(n) = (-1)^n$, and therefore $f(\infty)$ does not exist.

It must be emphasized that, in the statement and the proof of the final value theorem, the assumption is made that $f(\infty)$ exists and is a finite constant. It can be shown that this limit exists provided that $F(z)[(z - 1)/z]$ is analytic on and outside the unit circle $|z| = 1$ in the z-plane.

Note the similarity with the final value theorem of the Laplace transform, where

$$\lim_{t \to \infty} f(t) = \lim_{s \to 0} sF(s)$$

provided $sF(s)$ is analytic on the $j\omega$-axis and in the right half of the s-plane.

■

Convolution

Let $F_1(z)$ and $F_2(z)$ be, respectively, the transforms of $f_1(n)$ and $f_2(n)$. Then $F_3(z) = F_1(z)F_2(z)$ is the transform of the convolution of $f_1(n)$ and $f_2(n)$ given by

$$f_3(n) = \sum_{k=0}^{n} f_1(k)f_2(n - k) \tag{5.30}$$

To prove it, we write

$$F_1(z)F_2(z) = \sum_{k=0}^{\infty} f_1(k)z^{-k}F_2(z) \tag{5.31}$$

and use the shifting property, Equation 5.16, for $z^{-k}F_2(z)$. Therefore,

$$F_1(z)F_2(z) = \sum_{k=0}^{\infty} f_1(k) \, \mathscr{L}\left[f_2(n - k) \right] =$$

$$= \sum_{k=0}^{\infty} f_1(k) \sum_{n=0}^{\infty} f_2(n - k)z^{-n} = \sum_{n=0}^{\infty} \left\{ \sum_{k=0}^{n} f_1(k)f_2(n - k) \right\} z^{-n} =$$

$$= \mathscr{L}\{f_3(n)\} \tag{5.32}$$

5.4   THE INVERSE Z-TRANSFORM

Formally, we write

$$\mathscr{L}^{-1}\{F(z)\} = f(n) \tag{5.33}$$

to designate the inversion of $F(z)$ in order to obtain the discrete function $f(n)$. As in the case of the inverse Laplace transform, there are several methods here.

One method is based on the successive applications of the initial value theorem, as shown in Equations 5.23–5.25 and in Example 5.14. Here we obtain the numerical sequence $f(0), f(1), f(2), \ldots$, and hence we have $f(n)$.

A related method is the *power series expansion* of $F(z)$. Since $F(z)$ is analytic for $|z| > R$ (see Equation 5.12), we can expand $F(z)$ in a power series in z^{-1}. This is the principal part of the Laurent series of $F(z)$, expanded about the point $z_0 = 0$. The coefficient of z^{-n} in the series is $f(n)$:

$$F(z) = f(0) + f(1)z^{-1} + f(2)z^{-2} + \cdots + f(n)z^{-n} + \cdots \tag{5.34}$$

Example 5.17   Let $F(z) = z/(z - 1)^2$. Then, by longhand division, we obtain the power series in z^{-1}

$$F(z) = \frac{1}{z} + \frac{2}{z^2} + \frac{3}{z^3} + \cdots$$

Hence $f(0) = 0, f(1) = 1, \ f(2) = 2, \ldots$, and $f(n) = n$. ∎

Note that both previous methods yield numerical answers, i.e., the sequence $f(0)$, $f(1), \ldots$, even if a formal identification of the function f is not possible.

We now extend the power series method to the case when $F(z)$ is, in general, a ratio of two polynomials: A power series expansion in z^{-1}, via longhand division or another method, will yield Equation 5.34.

Example 5.18   Consider the function[7]

$$F(z) = \left(\frac{z + a}{z}\right)^{\beta}$$

where β is real and noninteger. Write the function as

$$\left(\frac{z + a}{z}\right)^{\beta} = (1 + az^{-1})^{\beta}$$

and expand $F(z^{-1}) = (1 + az^{-1})^{\beta}$ in a power series

$$F(z^{-1}) = a_0 + a_1 z^{-1} + a_2 z^{-2} + \cdots$$

where, as usual,

$$a_n = \frac{F^{(n)}(z^{-1})}{n!}\bigg]_{z^{-1} = 0}$$

Here $F^{(n)}$ is the nth derivative of F with respect to z^{-1}. We obtain, therefore,

$$(1 + az^{-1})^{\beta} = \sum_{n=0}^{\infty} \frac{1}{n!} \beta(\beta - 1)(\beta - 2)\cdots(\beta - n + 1)a^n z^{-n}$$

Consequently,

$$f(n) = \frac{1}{n!} \beta(\beta - 1)(\beta - 2)\ldots(\beta - n + 1)a^n$$

Using the definition of the gamma function

$$\Gamma(\beta + 1) = \beta(\beta - 1)(\beta - 2)\ldots(\beta - n + 1)\,\Gamma(\beta - n + 1)$$

and

$$\Gamma(n + 1) = n!$$

we have, finally,

$$F(n) = \frac{\Gamma(\beta + 1)a^n}{\Gamma(n + 1)\Gamma(\beta - n + 1)} = \binom{\beta}{n}a^n \qquad \blacksquare$$

The method of *partial fraction expansion* also can be used for inverting $F(z)$. Given $F(z)$, which can be written as

$$F(z) = F_1(z) + F_2(z) + \cdots \tag{5.35}$$

then

$$\mathcal{L}^{-1}\{F(z)\} = \mathcal{L}^{-1}\{F_1(z)\} + \mathcal{L}^{-1}\{F_2(z)\} + \cdots \tag{5.36}$$

where the simpler functions $F_1(z)$, $F_2(z) \ldots$ may be found in tables.

Example 5.19   Given

$$F(z) = \frac{3z^2}{z^2 + z - 2}$$

write

$$F(z) = \frac{3z^2}{(z - 1)(z + 2)} = z \frac{3z}{(z - 1)(z + 2)}$$

Note that we have "saved" one z as a multiplier, in order to find the suitable entries in the table. Therefore, expand

$$\frac{3z}{(z - 1)(z + 2)} = \frac{A}{z - 1} + \frac{B}{z + 2} = \frac{1}{z - 1} + \frac{2}{z + 2}$$

and, consequently,

$$F(z) = \frac{z}{z - 1} + \frac{2z}{z + 2}$$

From the table of Z-transforms (Appendix D) we read

$$f(n) = u(n) + 2[-2]^n$$ ■

The previous method is a special case of the more general method of *complex contour integration*. As in the case of the inverse Laplace transform, we rely on Cauchy's residue theorem.

Consider the power series of $F(z)$

$$F(z) = \sum_{n=0}^{\infty} f(n)z^{-n} \tag{5.37}$$

This function is analytic for $|z| > R$. Let us multiply Equation 5.37 by z^{n-1}, and then integrate around a circle C of radius $R_1 > R$, as shown in Figure 5.5. Since this contour

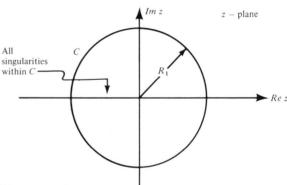

FIGURE 5.5   Contour of integration.

encloses all the singularities of the integrand, Cauchy's theorem yields

$$\oint_C F(z)z^{n-1}dz = 2\pi j\, f(n) \tag{5.35}$$

because $f(n)$ is the residue of the integrand, being the coefficient of z^{-1} in $F(z)z^{n-1}$. Therefore we have

$$f(n) = \frac{1}{2\pi j} \oint_C F(z)z^{n-1}dz \qquad (5.36)$$

as the inversion integral for the Z-transform.

Example 5.20 Let us repeat Example 5.19, using the inversion integral. The singularities of $F(z)$ are simple poles, located at $z = 1$ and $z = -2$. Circle C therefore will be of radius $R_1 > 2$.

$$f(n) = \frac{1}{2\pi j} \oint_C F(z)z^{n-1}dz = \sum [\text{residues of } F(z)z^{n-1} \text{ enclosed}]$$

Here the residues are

$$\text{Res}[F(z)z^{n-1}]_{z=1} = [F(z)z^{n-1} (z - 1)]_{z=1} = 1^{n+1} = 1(1)^n = u(n)$$
$$\text{Res}[F(z)z^{n-1}]_{z=-2} = [F(z)z^{n-1} (z + 2)]_{z=-2} = (-z)(z^n)]_{z=-2} = 2(-2)^n$$

Therefore, $f(n) = u(n) + 2(-2)^n$. ∎

Example 5.21 Consider

$$F(z) = \frac{3z}{(z - 1)^2(z + 2)}$$

Here $F(z)z^{n-1}$ has a second-order pole at $z = 1$ and a simple pole at $z = -2$. Recall (Chapter 2) that for a pole of order r, the residue is given by

$$\text{Res}[F(z)z^{n-1}]_{z=z_0} = \frac{1}{(r - 1)!} \frac{d^{r-1}}{dz^{r-1}} [F(z)(z - z_0)^r z^{n-1}]_{z=z_0}$$

Consequently, we have here

$$\text{Res}[F(z)z^{n-1}]_{z=1} = \frac{d}{dz} \left[\frac{3z^n}{z + 2} \right]_{z=1} = \frac{1}{3} (3n - 1) = n - \frac{1}{3} u(n)$$

and

$$\text{Res}[F(z)z^{n-1}]_{z=-2} = \left[\frac{3z}{(z - 1)^2} z^{n-1} \right]_{z=-2} = \frac{1}{3} (-2)^n$$

Finally,

$$f(n) = n - \frac{1}{3} u(n) + \frac{1}{3} (-2)^n$$ ∎

Example 5.22 Let us rework Example 5.18 using contour integration.[7]

Given

$$F(z) = \left(\frac{z + a}{z} \right)^\beta$$

let us first substitute $z = aw$, $(w = u + jv)$ to normalize the constant a to unity. Then

$$f(n) = \mathcal{Z}^{-1}\{F(z)\} = \frac{a^n}{2\pi j}\oint_C \left(\frac{w+1}{w}\right)^{\beta} w^{n-1}\, dw$$

The function $F(w)$ has a branch point at $w = 0$ and at $w = -1$, and a branch cut from $w = 0$ to $w = -1$. Therefore the contour will be as shown in Figure 5.6. It is easy to show (see Chapter

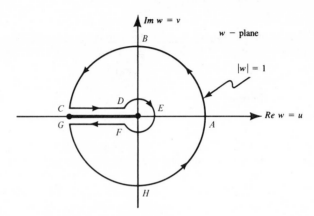

FIGURE 5.6   Contour of integration for Example 5.22.

2) that the integrals along ABC and GHA vanish. Also, the integral along DEF, where $w = \rho e^{j\phi}$, vanishes as $\rho \to 0$. Therefore, $f(n)$ can be obtained by integrating along GF and DC. On GF, $w = ue^{-j\pi}$, and on DC, $w = ue^{j\pi}$, and so

$$f(n) = \frac{a^n}{2\pi j}\left\{\int_1^0 \left[\frac{ue^{-j\pi}+1}{ue^{-j\pi}}\right]^{\beta} u^{n-1} e^{-jn\pi}\, du + \int_0^1 \left[\frac{ue^{j\pi}+1}{ue^{j\pi}}\right]^{\beta} u^{n-1} e^{jn\pi}\, du\right\}$$

If we change the limits of integration in the first integral properly, we get

$$f(n) = \frac{a^n}{2\pi j}\left\{\int_0^1 u^{n-1-\beta}(1-u)^{\beta} e^{j\pi(n-\beta)}\, du + \int_0^1 u^{n-1-\beta}(1-u)^{\beta} e^{-j\pi(n-\beta)}\, du\right\} =$$

$$= a^n \frac{\sin(n-\beta)\pi}{\pi}\int_0^1 u^{n-1-\beta}(1-u)^{\beta}\, du$$

The following identities hold for the gamma function:

$$\frac{\Gamma(m)\Gamma(k)}{\Gamma(m+k)} = \int_0^1 u^{m-1}(1-u)^{k-1}\, du$$

$$\Gamma(m)\Gamma(1-m) = \frac{\pi}{\sin m\pi}$$

Therefore we get, finally,

$$f(n) = a^n \frac{\Gamma(\beta+1)}{\Gamma(n+1)\Gamma(\beta-n+1)} = \binom{\beta}{n} a^n$$

as before. Note that this result also holds true for β an integer, in which case there is no branch point and no branch cut, but a pole at $w = 0$. ∎

5.5 ADDITIONAL APPLICATIONS OF THE Z-TRANSFORM

Let a constant continuous linear system be described by the state matrix differential equation

$$\dot{\mathbf{x}}(t) = \mathbf{A}\mathbf{x}(t) + \mathbf{B}\mathbf{u}(t) \tag{5.40}$$

and the output equation

$$\mathbf{y}(t) = \mathbf{C}\mathbf{x}(t) + \mathbf{D}\mathbf{u}(t) \tag{5.41}$$

These were discussed in Chapters 1 and 3 (see Section 3.13 and Problems 3-19 and 3-20). The results obtained there via the Laplace transform can be similarly applied to discrete systems.

In particular, let a continuous system be connected with discrete systems, as shown in Figure 5.7. Here the continuous output $\mathbf{y}(t)$ is sampled every Δ seconds by

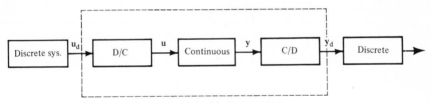

FIGURE 5.7 A continuous system connected with discrete systems.

a *sampler,* which is a continuous-to-discrete (C/D) converter. See also Figure 5.1. The sequence $\mathbf{y}(0)$, $\mathbf{y}(\Delta)$, $\mathbf{y}(2\Delta)$, . . . , is fed into a discrete system (a computer, for example). From the left side, the output of a discrete system is converted into a continuous signal by a discrete-to-continuous (D/C) converter. One simple D/C converter is called a *zero-order hold,* a device that maintains as constant the previous value of its input until the next one is available. See Figure 5.8, where a constant sampling time Δ is assumed.

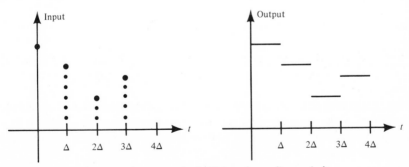

FIGURE 5.8 Input and output of a zero-order hold (equal sampling period).

To analyze this system, it is convenient to represent the continuous system together with the D/C and C/D converters by an *equivalent* discrete system.[8] The resulting system equations are*

$$x(k + 1) = A_d x(k) + B_d u(k) \tag{5.42}$$

$$y(k) = C_d x(k) + D_d u(k) \tag{5.43}$$

where, as mentioned, the continuous system is time invariant. The equivalent discrete system is also time invariant and its matrices A_d, B_d, C_d, and D_d are given by

$$A_d = e^{A\Delta}, \qquad B_d = \left(\int_0^\Delta e^{A\tau} d\tau \right) B$$

$$C_d = Ce^{A\Delta'}, \qquad D_d = C\left(\int_0^{\Delta'} e^{A\tau} d\tau \right) B + D \tag{5.44}$$

The complete analogy of Equations 5.42 and 5.43 to their continuous counterparts is obvious. Equation 5.42 is a linear, constant-coefficient, first-order matrix difference equation. It is the state equation for the system, whereas Equation 5.43 is the (algebraic) output equation for the system.

The solution of Equation 5.42 can be written *by inspection*—unlike the continuous case, Equation 5.40. We start with the given initial state

$$x(0) = x_0 \tag{5.45}$$

and therefore Equation 5.42 yields successively

$$x(1) = A_d x_0 + B_d u(0) \tag{5.46a}$$

$$x(2) = A_d x(1) + B_d u(1) = A_d^2 x_0 + A_d B_d u(0) + B_d u(1) \tag{5.46b}$$

$$x(3) = A_d^3 x_0 + A_d^2 B_d u(0) + A_d B_d u(1) + B_d u(2) \tag{5.46c}$$

or, in general,

$$x(k) = A_d^k x_0 + \sum_{p=0}^{k-1} A_d^{k-p-1} B_d u(p) \tag{5.47}$$

The output solution, Equation 5.43, then becomes

$$y(k) = C_d A_d^k x_0 + \sum_{p=0}^{k-1} C_d A_d^{k-p-1} B_d u(p) + D_d u(k) \tag{5.48}$$

As in the continuous case, the state $x(k)$ and the output $y(k)$ consist of the sum of the zero-input term (those containing no u) and the zero-state term, the response when $x_0 = 0$.

The application of the Z-transform to the matrix state equation and output equation follows very closely the earlier derivations for continuous systems with the Laplace transform. For this reason we merely outline the steps and urge the student to supply the necessary details.

Taking the Z-transform of Equation 5.42, and solving for $X(z)$, we obtain

---

*The student should distinguish between the present (and standard) notation of **x** for the state variables and the earlier designation of *x* for the input, as in Section 5.1. Here the input is designated by **u**.

$$X(z) = (z\mathbf{I} - \mathbf{A}_d)^{-1}\mathbf{B}_d U(z) + (z\mathbf{I} - \mathbf{A}_d)^{-1}z\mathbf{x}(0) \tag{5.49}$$

where we use $\mathbf{I}$ for the unit matrix and $U(z) = \mathscr{Z}\{\mathbf{u}\}$. The state transition matrix here is

$$\mathbf{\Phi}(z) = (z\mathbf{I} - \mathbf{A}_d)^{-1} \tag{5.50}$$

The Z-transform of Equation 5.43 yields

$$Y(z) = \mathbf{C}_d X(z) + \mathbf{D}_d U(z) \tag{5.51}$$

The transfer matrix function relating the zero-state output to the input can be obtained by eliminating $X(z)$ between Equations 5.49 and 5.51, with $\mathbf{x}(0) = \mathbf{0}$. The result is

$$Y(z) = \mathbf{H}(z)U(z) \tag{5.52}$$

where

$$\mathbf{H}(z) = \mathbf{C}_d \mathbf{\Phi}(z)\mathbf{B}_d + \mathbf{D}_d \tag{5.53}$$

is the transfer matrix function for the system.

Finally, several aspects of stability, impulse response, and frequency response are considered in the problems at the end of this chapter.

5.6   THE DISCRETE FOURIER TRANSFORM

Recall that the exponential Fourier transform pair was defined as

$$F(\omega) = \int_{-\infty}^{\infty} f(t)e^{-j\omega t}dt \tag{5.54}$$

and

$$f(t) = \frac{1}{2\pi}\int_{-\infty}^{\infty} F(\omega)e^{j\omega t}d\omega \tag{5.55}$$

In this section we find representations of sampled, or discrete, data in the time and frequency domains. Just as the Z-transform can be interpreted as a limiting case of the Laplace transform for sampled data, the limiting case of Fourier transforms for discrete samples is called a discrete Fourier transform (DFT) pair. We now find the DFT pair by considering Equation 5.54.

A fundamental theorem of calculus enables us to approximate $F(\omega)$ as the sum

$$F(\omega) = \sum_{n=-\infty}^{\infty} f(t_n)e^{-j\omega t_n}\Delta t \tag{5.56}$$

where $t_n = n\Delta t$.

We shall, for convenience, restrict our discussion temporarily to signals $f(t_n)$ which are real, and to functions $F_R(\omega)$ which are real. Then

$$F_R(\omega) = \sum_{n=-\infty}^{\infty} f(t_n)\cos \omega t_n\Delta t \tag{5.57}$$

The frequency ω may be discretized by setting $\omega = k\Delta\omega$, where k is any integer. Then, on defining $F_R(k\Delta\omega)$ as $F_R(k)$ and $f(t_n) = f(n\Delta t)$ as $f(n)$, we have

$$F_R(k) = \sum_{n=-\infty}^{\infty} f(n) \cos (kn\Delta\omega\Delta t)\Delta t \qquad (5.58)$$

It is conventional to choose the product of the frequency sampling interval and the time sampling interval so that they satisfy the relation

$$\Delta\omega\Delta t = 2\pi/N \qquad (5.59)$$

where N is an arbitrary integer that determines the total number of samples in $f(n)$. Then

$$F_R(k) = \Delta t \sum_{n=-\infty}^{\infty} f(n) \cos (2\pi kn/N) \qquad (5.60)$$

If k is increased by the integer N, we have

$$F_R(k + N) = F_R(k) \qquad (5.61)$$

Thus far more information than is necessary is contained in Equation 5.60. Our interest is in finding a minimum number of samples of $F_R(k)$ so as to convey accurately the information concerning the discrete frequency spectrum of $F_R(k)$. If $f(n)$ is periodic with period $T = N\Delta t$, then all the information necessary to determine $F_R(k)$ accurately will be gathered in time T. If $f(n)$ is nonperiodic, and if T is of sufficient length, then a sample of length T will yield an accurate estimate of $F_R(k)$. We shall, therefore, truncate the series in Equation 5.60 by writing

$$F_R(k) = \Delta t \sum_{n=0}^{N-1} f(n) \cos (2\pi kn/N) \qquad (5.62)$$

The reason for the choice of $(N - 1)$ rather than N for the upper limit of the sum is as follows: The terms

$$f(0) = f(N) \cos (2\pi k) = f(N) \qquad (5.63)$$

are identical if $f(n)$ is periodic with period N. Thus no additional information concerning $F_R(k)$ accrues for $n = N$.

Reverting to complex notation, we define the discrete Fourier transform of a sequence $f(n)$ as follows:

$$F_d(k) = \sum_{n=0}^{N-1} f(n)e^{-2\pi jkn/N} \qquad (5.64)$$

Then we find $f(n)$ by forming

$$\sum_{k=0}^{N-1} F_d(k)e^{2\pi jkl/N} = \sum_{n=0}^{N-1} \sum_{k=0}^{N-1} f(n)e^{-2\pi jk(n-l)/N} \qquad (5.65)$$

The following identity is easy to establish:

$$\sum_{n=0}^{N-1} a^n = \frac{1 - a^N}{1 - a} \qquad (5.66)$$

Therefore, with $a = e^{-2\pi j(n-l)/N}$, we can write

$$\sum_{k=0}^{N-1} e^{-2\pi jk(l-n)/N} = \frac{1 - e^{-2\pi j(l-n)}}{1 - e^{-2\pi j(l-n)/N}} \qquad (5.67)$$

If $l \neq n$, the denominator of the right-hand side of Equation 5.67 is finite, nonzero, while the numerator vanishes. If $l = n$, the right-hand side is equal to N. Thus,

$$\sum_{k=0}^{N-1} e^{-2\pi jk(l-n)/N} = N\delta_{l,n} \qquad (5.68)$$

where $\delta_{l,n}$ is the Kronecker delta previously introduced. Equation 5.65 then becomes

$$f(l) = \frac{1}{N} \sum_{k=0}^{N-1} F_d(k)e^{2\pi jkl/N} \qquad (5.69)$$

The discrete Fourier transform (DFT) pair is defined as the set of relations

$$F_d(k) = \sum_{n=0}^{N-1} f_d(n)e^{-2\pi jnk/N} \qquad (5.70a)$$

and

$$f_d(n) = \frac{1}{N} \sum_{k=0}^{N-1} F_d(k)e^{2\pi jnk/N} \qquad (5.70b)$$

As has been mentioned, N is an arbitrary integer that is the total number of samples. Both n and k range over the integers $[0, 1, \ldots, N - 1]$ since both are regarded as periodic sequences of length N.

Let us now study in more detail some properties of the functions given in Equations 5.70a and 5.70b. We first note that if $f(n)$ is real, $F_d(k)$ is, in general, complex.

Linearity

The DFT is a linear operation. That is, if we are given two sequences $f(n)$ and $g(n)$, and two constants a and b, then

$$\text{DFT}\{af(n) + bg(n)\} = a\text{DFT}\{f(n)\} + b\text{DFT}\{g(n)\} \qquad (5.71)$$

This property follows directly from the defining equations.

Shifting

In analogy to the shifting theorems for continuous functions, there is a corresponding relation for the DFT. We want to find the DFT of the sequence $f(n - m)$. It is defined according to Equation 5.70a as

$$\text{DFT}\{f(n - m)\} = \sum_{n=0}^{N-1} f(n - m)e^{-2\pi jkn/N} \qquad (5.72)$$

Let $n - m = l$ so that $-m \leq l \leq N - 1 - m$. Then

$$\text{DFT}\{f(n - m)\} = e^{-2\pi jkm/N} \sum_{l=-m}^{N-1-m} f(l)e^{-2\pi jkl/N} \tag{5.73}$$

But $f(l)$ is a periodic sequence such that $f(-m) = f(-m + N)$. Thus the summation over l can be changed so that it runs over the integers $0 \le l \le N - 1$. Then, with n replacing l,

$$\text{DFT}\{f(n - m)\} = e^{-2\pi jkm/N}\text{DFT}\{f(n)\} \tag{5.74}$$

Equation 5.74 is the statement of the shifting theorem for the DFT.

Convolution

Let $F_d(k) = \text{DFT}\{f_d(n)\}$ and $G_d(k) = \text{DFT}\{g_d(n)\}$. Let us find the sequence $h(n)$ given by

$$h(n) = \frac{1}{N} \sum_{k=0}^{N-1} F_d(k)G_d(k)e^{2\pi jkn/N} \tag{5.75}$$

Inserting the expressions for $F_d(k)$ and $G_d(k)$ gives

$$h(n) = \frac{1}{N} \sum_{k=0}^{N-1} \sum_{l=0}^{N-1} \sum_{m=0}^{N-1} f(l)g(m)e^{2\pi jk(l-m-n)/N} \tag{5.76}$$

Assuming the convergence of the summations, we may sum first over the integer k. Denoting the sum by S, we have

$$S = \sum_{k=0}^{N-1} e^{2\pi jk(n-l-m)/N} = \frac{1 - e^{2\pi j(n-l-m)}}{1 - e^{2\pi j(n-l-m)/N}} \tag{5.77}$$

For any $n - l - m \ne 0$, the numerator of Equation 5.77 is zero and the denominator is finite, nonzero. For $n - l - m = 0$, the sum is equal to N. Thus,

$$S = N\delta_{l,n-m} \tag{5.78}$$

Consequently, the expression for $h(n)$ becomes

$$h(n) = \sum_{l=0}^{N-1} \sum_{m=0}^{N-1} f(l)g(m)\delta_{l,n-m} \tag{5.79}$$

or, finally,

$$h(n) = \sum_{m=0}^{N-1} f(n - m)g(m) \tag{5.80}$$

Equation 5.80 is the statement of the convolution theorem for the two discrete sequences $f(n)$ and $g(n)$.

Let us interpret more closely the meaning of the DFT of a sequence $f(n)$. Consider a sample of continuous data, as in Equation 5.2, written as

$$f(t) = \sum_{n=0}^{N-1} f(n\Delta t)\delta(t - n\Delta t) \tag{5.81}$$

The Fourier transform of this signal is

$$F(\omega) = \int_{-\infty}^{\infty} \sum_{n=0}^{N-1} f(n\Delta t)\delta(t - n\Delta t)e^{-j\omega t}dt \qquad (5.82)$$

Assuming that the right-hand side of Equation 5.82 converges, the order of integration and summation can be interchanged, with the result

$$F(\omega) = \sum_{n=0}^{N-1} f(n)e^{-j\omega t_n} \qquad (5.83)$$

where $t_n = n\Delta t$ and $f(n) = f(n\Delta t)$ are again introduced as our notation. When Equation 5.83 is evaluated at discrete frequencies $\omega = \omega_k = k\Delta\omega$, the result is identical with Equation 5.70a. We therefore have the interpretation that the DFT$\{f(n)\}$ is identical with the Fourier transform of the sampled function.

Another way of writing Equation 5.81, which follows from the properties of the delta function, is

$$f(t) = \sum_{n=0}^{N-1} f(t)\delta(t - n\Delta t) \qquad (5.84)$$

We shall find a Fourier series representation for the delta function contained in Equation 5.84 and then determine the Fourier transform of the resulting signal $f(t)$. In this way, an additional interpretation of the DFT$\{f(n)\}$ will be found and the phenomenon of *aliasing* will be introduced. The latter is one of the chief sources of difficulty in using the DFT if care is not taken. We write

$$\delta(t - n\Delta t) = \sum_{l=-\infty}^{\infty} a_l e^{j\omega_l t} \qquad (5.85)$$

where $\omega_l = 2\pi l/T$, with T the period. The coefficients a_l are calculated by forming

$$\int_{-T/2}^{T/2} e^{-j\omega_p t}\delta(t - n\Delta t)dt = \sum_{l=-\infty}^{\infty} a_l \int_{-T/2}^{T/2} e^{j(\omega_l - \omega_p)t}dt \qquad (5.86)$$

with the result

$$a_l = \frac{1}{T} e^{-j\omega_l n\Delta t} \qquad (5.87)$$

Consequently, we can write

$$\delta(t - n\Delta t) = \frac{1}{T} \sum_{l=-\infty}^{\infty} e^{j\omega_l(t - n\Delta t)} \qquad (5.88)$$

Therefore, using Equation 5.84, $f(t)$ can be written as

$$f(t) = \frac{1}{T} \sum_{n=0}^{N-1} f(t) \sum_{l=-\infty}^{\infty} e^{j\omega_l(t - n\Delta t)} \qquad (5.89)$$

The Fourier transform of this function is a DFT, by virtue of Equation 5.83 when evaluated at discrete frequencies. Thus, for $\omega = \omega_k$,

$$F_d(\omega_k) = \frac{1}{T} \int_{-\infty}^{\infty} e^{-j\omega_k t} \left\{ \sum_{n=0}^{N-1} f(t) \sum_{l=-\infty}^{\infty} e^{j\omega_l(t-n\Delta t)} \right\} dt \qquad (5.90)$$

Again, with the interchange of the summations and integration, we have, using the shifting theorem for Fourier transforms,

$$F(\omega_k - \omega_l) = \int_{-\infty}^{\infty} e^{-j(\omega_k-\omega_l)t} f(t) dt \qquad (5.91)$$

Upon substituting this result into Equation 5.90, we find that

$$F_d(\omega_k) = \frac{N}{T} \sum_{l=-\infty}^{\infty} F\left(\omega_k - \frac{2\pi l}{T} \right) \qquad (5.92)$$

or, since $T = N\Delta t$ and $\Delta t = 2\pi/\Delta\omega$,

$$F_d(\omega_k) = \frac{\Delta\omega}{2\pi} \sum_{l=-\infty}^{\infty} F(\omega_k - l\Delta\omega) \qquad (5.93)$$

Therefore the DFT$\{f(n)\}$ can be interpreted as an infinite series of shifted Fourier transforms. It is precisely this fact that leads to one of the major problems in the use of the DFT: If care is not taken in the choice of a sampling rate, these Fourier transforms can overlap, with the result that aliasing will occur.

The Sampling Theorem and Aliasing

It is convenient to begin discussion of the sampling theorem and of aliasing by means of intuitive reasoning, and then discuss them more rigorously. In Figure 5.9 we see a group of sample points through which can pass several continuous functions of time, $f_1(t)$, $f_2(t)$, and $f_3(t)$.

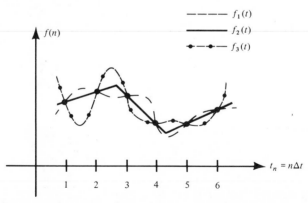

FIGURE 5.9 Discrete sample points and several fitting continuous functions.

The problem is then: Which function is "correct"? The answer is that each of them is correct, given the collection of data $f(n)$ as shown. If the sampling interval were decreased so that samples taken over the time interval shown resulted in $f(n)$ of Figure 5.10, then we would conclude immediately that $f_3(t)$ is the "correct" signal.

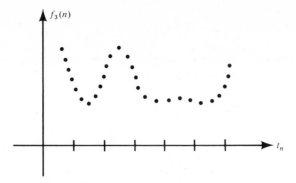

FIGURE 5.10   Discrete sample points for $t_n = n\Delta t$, with $\Delta t \to 0$.

Intuitively, then, we reach the conclusion that we need a criterion on the sampling rate in order to provide an accurate reconstruction of a continuous function $f(t)$ from $f_d(n)$. The *sampling theorem* provides the answer: Given a continuous function $f(t)$, we must sample it at a rate that is greater than twice the highest frequency contained in $f(t)$ in order to be able to reconstruct it exactly.

To prove the sampling theorem, we return to Equation 4.148 of Chapter 4. In connection with a discussion of filters, we established the identity

$$F_d(k) = \frac{1}{\pi} \sum_{n=-L}^{L} F_d(n) \frac{\sin (k - n)\pi}{k - n} \tag{4.148}$$

Note that if $k = n$, the sample $F_d(k)$ is exactly reproduced. Thus, if $-L \le n \le L$, we must have exactly $k = 2L + 1$ values of the frequency for a discertized signal to be reproduced exactly. We state without proof that if $k > 2L + 1$, then the mean square error between an exact $F_d(k)$ and its approximation will be minimized.

In sampling theory, Equation 4.148 is known as Whittaker's cardinal function. Here the fundamental period is taken to be 2π so that $2L\pi$ is the highest frequency contained in $F_d(k)$. If $k < 2L + 1$, the signal $F_d^{(a)}(k)$ is said to be *aliased*. The difference between the aliased and the exact signal is defined as the error signal $E_a(k)$, i.e.,

$$E_a(k) = F_d^{(a)}(k) - F_d(k)$$

Obviously, $E_a(k) \equiv 0$ if $k = n$ and $-L \le k \le L$.

However, this is not the case when $k \ne n$. A few problems on sample size and its effect at the end of this chapter illustrate this discussion.

We now turn to a few examples of the calculation of the DFT. In each, we first find the continuous Fourier transform of a given function, and then find the DFT and compare the two.

Example 5.23   Let $f(t) = u(t) - u(t - T_0)$. Its continuous Fourier transform is given by

$$F(\omega) = \int_0^{T_0} e^{-j\omega t} dt = 2T_0 e^{-jx} \frac{\sin x}{x}$$

with $x = \omega T_0 / 2$. The magnitude of $F(\omega)$ is

$$|F(\omega)| = 2T_0 \left| \frac{\sin x}{x} \right|$$

We now calculate the DFT of this function by choosing our sample of the periodic square wave as

$$f(n) = \begin{cases} 1 & 0 \le n \le (N-1)/2 \\ 0 & (N-1)/2 < n \le N-1 \end{cases}$$

Then

$$F_d(k) = \sum_{n=0}^{(N-1)/2} e^{-2\pi jkn/N} = \frac{1 - e^{-j\pi k}}{1 - e^{-2\pi jk/N}}$$

The relation for $F_d(k)$ can be written as

$$F_d(k) = e^{-jnk(\frac{1}{2}-\frac{1}{N})} \frac{\sin(\pi k/2)}{\sin(\pi k/N)}$$

The complex nature of $F_d(k)$ for the real sequence $f(n)$ is clearly seen in this last expression. Our interest is in comparing the magnitude of $F_d(k)$ with $|\sin x/x|$. We have

$$|F_d(k)| = \left| \frac{\sin(\pi k/2)}{\sin(\pi k/N)} \right|$$

For $k = 0$, $|F_d(k)| = N/2$. If k is even, $|F_d(k)| = 0$. If N is very large,

$$|F_d(k)| \to \frac{N}{2} \left| \frac{\sin x_k}{x_k} \right|$$

where $x_k = \pi k/2$. We therefore expect that a good approximation to the continuous frequency spectrum, apart from a multiplicative constant, will be given by the discrete Fourier transform. In one of the problems at the end of the chapter, the effect of changing the number of sample points on the form of $|F_d(k)|$ is considered.   ∎

Example 5.24   Let $f(t) = \sin \omega_0 t$ with a period $T_0 = 2\pi/\omega_0$. The continuous Fourier transform of this function is

$$F(\omega) = \frac{1}{2j} \int_{-\infty}^{\infty} (e^{-j(\omega-\omega_0)t} - e^{-j(\omega+\omega_0)t})\, dt = j \frac{\pi}{2} \{-\delta(\omega - \omega_0) + \delta(\omega + \omega_0)\}$$

The magnitude of this frequency spectrum consists of two delta functions at the points $\omega = \pm \omega_0$.

A discrete sample of $f(t)$ is given by the sequence

$$f_d(n) = \sin(2\pi n/N)$$

We first show that the DFT $\{f_d(n)\}$ satisfies a difference equation. The exponential representation of the sine function allows us to write

$$F_d(k) = \frac{1}{2j} \sum_{n=0}^{N-1} [e^{-(2\pi jn/N)(k-1)} - e^{-(2\pi jn/N)(k+1)}]$$

which is, by definition, the difference equation

$$F_d(k) = \frac{j}{2}\{F_d(k+1) - F_d(k-1)\}$$

We can find an explicit representation of $F_d(k)$ by performing the summations over n, with the result

$$F_d(k) = \frac{1}{2j}\left\{\frac{1 - e^{-2\pi j(k-1)}}{1 - e^{-2\pi j(k-1)/N}} - \frac{1 - e^{-2\pi j(k+1)}}{1 - e^{-2\pi j(k+1)/N}}\right\}$$

The numerator of the first term within the brackets vanishes unless $k = 1$, while the second term is zero unless $k = -1$. Therefore the absolute value of $F_d(k)$ is

$$|F_d(k)| = \frac{N}{2}\delta_{k\pm1}$$

Since $\omega_k = k\omega_0$, there are spikes of height $N/2$ at $\pm \omega_0$.   ∎

Example 5.25   In this example we illustrate the calculation of the convolution of the two functions $f(t) = \sin \omega_0 t$ and $h(t) = u(t) - u(t - T_0)$, under the assumption that $\omega_0 T_0 = \pi$. Then both functions will have the same period of $2T_0$. The continuous convolution integral is a function $g(t)$,

$$g(t) = \int_{-\infty}^{\infty} f(t - \tau)h(\tau)d\tau$$

which here becomes

$$g(t) = \int_0^{T_0} \sin \omega_0(t - \tau)d\tau = -\frac{2}{\omega_0}\cos \omega_0 t$$

The discrete convolution of the functions $f(n)$ and $h(n)$ is, according to Equation 5.80, a function $g(n)$, given by

$$g(n) = \sum_{m=0}^{L-1} f(n - m)h(m)$$

where L will be determined later by using the sampling theorem. We shall take $f(n)$ and $h(n)$ to be the sampled functions

$$f(n) = \sin(\pi n/N)$$

and

$$h(n) = \begin{cases} 1 & 0 \le n \le (L-1)/2 \\ 0 & \dfrac{L-1}{2} < n < L - 1 \end{cases}$$

Since the continuous frequency corresponding to a period T_0 is twice the frequency ω_0, we must take $L = 2N + 1$, whereupon

$$g(n) = \sum_{m=0}^{N} \sin \frac{\pi}{N}(n - m)$$

We write $g(n)$ as

$$g(n) = \operatorname{Im} \sum_{m=0}^{N} e^{j\pi(n-m)/N}$$

which becomes

$$g(n) = \operatorname{Im} \left\{ e^{j\pi n/N} \frac{1 - e^{-j\pi(N+1)/N}}{1 - e^{-j\pi/N}} \right\}$$

We find that $g(n)$ is given by

$$g(n) = \operatorname{ctn} \frac{\pi}{2N} \sin\left(\frac{n\pi}{N} - \frac{\pi}{2}\right)$$

or, alternatively, by

$$g(n) = -\operatorname{ctn} \frac{\pi}{2N} \cos\left(\frac{n\pi}{N}\right)$$

For N large, we have, therefore,

$$g(n) \rightarrow -\frac{2n}{\pi} \cos\left(\frac{n\pi}{N}\right)$$

which is exactly what we find on direct discretization of the continuous result.   ∎

We conclude this section with final remarks about efficient algorithms for computing DFT pairs. In the expression for $F_d(k)$, let $W = e^{-2\pi j/N}$. Then we can write $F_d(k)$ as

$$F_d(k) = \sum_{n=0}^{N-1} W^{nk} f_d(n) \tag{5.94}$$

Equation 5.94 is, in component notation, a matrix relation that transforms an N-dimensional vector $\mathbf{f}_d(n)$ containing sampled time data to a corresponding N-dimensional vector $\mathbf{F}_d(k)$ in the frequency space. The matrix of the transformation has elements W^{nk}. Thus we can write

$$\mathbf{F}_d(k) = \mathbf{W}\mathbf{f}_d(n) \tag{5.95}$$

By inversion, $\mathbf{f}_d(n)$ is found to be

$$\mathbf{f}_d(n) = \mathbf{W}^{-1}\mathbf{F}_d(k) \tag{5.96}$$

The matrix $\mathbf{W}$ is symmetric, $W^{nk} = W^{kn}$, and $W^{n0} = W^{0k} = 1$ for all n and k. Further, all the elements of $\mathbf{W}$ are of modulus unity. Since $\mathbf{W}$ is an $N \times N$ symmetric matrix, at most only $N(N + 1)2$ of its elements are independent. We can think of the elements W^{kn} for varying n and fixed k as being spaced $2\pi k/N$ radians about a circle of unit radius, so that further symmetry relations can be found. These remarks serve to illustrate the way in which the machine computation time of a DFT pair can be minimized. The efficient numerical fast Fourier transform (FFT) algorithm is based on such considerations. We do not discuss the details of the algorithm for the FFT but close with an example.

Example 5.26   Let $N = 4$ and find general expressions for $F_d(k)$ in terms of $f_d(n)$. With $N = 4$, $W = e^{-\pi j/2} = -j$. Then, in matrix notation, we have

$$
\begin{bmatrix} F_d(0) \\ F_d(1) \\ F_d(2) \\ F_d(3) \end{bmatrix}
=
\begin{bmatrix} 1 & 1 & 1 & 1 \\ 1 & -j & -1 & j \\ 1 & -1 & 1 & -1 \\ 1 & j & -1 & -j \end{bmatrix}
\begin{bmatrix} f_d(0) \\ f_d(1) \\ f_d(2) \\ f_d(3) \end{bmatrix}
$$

from which we find

$$
F_d(0) = \sum_{n=0}^{3} f_d(n)
$$

$$
F_d(1) = F_d{}^*(3) = \sum_{n=0}^{\infty} (-j)^n f_d(n)
$$

and

$$
F_d(2) = \sum_{n=0}^{3} (-1)^n f_d(n)
$$

In this case, with the $f_d(n)$ known, computation time is minimized by finding the matrix coefficients and forming the expressions for the $F_d(k)$ shown. This can be generalized to arbitrary n and k. ∎

PROBLEMS

5-1 The *forward difference operator* Δ is defined as follows:

$$
\Delta f(k) = f(k+1) - f(k)
$$

where $\Delta f(k)$ is known as the first forward difference of $f(k)$. The second difference is then

$$
\Delta^2 f(k) = \Delta[\Delta f(k)] = f(k+2) - 2f(k+1) + f(k)
$$

(a) Obtain the expression for the nth difference of $f(k)$.
(b) Prove that Δ is a linear operator, i.e.,

$$
\Delta[c_1 f_1(k) + c_2 f_2(k)] = c_1 \Delta f_1(k) + c_2 \Delta f_2(k)
$$

for c_1 and c_2 constants.
(c) Relate the difference operator to the *shifting operator* E defined by

$$
E[f(k)] = f(k+1)
$$

and express the nth difference of $f(k)$ in terms of the operator E.
(d) The *backward difference operator* ∇ is similarly defined by

$$
\nabla f(k) = f(k) - f(k-1)
$$

Obtain expressions for $\nabla^2 f(k), \ldots, \nabla^n f(k)$; prove that ∇ is a linear operator. Also, show that $\nabla = 1 - E^{-1}$.
(e) Compare the difference operators Δ and ∇ with the differential operator $D = d/dt$. Recall that

$$\frac{df(t)}{dt}\bigg]_{t=t_0} = Df(t) = \lim_{h \to 0} \frac{f(t_0 + h) - f(t_0)}{h}$$

5-2   A digital filter is called *recursive* if its response $y(n)$ is a function of the past values of the input and of past values of response as well; more specifically,

$$y(n) = \sum_{k=0}^{N} c_k x(n-k) + \sum_{k=1}^{N} d_k y(n-k)$$

describes a linear, time-invariant (c_k, d_k are constant) recursive filter of order N. When all the coefficients d_k are zero, the filter is *nonrecursive*.

(a) The numerical integration known as the trapezoid rule

$$y(n) = y(n-1) + \frac{1}{2}[x(n) + x(n-1)]$$

can be considered a digital filter. Classify it, then draw its block diagram, similar to Figure 5.4.

(b) Repeat part (a) for

$$y(n) = x(n) + \frac{1}{2}x(n-1)$$

5-3   Show that the Laplace transform of $f_a(t)$, Equation 5.6, is a periodic function in s; that is,

$$F_a(s) = F_a\left(s + j\frac{2\pi}{T}\right)$$

and therefore has an infinite number of poles and zeros. Its inversion (say, by partial fractions) is then difficult.

5-4   Show that the Z-transform does not depend on the sampling interval T. Therefore we use the notations $f(nT)$ and $f(n)$ interchangeably.

5-5   Derive the Z-transform and the region of its convergence for:

(a) $f(n) = \cos n\omega_0\, u(n)$
(b) $f(n) = a^{|n|}$, $n = 0, \pm 1, \pm 2, \ldots$
(c) $f(n) = |n|a^{|n|}$, $n = 0, \pm 1, \pm 2, \ldots$

5-6   Establish the region of convergence for $F(z)$ of:

(a) $f(n) = e^{-an}$
(b) $f(n) = n^2$
(c) $f(n) = \cos n\omega_0$
(d) $f(n) = \sinh n\omega_0$
(e) $f(n) = \cosh n\omega_0$.

5-7   Complete the solution of the resistive ladder network, Example 5.13, as follows:

(a) Rearrange the expression of $V(z)$ to contain only $v(0)$, using the first "boundary" condition that relates $v(1)$ to $v(0)$—see Example 5.2.

(b) Compare this expression of $V(z)$ with the Z-transforms of $\sinh \omega_0 n$ and $\cosh \omega_0 n$ to obtain[1]

$$v(n) = v(0)\left[\cosh \omega_0 n + \frac{1/2 - [I/v(0)]}{\sqrt{5}/2}\sinh \omega_0 n\right]$$

where $\cosh \omega_0 = 3/2$ and $\sinh \omega_0 = \sqrt{5}/2$.

(c) To evaluate $v(0)$, use this last equation for $n = N$, the second given "boundary" condition.

5-8 (a) Obtain the transfer function $H(z) = Y(z)/X(z)$ for Example 5.3, defined with all boundary conditions zero. Also find the impulse response, $h(n)$, when $x(n) = \delta(n)$.
(b) Find $H(z)$ for the general difference equation given by Equation 5.5. Compare your result with $H(s)$, the transfer function of the Laplace transform.
(c) In part (b) write[12]

$$Y(z) = W(z) \sum_i b_i z^{-1}$$

and

$$W(z) = X(z) \frac{1}{\sum_i a_i z^{-1}}$$

Here $W(z)$ is defined as an intermediate variable, corresponding to an intermediate sequence $w(nT)$, between input and output. Write the corresponding two difference equations relating $w(nT)$ and $x(nT)$, and $y(nT)$ and $w(nT)$. From these equations draw a block diagram for realizing the digital filter, using delay units, multipliers, and summation nodes (see Example 5.3).

5-9 Prove that

$$\mathcal{L}\{nf(n)\} = -z \frac{dF(z)}{dz}$$

by setting up the defining sum of the Z-transform of $nf(n)$.

5-10 Using the initial value property, Equations 5.22 and 5.23, prove that if $f(0) = 0$ then $f(1) = \lim_{z \to \infty} zF(z)$. Also obtain $f(2), f(3), \ldots$ in this case.

5-11 Prove the following property of the Z-transform:

$$\mathcal{L}\left\{ \sum_{p=0}^{n} f(p) \right\} = \frac{z}{z-1} F(z)$$

This property corresponds to the finite integration (between 0 and t) in the Laplace transform. *Hint* Let the finite sum be designated by $g(n)$; write a difference equation relating $f(n)$ and $g(n)$, and apply the Z-transform to it.

5-12 Using the inversion integral, prove that
(a) $\mathcal{L}^{-1}\{\sinh(a/z)\} = a^n/n!$ for $n = 1,3,5,\ldots$
(b) $\mathcal{L}^{-1}\{\cosh(a/z)\} = a^n/n!$ for $n = 0,2,4\ldots$

5-13 Using the inversion integral, prove that

$$\mathcal{L}^{-1}\left\{ \ln\frac{z}{z-1} \right\} = \frac{1}{n} \quad \text{for } n > 0$$

5-14 Evaluate
(a) $\mathcal{L}^{-1}\left\{ \dfrac{z}{(z-a)(z-b)} \right\}$

(b) $\mathcal{L}^{-1}\left\{ \dfrac{1}{z^2 - a^2} \right\}$

by partial fractions. Repeat by contour integration.

5-15 Convolve the two functions $f_1(n) = a^n u(n)$ and $f_2(n) = u(n)$ to obtain $f_3(n)$. Then use the product $F_1(z)F_2(z)$ to verify your answer. Give regions of convergence.

5-16 (a) Give a tabular listing for the convolution of $f_1(n)$ with $f_2(n)$ in accordance with Equation 5.30, i.e.,

$$f_3(0) = f_1(0)f_2(0)$$
$$f_3(1) = f_1(0)f_2(1) + f_1(1)f_2(0)$$

etc. Show it graphically.
(b) Write a computer program for it.

5-17 As in the case of Laplace transforms, the convolution theorem in the discrete case can be used to calculate the zero-state response of a linear, constant, discrete system to a discrete input. Let $h(n)$ designate the impulse response of such a system. Then, for an input $x(n)$, the output $y(n)$ will be the convolution of h and x, i.e.,

$$y(n) = \sum_{k=0}^{n} h(k)x(n - k)$$

The corresponding transfer function $H(z)$ is defined from

$$Y(z) = H(z)X(z)$$

(a) Find $H(z)$ for the digital filter in Example 5.3. Find its impulse response.
(b) Calculate its response to the discrete unit step input $u(n)$.

5-18 A stability criterion for discrete systems can be established in a similar way to the continuous case. The bounded-input/bounded-output (BIBO) criterion states that a system is stable if every bounded input $x(n)$ produces a bounded ouput $y(n)$. Prove that a necessary and sufficient condition for BIBO stability is

$$\sum_{n=0}^{\infty} |h(n)| < \infty$$

where $h(n)$ is the impulse response.

5-19 A digital (and causal) filter is known as a *finite-impulse-response* (FIR) filter of length N (N = a finite integer) if its impulse response $h(n) = 0$ for $n \geq N$. Prove that a FIR filter is BIBO stable.

5-20 Let a causal discrete system be described by a rational transfer function $H(z)$. Prove that this system is BIBO stable if, and only if, all the poles of $H(z)$ are inside the unit circle, $|z| < 1$.

5-21 The vast knowledge available on continuous filter design can provide several approaches to digital filter design. One such approach is via the *impulse invariance* method.[12] Let the impulse response of a continuous filter be $h(t)$, where $h(t)$ is the inverse Laplace transform of the transfer function $H(s)$. To be specific, let $H(s)$ be given as

$$H(s) = \sum_{i=1}^{m} \frac{K_i}{s + p_i}$$

with only simple poles p_i. Then

$$h(t) = \sum_{i=1}^{m} K_i e^{-p_i t}$$

For the digital filter, its impulse response $h(nT)$ is the inverse Z-transform of $H(z)$. The criterion of impulse invariance requires

$$h(nT) = h(t) \qquad t = 0, T, 2T, \ldots$$

i.e. the impulse response of the digital filter must be equal to the sampled impulse response of a given continuous filter.

(a) Show that

$$H(z) = \sum_{i=1}^{m} \frac{K_i}{1 - e^{-p_i T} z^{-1}}$$

where the K_i and p_i are already known from the continuous filter.

(b) Illustrate the previous result by considering a simple, one-pole, RC low-pass filter with

$$H(s) = \frac{a}{s + a}$$

Obtain the corresponding $H(z)$ and plot the frequency responses, $|H(j\omega)|$ and $|H(e^{j\omega T})|$, respectively, for several choices of a, $a = 1.0, 0.1$, and 0.01, and unity sampling rate, $T = 1$.

5-22 (a) Write the two-sided Z-transform, Equation 5.9, in its polar form, with

$$z = re^{j\theta}$$

and relate it to the Fourier transform of $f(nT)$ when $r = 1$.

(b) Consider the inversion integral for $F(z)$, i.e.,

$$f(nT) = \frac{1}{2\pi j} \oint_C F(z) z^{n-1} dz$$

and let the region of convergence of $F(z)$ include the unit circle $|z| = 1$. Then we can write (see Equation 5.7)

$$z = e^{j\omega T}$$

Show that in this case the inversion integral for $f(nT)$ yields its Fourier series, with a period $\omega = 2\pi/T$.

5-23 An important class of FIR digital filters has a transfer function

$$H(z) = \sum_{k=0}^{N-1} a_k z^{-1}$$

Write the difference equation relating $y(k)$ to $x(k)$. Draw the block diagram implementation using delay units, multipliers, and only one summing node. Are these filters recursive or nonrecursive?

5-24 Prove that the region of convergence for $F(z)$ always includes the unit circle $|z| = 1$ if $f(n)$ is a *finite* sequence.

5-25 Consider an extension of the resistive ladder network in Examples 5.2 and 5.3 and Problem 5-7 as follows: Let the branches be Z_1 and Z_2, under sinusoidal steady-state operation. See Figure 5.11. Let us use loop analysis here with loop currents (phasors) $I(0), \ldots I(k), \ldots$, as shown.

(a) Derive the two first-order difference equations for $I(k)$ and $I(k + 1)$.

(b) With the boundary conditions V_{in} given and $Z(N) = \infty$ (open circuit), solve for the $I(k)$.

(c) Repeat (b) for the boundary conditions V_{in} given and $Z(N) = 0$ (short circuit).

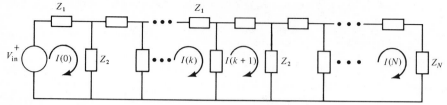

FIGURE 5.11   Problem 5-25.

5-26   Plot

$$|F_d(k)| = \left| \frac{\sin(\pi k/2)}{\sin(\pi k/N)} \right|$$

for $N = 5, 10, 50$. Write a program to accomplish this task, taking care to normalize the peak amplitude to unity. Compare your results with the continuous function $|\sin x/x|$ and discuss the influence of the sampling rate. Find the phase of the expression for $F_d(k)$ in Example 5.23 for the total number of samples as above.

5-27   The convolution of the functions $f(t) = \sin \omega_0 t$ and $h(t) = u(t) - u(t - T_0)$ was found, together with its discrete analog in Example 5.25. Compare the results for a number of sample points $N = 10, 20, 50$, and discuss your findings.

5-28   Repeat the derivation in Example 5.25 using a summation over $0 \leq m \leq (N - 1)/2$. Show that, in this case, a phase shift of $\pi/4$ radians appears in the argument of the sine function. This again illustrates the care that must be taken when using the sampling theorem.

5-29   The relationships between the DFT and the Z-transform can be further explored, as follows: Let $f(nT)$ be discrete, of finite duration, and let $f_p(nT)$ be of period NT:

$$f_p(nT) = \sum_{k=-\infty}^{\infty} f[(n + kN)T]$$

Write the DFT of f_p, and by letting $n = m - kN$ show that it is equal numerically to the sampling of $\mathscr{L}\{f(nT)\}$ on the unit circle $|z| = 1$.

SELECTED BIBLIOGRAPHY

1.   J. A. Aseltine, *Transform Method in Linear System Analysis.* New York: McGraw-Hill Book Company, Inc., 1958.

2.   E. O. Brigham, *The Fast Fourier Transform.* Englewood Cliffs, N.J.: Prentice-Hall, Inc., 1974.

3.   J. W. Cooley, P. A. W. Lewis, and P. D. Welch, "Application of the Fast Fourier Transform to Computation of Fourier Integrals, Fourier Series and Convolution Integrals," *IEEE Transactions in Audio and Electroacoustics,* vol. AU-15, pp. 79–84, June 1967.

4.   G. Doetsch, *Guide to the Applications of Laplace and Z-Transforms.* London: Van Nostrand Reinhold Co., 1971.

5.   F. B. Hildebrand, *Methods of Applied Mathematics.* Englewood Cliffs, N.J.: Prentice-Hall, Inc., 1961.

6. E. I. Jury, *Theory and Application of the Z-Transform*. New York: John Wiley & Sons, Inc., 1964.

7. E. I. Jury and C. A. Galtieri, "A Note on the Inverse Z-Transformation," *IRE Transactions on Circuit Theory,* vol. CT-9, no. 3, pp. 371–374, September 1961.

8. H. Kwakernaak and R. Sivan, *Linear Optimal Control Systems*. New York: Wiley-Interscience (a division of John Wiley & Sons, Inc.), 1972.

9. J. H. McClellan and Charles M. Rader, *Number Theory in Digital Signal Processing*. Englewood Cliffs, N.J.: Prentice-Hall, Inc., 1979.

10. C. D. McGillem and G. R. Cooper, *Continuous and Discrete Signal and System Analysis*. New York: Holt, Rinehart & Winston, Inc., 1974.

11. A. V. Oppenheim and R. W. Schafer, *Digital Signal Processing*. Englewood Cliffs, N.J.: Prentice-Hall, Inc., 1975.

12. C. M. Rader and B. Gold, "Digital Filter Design Techniques in the Frequency Domain," *Proceedings of the IEEE,* vol. 55, no. 2, pp. 149–171, February 1967.

13. T. S. Huang, *Two-Dimensional Digital Signal Processing: Transforms and Median Filters*. Berlin, Heidelberg, New York: Springer-Verlag, 1981.

CHAPTER 6

State

Variables

6.1 INTRODUCTION

In Chapter 1 we introduced briefly the concepts of eigenvalues and eigenvectors, matrix differential equations, and state variables. In Chapter 3 we discussed the formulation of state equations and their solution for constant, linear networks (see Section 3.13 and Problems 3.19–3.24). Here we elaborate on these topics and their applications in electrical networks.

If it were only for a better understanding of system behavior, we should welcome having yet another method of system analysis. However, the state variable characterization offers several additional important advantages.

1. It provides a better insight into the physical aspects of the problem.
2. It leads to a set of *first-order* differential equations, and the theory, properties, and solutions of such equations have been thoroughly studied.
3. These equations are suitable for solution by analog or digital computers.
4. The state variables provide a unified approach that is readily applicable to continuous or discrete systems, constant or time varying, linear or nonlinear.

Example 6.1 Let us review Example 1.50 in Chapter 1. There, a series *RLC* circuit is analyzed. Had we used loop analysis for it, we would have obtained

$$(R_1 + R_2)i(t) + L\frac{di(t)}{dt} + \frac{1}{C}\int_{-\infty}^{t} i(x)\,dx = 0$$

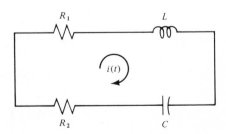

FIGURE 6.1 **Example 6.1.**

an integro-differential equation in the unknown loop current $i(t)$. Alternately, with the substitution $i(t) = dq/dt$, where $q(t)$ is the charge on the capacitor, we could get the equivalent second-order differential equation

$$L\frac{d^2q(t)}{dt^2} + (R_1 + R_2)\frac{dq(t)}{dt} + \frac{1}{C}q(t) = 0$$

Instead, using the linearly independent state variables $v_C(t)$ and $i_L(t)$, we obtained a first-order matrix differential equation,

$$\dot{\mathbf{x}} = \mathbf{Ax}, \qquad \mathbf{x}(t) = \begin{bmatrix} v_C(t) \\ i_L(t) \end{bmatrix}$$

where $\mathbf{x}(t)$ is the state vector. ∎

We observe that, indeed, the state variables provide better physical insight—the capacitor's voltage and the inductor's current are realistic, physical quantities, easily measured and displayed. By contrast, loop currents, in general, are merely mathematical variables, introduced to facilitate the writing of Kirchhoff's current law in "complicated" networks. Also, the initial state vector $\mathbf{x}(0_-)$ consists of the naturally given initial conditions. Finally, a single nth-order scalar differential equation was shown (Eqs. 1.104–1.107) to be equivalent to a single first-order matrix differential equation.

Example 6.2   In the network shown, the state variables are the capacitive voltages, $v_1(t)$ and $v_2(t)$, respectively,

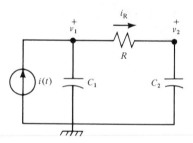

FIGURE 6.2   Example 6.2.

$$\mathbf{x}(t) = \begin{bmatrix} v_1(t) \\ v_2(t) \end{bmatrix}$$

and we are given the initial state vector

$$\mathbf{x}(0_-) = \begin{bmatrix} v_1(0_-) \\ v_2(0_-) \end{bmatrix}$$

Writing the two state equations, as outlined in Chapter 3, we get

$$\begin{bmatrix} \dot{v}_1 \\ \dot{v}_2 \end{bmatrix} = \begin{bmatrix} -\dfrac{1}{RC_1} & \dfrac{1}{RC_1} \\ \dfrac{1}{RC_2} & -\dfrac{1}{RC_2} \end{bmatrix} \begin{bmatrix} v_1 \\ v_2 \end{bmatrix} + \begin{bmatrix} \dfrac{1}{C_1} \\ 0 \end{bmatrix} i(t)$$

i.e., a non-homogeneous matrix differential equation

$$\dot{\mathbf{x}}(t) = \mathbf{Ax}(t) + \mathbf{Bu}(t)$$

where $\mathbf{u}(t)$ is, in general, the input vector; here, it is the scalar $i(t)$. ∎

Let us make a few observations:

1. The initial state vector $\mathbf{x}(0_-)$ completely describes the network at $t = 0_-$.
2. For any time in the future, t_1, the knowledge of the state vector $\mathbf{x}(t_1)$ and of the input $\mathbf{u}(t_1)$ completely describes the network. In other words, the solution of the state equation provides the solution of the network.
3. For linear networks, superposition is applicable, and the total solution for $\mathbf{x}(t)$ will consist of the sum of the *zero-input* state vector the solution of the homogeneous state equation when $\mathbf{u}(t) = \mathbf{0}$, plus the *zero-state* state vector, the solution of the state equation when $\mathbf{x}(0_-) = \mathbf{0}$. For linear, constant networks, the solution is given by Equation 3.171, repeated here for convenience

$$\mathbf{x}(t) = e^{\mathbf{A}t}\mathbf{x}(0_-) + \int_{0_-}^{t} e^{\mathbf{A}(t-\tau)}\mathbf{B}\mathbf{u}(\tau)d\tau \qquad (3.171)$$

where the first term on the right is the zero-input part and the integral (convolution) is the zero-state part.

4. The state transition matrix for linear, constant networks is

$$\boldsymbol{\phi}(t) = e^{\mathbf{A}t} \qquad (6.1)$$

and its Laplace transform is (here $\mathbf{I}$ is the unit matrix)

$$\boldsymbol{\Phi}(s) = (s\mathbf{I} - \mathbf{A})^{-1} \qquad (6.2)$$

In terms of $\boldsymbol{\phi}(t)$, the solution for $\mathbf{x}(t)$ is

$$\mathbf{x}(t) = \boldsymbol{\phi}(t)\mathbf{x}(0_-) + \int_{0_-}^{t} \boldsymbol{\phi}(t - \tau)\mathbf{B}\mathbf{u}(\tau)d\tau \qquad (6.3)$$

5. The *state space* $\mathbf{S}^n$ is the vector space defined by the state vectors. It is, in general, of dimension n. Here, $n = 2$, and it is shown in Figure 6.3. The vector $\mathbf{x}(t)$ is shown for various values of time, $t = 0_-$, $t = t_1$, $t = t_2$.

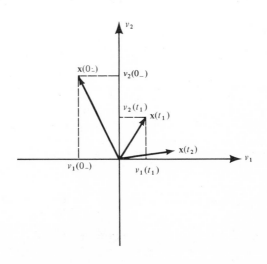

FIGURE 6.3 State space S^2.

Example 6.3   The network shown in Figure 6.4 is a length Δx of two coupled lossless transmission lines.

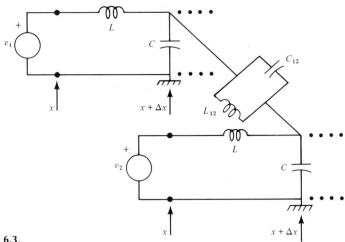

FIGURE 6.4   Example 6.3.

Kirchhoff's voltage and current laws for the circuit yield the relations

$$-\frac{\partial v_1}{\partial x} = (L - L_{12}) \frac{\partial i_1}{\partial t} + L_{12} \frac{\partial i_2}{\partial t}$$

and

$$-\frac{\partial v_2}{\partial x} = (L - L_{12}) \frac{\partial i_2}{\partial t} + L_{12} \frac{\partial i_1}{\partial t}$$

as well as

$$-\frac{\partial i_1}{\partial x} = (C + C_{12}) \frac{\partial v_1}{\partial t} - C_{12} \frac{\partial v_2}{\partial t}$$

and

$$-\frac{\partial i_2}{\partial x} = (C + C_{12}) \frac{\partial v_2}{\partial t} - C_{12} \frac{\partial v_1}{\partial t}$$

Here, L and C are the inductance and capacitance per unit length, with L_{12} the mutual inductance and C_{12} the coupling capacitance per unit length between the lines.

It is preferable to work here with the even and odd mode voltages and currents, defined in terms of the variables v_1, v_2, i_1, and i_2 as follows:

$$v_e = v_1 + v_2, \quad v_o = v_1 - v_2$$

and

$$i_e = i_1 + i_2, \quad i_o = i_1 - i_2$$

Then we obtain the equivalent equations

$$-\frac{\partial v_e}{\partial x} = L\,\frac{\partial i_e}{\partial t}$$

$$-\frac{\partial v_o}{\partial x} = (L - 2L_{12})\,\frac{\partial i_o}{\partial t}$$

and

$$-\frac{\partial i_o}{\partial x} = C\,\frac{\partial v_e}{\partial t}$$

$$-\frac{\partial i_o}{\partial x} = (C + 2C_{12})\,\frac{\partial v_o}{\partial t}$$

We now assume that voltage and current vary sinusoidally with time as $e^{j\omega t}$; that is, for example, $v_e(x,t) = V_e(x)\,e^{j\omega t}$, with similar expressions for v_o, i_e, and i_o. Then

$$-\frac{dV_e}{dx} = j\omega L I_e$$

$$-\frac{dV_o}{dx} = j\omega L' I_o$$

and

$$-\frac{dI_e}{dx} = j\omega C\,V_e$$

$$-\frac{dI_o}{dx} = j\omega C'\,V_o$$

where $L' = L - 2L_{12}$ and $C' = C + 2C_{12}$. We now define a vector

$$\mathbf{w}(x) = \begin{bmatrix} V_e(x) \\ V_o(x) \\ I_e(x) \\ I_o(x) \end{bmatrix}$$

and a matrix

$$= \left[\begin{array}{cc:cc} 0 & 0 & j\omega L & 0 \\ 0 & 0 & 0 & j\omega L' \\ \hdashline j\omega C & 0 & 0 & 0 \\ 0 & j\omega C' & 0 & 0 \end{array}\right]$$

so that the last equations become the state matrix equation

$$-\frac{d\mathbf{w}}{dx} = -\mathbf{\Lambda w}$$

With $\mathbf{w}(0_-)$ given, the solution is

$$\mathbf{w}(x) = e^{-\mathbf{\Lambda} x}\mathbf{w}(0_-) \qquad\blacksquare$$

State equations also occur in probability theory, many aspects of which are of importance in engineering. In the following example we discuss the Poisson distribution of probabilities. The Poisson distribution, and its generalizations, have important applications to such diverse topics as radioactive decay, expected loads in electric power systems, and the control of aircraft in the vicinity of airports.

Example 6.4   Let a system have N possible states, labeled $S_0, \ldots, S_{N-1}$, and let the probability of occupation of the nth state at time t be denoted by $p_n(t)$. The initial distribution of probabilities is given as

$$p_n(0) = \delta_{n0} = \begin{cases} 1 & n = 0 \\ 0 & \text{otherwise} \end{cases}$$

We shall assume that transitions can occur between nearest neighbors only. Then, as time passes, transitions from the $(n - 1)$st to the nth state occur with probability λ per unit time, while the probability of occupation of the nth state will decrease due to transitions to the $(n + 1)$st state, again with an assumed probability per unit time of λ. In a time Δt, we have a balance equation for the $p_n(t)$ as follows:

$$p_n(t + \Delta t) = p_n(t) - \lambda p_n(t)\Delta t + \lambda p_{n-1}(t)\Delta t$$

As $\Delta t \to 0$, this equation becomes

$$\frac{dp_n}{dt} + \lambda p_n = \lambda p_{n-1}$$

Its solution, the Poisson distribution of probabilities, will now be found. Let $\mathbf{p}$ be the vector whose components are p_n and denote by $\mathbf{q}$ the vector whose components are p_{n-1}, with $p_{-1} \equiv 0$. Then the equation can be written as the state equation

$$\frac{d\mathbf{p}}{dt} + \lambda \mathbf{I} \mathbf{p} = \lambda \mathbf{I} \mathbf{q}$$

where $\mathbf{I}$ is the unit matrix. The solution, according to Equation 3.171, is given by

$$\mathbf{p}(t) = e^{-\lambda \mathbf{I} t}\mathbf{p}(0_-) + \lambda \int_{0_-}^{t} e^{-\lambda \mathbf{I}(t-\tau)} \mathbf{I}\mathbf{q}(\tau)d\tau$$

where $e^{-\lambda \mathbf{I} t} \equiv \mathbf{I} e^{-\lambda t}$. The components $p_n(t)$ are found according to

$$\begin{bmatrix} p_0(t) \\ \cdot \\ \cdot \\ \cdot \\ \cdot \\ \cdot \\ \cdot \\ p_{N-1}(t) \end{bmatrix} = e^{-\lambda t} \begin{bmatrix} 1 \\ 0 \\ 0 \\ \cdot \\ \cdot \\ \cdot \\ \cdot \\ 0 \end{bmatrix} + \lambda \int_{0_-}^{t} e^{-\lambda(t-\tau)} \begin{bmatrix} 0 \\ p_0(\tau) \\ \cdot \\ \cdot \\ \cdot \\ \cdot \\ \cdot \\ p_{N-2}(\tau) \end{bmatrix} d\tau$$

since $\mathbf{I}\,\mathbf{p}(0) \equiv \mathbf{p}(0)$.

In particular, then,

$$p_0(t) = e^{-\lambda t}$$

and

$$p_1(t) = \lambda t e^{-\lambda t}$$

while, in general,

$$p_n(t) = \lambda e^{-\lambda t} \int_{0_-}^{t} e^{\lambda \tau} p_{n-1}(\tau) \, d\tau$$

We find that the Poisson distribution is, therefore,

$$p_n(t) = \frac{(\lambda t)^n}{n!} e^{-\lambda t}, \quad (t \geq 0)$$

From our earlier work with Laplace transforms, it is clear that

$$\int_{0}^{\infty} p_n(t)\lambda \, dt = 1$$

for every n. ∎

6.2 FORMULATION FOR TIME-VARYING AND NONLINEAR NETWORKS

As mentioned in the introduction, the state variable formulation also offers a unified approach for time-varying networks. The topological relations (Kirchhoff's current and voltage laws) remain, of course, the same regardless of the nature of the elements. A linear time-varying resistor is defined by

$$v_R(t) = R(t) \, i_R(t) \tag{6.4}$$

Changes occur in the expressions for voltages and currents for linear time-varying inductors and capacitors; for an inductor, with ϕ_L designating the flux, we have

$$v_L(t) = \frac{d}{dt} \phi_L(t) = \frac{d}{dt} [L(t) \, i_L(t)] = \dot{L}(t) \, i_L(t) + L(t) \, \dot{i}_L(t) \tag{6.5}$$

For a capacitor, with q_c designating the charge, we have

$$i_C(t) = \frac{d}{dt} q_C(t) = \frac{d}{dt} [C(t) \, v_C(t)] = \dot{C}(t) \, v_C(t) + C(t) \, \dot{v}_C(t) \tag{6.6}$$

Here the dot indicates, as usual, time differentiation. We see, therefore, the additional terms $\dot{L}(t) \, i_L(t)$ and $\dot{C}(t) \, v_C(t)$, respectively.

Example 6.5 Consider again the series RLC circuit of Example 6.1. Let all the elements be linear and time-varying. The fundamental cut-set equation for the capacitor is

$$i_C(t) = i_L(t)$$

or

$$\dot{C}(t) \, v_C(t) + C(t) \, \dot{v}_C(t) = i_L(t)$$

The fundamental loop equation for the inductor is

$$v_L(t) + v_C(t) + v_{R_1}(t) + v_{R_2}(t) = 0$$

or

$$\dot{L}(t)i_L(t) + L(t)\dot{i}_L(t) + [R_1(t) + R_2(t)]i_L(t) + v_C(t) = 0$$

These two equations, when rearranged, become

$$
\begin{bmatrix} \dot{v}_C(t) \\ \\ \dot{i}_L(t) \end{bmatrix}
=
\begin{bmatrix} -\dfrac{\dot{C}(t)}{C(t)} & \dfrac{1}{C(t)} \\ \\ -\dfrac{1}{L(t)} & -\dfrac{R_1(t) + R_2(t) + \dot{L}(t)}{L(t)} \end{bmatrix}
\begin{bmatrix} v_C(t) \\ \\ i_L(t) \end{bmatrix}
$$

In other words, the homogeneous matrix state equation is

$$\dot{\mathbf{x}}(t) = \mathbf{A}(t)\mathbf{x}(t)$$

where the matrix **A** is now time dependent. In passing, we observe that for the linear constant case, $\mathbf{A}(t)$ becomes the constant matrix **A** in Example 6.1. ∎

To emphasize the unified approach for constant and time-varying elements, we can choose as state variables the capacitors' charges and the inductors' fluxes. The new state vector is

$$
\hat{\mathbf{x}}(t) =
\begin{bmatrix} q_{C_1}(t) \\ q_{C_2}(t) \\ \vdots \\ \phi_{L_1}(t) \\ \phi_{L_2}(t) \\ \vdots \end{bmatrix}
\tag{6.7}
$$

and is equally suitable for constant or time-varying elements. In the former case the only difference between **x** (voltages and currents) and $\hat{\mathbf{x}}$ (charges and fluxes) is a set of constant multipliers; in the latter case the choice of $\hat{\mathbf{x}}$ avoids the terms $\dot{C}(t)$ and $\dot{L}(t)$, as illustrated in the following example.

Example 6.6   For the same circuit as in Example 6.5 choose

$$\hat{\mathbf{x}}(t) = \begin{bmatrix} q_C(t) \\ \phi_L(t) \end{bmatrix}$$

Then the fundamental cut-set equation becomes

$$\dot{q}_C(t) = \frac{1}{L(t)}\,\phi_L(t)$$

while the fundamental loop equation reads

$$\dot{\phi}_L(t) + \frac{1}{C(t)}\,q_C(t) + [R_1(t) + R_2(t)]\,\dot{q}_C(t) = 0$$

Together, these become

$$
\begin{bmatrix} \dot{q}_C(t) \\[2em] \dot{\phi}_L(t) \end{bmatrix} = \begin{bmatrix} 0 & \dfrac{1}{C(t)} \\[2em] -\dfrac{1}{C(t)} & -\dfrac{R_1(t) + R_2(t)}{L(t)} \end{bmatrix} \begin{bmatrix} q_C(t) \\[2em] \phi_L(t) \end{bmatrix}
$$

that is,

$$
\dot{\mathbf{x}}(t) = \hat{\mathbf{A}}(t)\hat{\mathbf{x}}(t) \qquad\qquad \blacksquare
$$

Example 6.7   Another application of state variables is found in time-varying quantum mechanics. In what follows we derive an expression for time-dependent transition probabilities in typical physics notation, and then cast our results into the notation of this text.

The time-dependent nonrelativistic Schroedinger equation is

$$
j\hbar\, \frac{\partial \Psi}{\partial t} = \mathcal{H}\Psi
$$

Here $\hbar = h/2\pi$ is a constant, $\Psi(\mathbf{r},t)$ is a state vector of the system under discussion, and $\mathcal{H}$ is the Hamiltonian operator given by

$$
\mathcal{H} = -\frac{\hbar^2}{2m}\, \nabla^2 + V(\mathbf{r}) + \mathcal{H}'
$$

$\mathcal{H}_0 = -\dfrac{\hbar^2}{2m}\, \nabla^2 + V(\mathbf{r})$ is an unperturbed Hamiltonian and $\mathcal{H}'$ can be regarded as a (not necessarily small) perturbation.

We set

$$
\Psi(\mathbf{r},t) = \sum_{n=1}^{N} a_n(t) e^{-jE_n t/\hbar} \phi_n(\mathbf{r})
$$

Here the E_n are the energy eigenvalues of the system and the $\phi_n(\mathbf{r})$ are a complete orthonormal set of functions that may, in general, be complex. Then

$$
\int_{V(\mathbf{r})} \phi_K^*(\mathbf{r})\phi_n(\mathbf{r})\, dV(\mathbf{r}) = \delta_{Kn}
$$

is the expression of the orthonormality condition. It is customary, in quantum mechanics, to regard to quantity $\Psi^*\Psi$ as a probability density, so that

$$
\int_{V(\mathbf{r})} \Psi * \Psi\, dV(\mathbf{r}) = 1
$$

On substituting the equation for Ψ, we find that if there is a total of N available states,

$$
\sum_{n=1}^{N} |a_n(t)|^2 = 1
$$

Thus the quantity $|a_K(t)|^2$ is the probability of occupancy of the kth state of the system. A matrix state equation will govern the behavior of the $a_K(t)$.

On substituting Ψ into the Schroedinger equation, we find that

$$
j\hbar \sum_{n=1}^{N} \left(\frac{da_n}{dt} - jE_n a_n/\hbar \right) e^{-jE_n t/\hbar} \phi_n(\mathbf{r}) = \sum_{l=1}^{N} (\mathcal{H}_0 + \mathcal{H}') a_l(t) e^{-jE_l t/\hbar} \phi_l(\mathbf{r})
$$

Upon multiplying both sides of this equation by $\phi_K^*(\mathbf{r})$ and integrating over the volume occupied by the system, we have, on using the orthonormality condition,

$$j\hbar \frac{da_K}{dt} + E_K a_K = \sum_{l=1}^{N} e^{j\omega_{Kl}t} a_l(t) \int_{V(\mathbf{r})} \phi_K^* (\mathcal{H}_0 + \mathcal{H}') \phi_l dV(\mathbf{r})$$

where $\omega_{kl} = (E_K - E_l)/\hbar$.

Now, the unperturbed time-independent Schroedinger equation is

$$\mathcal{H}_0 \phi_l = E_l \phi_l$$

so that

$$\int \phi_K^* \mathcal{H}_0 \phi_l dV(\mathbf{r}) = E_l \delta_{Kl}$$

Then the equation for a_K reduces to

$$j\hbar \frac{da_K}{dt} = \sum_{l=1}^{N} \mathcal{H}_{Kl} e^{j\omega_{Kl}t} a_l(t)$$

where the matrix elements $\mathcal{H}_{Kl}$ are given by

$$\mathcal{H}_{Kl} = \int_{V(\mathbf{r})} \phi_K^* \mathcal{H}' \phi_l dV(\mathbf{r})$$

Thus far the development leading to these equations is standard and may be found in texts on quantum mechanics.

The equation for a_K can be written as

$$\frac{da_K}{dt} = \sum_{l=1}^{N} \Lambda_{Kl}(t) a_l(t)$$

where the transition matrix $\Lambda(t)$ has elements Λ_{Kl} given by

$$\Lambda_{Kl}(t) = -\frac{j}{\hbar} \mathcal{H}_{Kl} e^{j\omega_{Kl}t}$$

Since $\omega_{Kl}t = (E_K - E_l)t/\hbar$ must be dimensionless, it is seen that the constant $\hbar$ must have the units of energy multiplied by time, which is called action. Now, $\mathcal{H}_{Kl}$ has the units of energy so that $\Lambda_{Kl}(t)$ is, dimensionally, a reciprocal time. The last equation can then be thought of in the following terms: The transition matrix operates on the state vector components $a_l(t)$ and, when summed over the states of the system, yields the rate at which the state K is being populated at the expense of all remaining states. In our standard matrix notation, the last equation is written as

$$\frac{d\mathbf{a}}{dt} = \Lambda(t)\mathbf{a}(t) \qquad \blacksquare$$

Finally, let us comment briefly on nonlinear elements. We should again expect nothing higher than first derivatives ($\dot{q}_C$, $\dot{\phi}_L$), since Kirchhoff's laws are still applicable. However, because of the nonlinear elements, the relation between $\dot{\mathbf{x}}$ and $\hat{\mathbf{x}}$ in general will be nonlinear.

Example 6.8   For the same circuit as in Example 6.6, assume all the elements to be nonlinear.

To be specific, let the defining relation for each element be as follows:

$$v_{R_1}(t) = f_1[i_{R_1}(t)] \qquad v_{R_2}(t) = f_2[i_{R_2}(t)]$$
$$v_C(t) = f_3[q_C(t)] \qquad i_L(t) = f_4[\phi_L(t)]$$

These relations are illustrated in Figure 6.5. The fundamental cut-set equation reads $i_C = i_L$, i.e.,

$$\dot{q}_C = f_4(\phi_L)$$

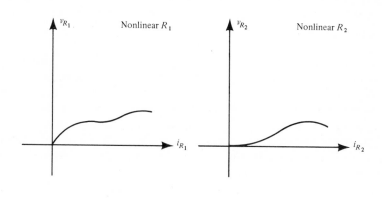

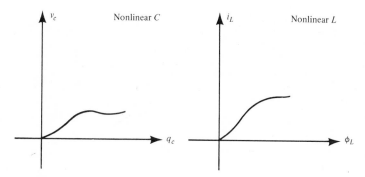

FIGURE 6.5 Nonlinear elements.

and the fundamental loop equation $v_L + v_{R_1} + v_{R_2} + v_C = 0$ becomes

$$\dot{\phi}_L = -f_1(\dot{q}_C) - f_2(\dot{q}_C) - f_3(q_C)$$

because $i_{R_1} = i_{R_2} = i_L = i_C = \dot{q}_C$. These two state equations are of the form

$$\dot{\mathbf{x}} = \mathbf{F}(\hat{\mathbf{x}})$$

where $\mathbf{F}$ designates a functional nonlinear relation.

In closing, it is worth mentioning that a first-order nonlinear differential equation such as the one obtained for state variables is much easier to solve (numerically!) than the equivalent n simultaneous (coupled) nonlinear equations obtained by loop or node analysis. ∎

6.3   THE ORDER
OF THE NETWORK

It should be clear that a purely resistive network—consisting of resistors and sources (dependent and independent)—is described by purely algebraic equations with no derivatives or integrals. Such equations can be solved by methods outlined in Chapter 1, and, for our present purposes, will be considered solved. No initial state is associated with such a network since it is *instantaneous*. A *dynamic* network, on the other hand, has one or more energy storage elements (inductors and capacitors), and the resulting differential equations will require for their solution some initial conditions—the initial state of the network.

The order of the network, *n,* designates the number of the *independent* state variables, with the state vector being a matrix of order ($n \times 1$). The need for *independent* state variables is obvious: Any system described by a set of equations must have only independent unknown variables. If one (or more) of these variables is dependent on the others, then, of course, it cannot qualify as an independent variable.

Capacitor voltages qualify as independent state variables provided there are no constraints of dependence among them. Such constraints can arise only if there exist "all-capacitive" loops in the network. In Figure 6.6, for example,[3] Kirchhoff's voltage law around the all-capacitive loop reads

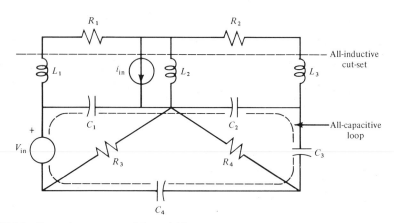

FIGURE 6.6   Dependence among state variables.

$$v_{C_1}(t) + v_{C_2}(t) + v_{C_3}(t) + v_{C_4}(t) = v_{in} \qquad (6.8)$$

(with proper reference polarities on these voltages). Therefore, only three of these four capacitive voltages qualify as independent state variables: Once these three are known, the fourth is determined by Equation 6.8. Also, the initial state vector, $\mathbf{x}(0_-)$, will have only three initial capacitive voltages, the fourth one being dependent on them.

In a dual fashion, inductor currents qualify as independent state variables as long as there are no "all-inductive" cut-sets. In Figure 6.6 we have Kirchhoff's current law

$$i_{L_1} + i_{L_2} + i_{L_3} = i_{in} \qquad (6.9)$$

as a constraint, making one of the inductive currents dependent on the remaining two.

In conclusion, then, the state vector for this network has five components: three capacitive voltages and two inductive currents. Hence the order of the network is $n = 5$.

We should recognize also that the topological formulation of state equations (Problem 3-22) achieves the same goal in an orderly fashion: The chosen tree contains all the voltage sources and a maximum number of capacitors. If there are no all-capacitive loops, every capacitor will be in that tree. Otherwise, with one or more all-capacitive loops, one or more capacitors will not be in the tree (since the tree, by definition, must not contain any loops). Also, a minimal number of inductors is included in this tree; specifically, no inductors are in the tree unless one or more cut-sets are all-inductive, and then we must include one or more inductors in the tree (since, by definition, the tree is connected).

If we designate the number of inductors by e_L, the number of capacitors by e_C, the number of independent all-capacitive loops by n_C, and the number of independent all-inductive cut-sets by n_L, we have

$$n = (e_C - n_C) + (e_L - n_L) \qquad (6.10)$$

In most networks this calculation can be established by inspection. See also Problem 6-2.

A final aspect related to the order of the network is the order of its characteristic equation. For linear constant networks, this equation is (see Problem 3-21)

$$\Delta = \det (s\mathbf{I} - \mathbf{A}) = 0 \qquad (6.11)$$

and since $\mathbf{A}$ is of order $(n \times n)$, the highest power of s in this equation will also be n. Furthermore, there will be n roots of the characteristic equation, the n characteristic values.

6.4 THE STATE TRANSITION MATRIX

In linear constant networks, the state transition matrix $\boldsymbol{\phi}(t)$ appears in both parts of the solution, i.e., in the zero-input part

$$\mathbf{x}(t) = \boldsymbol{\phi}(t)\mathbf{x}(0_-) \qquad (6.12)$$

and in the zero-state part

$$\mathbf{x}(t) = \int_{0_-}^{t} \boldsymbol{\phi}(t - \tau)\mathbf{B}\mathbf{u}(\tau)d\tau \qquad (6.13)$$

Its calculation, while tedious at times, is rather straightforward using the Laplace transform

$$\boldsymbol{\phi}(t) = \mathscr{L}^{-1}(s\mathbf{I} - \mathbf{A})^{-1} \qquad (6.14)$$

and its name describes it well: The initial state $\mathbf{x}(0_-)$, as in Equation 6.12, is transformed into a subsequent state $\mathbf{x}(t)$ via the matrix $\boldsymbol{\phi}(t)$. This matrix, then, provides the transition from $\mathbf{x}(0_-)$ to $\mathbf{x}(t)$.

Example 6.9 In Example 6.2 let $R = 1$ ohm, $C_1 = 0.5$ farad, and $C_2 = 1$ farad. Then

$$\mathbf{A} = \begin{bmatrix} -2 & 2 \\ 2 & -1 \end{bmatrix}$$

and

$$\Phi(s) = \begin{bmatrix} s+2 & -2 \\ -1 & s+1 \end{bmatrix}^{-1} = \frac{1}{s^2 + 3s}\begin{bmatrix} s+1 & 2 \\ 1 & s+2 \end{bmatrix} = \begin{bmatrix} \dfrac{s+1}{s(s+3)} & \dfrac{2}{s(s+3)} \\ \dfrac{1}{s(s+3)} & \dfrac{s+2}{s(s+3)} \end{bmatrix}$$

Consequently,

$$\Phi(t) = \mathcal{L}^{-1}\Phi(s) = \begin{bmatrix} 1/3u(t) + 2/3e^{-3t} & 2/3u(t) - 2/3e^{-3t} \\ 1/3u(t) - 1/3e^{-3t} & 2/3u(t) + 1/3e^{-3t} \end{bmatrix}$$

Then, according to Equation 6.12, the zero-input solution for the state is

$$\begin{bmatrix} v_1(t) \\ v_2(t) \end{bmatrix} = \begin{bmatrix} 1/3u(t) + 2/3e^{-3t} & 2/3u(t) - 2/3e^{-3t} \\ 1/3u(t) - 1/3e^{-3t} & 2/3u(t) + 1/3e^{-3t} \end{bmatrix}\begin{bmatrix} v_1(0_-) \\ v_2(0_-) \end{bmatrix}$$

The characteristic equation here is

$$\Delta = \det (s\mathbf{I} - \mathbf{A}) = s^2 + 3s = 0$$

and the two characteristic values, $s = 0$ and $s = -3$, appear in the exponentials of the solution.
∎

Several methods are available for a direct computation of $\phi(t)$ in the time domain.[8] Some properties of $\phi(t)$ are

$$\phi(0) = \mathbf{I} \tag{6.15}$$

the unit matrix,

$$\phi(t_1) \cdot \phi(t_2) = \phi(t_2) \cdot \phi(t_1) = \phi(t_1 + t_2) \tag{6.16}$$

$$[\phi(t)]^{-1} = e^{-\mathbf{A}t} \tag{6.17}$$

$$\phi(t_2 - t_1) = [\phi(t_1 - t_2)]^{-1} \tag{6.18}$$

In linear time-varying networks, the state transition matrix is dependent both on the initial time t_0 and the subsequent time t. Its designation is $\phi(t,t_0)$. For constant time-invariant networks we had $\phi(t) = \phi(t - t_0)$ dependent on the *difference* $t - t_0$, and, without loss of generality, we set $t_0 = 0$. The linear time-varying state transition matrix itself obeys the state equation

$$\dot{\phi}(t,t_0) = \mathbf{A}(t)\phi(t,t_0) \tag{6.19}$$

with $\phi(t_0,t_0) = \mathbf{I}$.

The zero-input solution to the state equation

$$\dot{\mathbf{x}}(t) = \mathbf{A}(t)\mathbf{x}(t) \tag{6.20}$$

with the initial state $\mathbf{x}(t_0)$ given, is

$$\mathbf{x}(t) = \phi(t,t_0)\mathbf{x}(t_0) \tag{6.21}$$

In order to obtain an expression for $\boldsymbol{\phi}(t,t_0)$, let us consider a first-order network. Here the state equation is the scalar differential equation

$$\dot{x}(t) = a(t)x(t) \tag{6.22}$$

Separating variables, we get

$$\frac{dx}{x} = a(t)dt \tag{6.23}$$

Integration from an initial time t_0 to t yields

$$x(t) = \exp\left[\int_{t_0}^{t} a(\tau)d\tau\right]x(t_0) \tag{6.24}$$

We may be tempted to extend this solution to higher order networks and write

$$\mathbf{x}(t) = \exp\left[\int_{t_0}^{t} \mathbf{A}(\tau)d\tau\right]\mathbf{x}(t_0) \tag{6.25}$$

However, if this trial solution is substituted into Equation 6.20, we see that it is correct when $\mathbf{A}(t)$ and $\int_{t_0}^{t} \mathbf{A}(\tau)d\tau$ commute. This is true when $\mathbf{A}(t)$ is diagonal, or when $\mathbf{A}(t)$ satisfies[4]

$$\mathbf{A}(t_1)\mathbf{A}(t_2) = \mathbf{A}(t_2)\mathbf{A}(t_1) \tag{6.26}$$

for all t_1 and t_2.

Example 6.10   Let

$$\mathbf{A}(t) = \begin{bmatrix} -t & 0 \\ 0 & t \end{bmatrix}$$

Then the commutative condition is satisfied, or, alternately, Equation 6.26 is satisfied, and therefore

$$\boldsymbol{\phi}(t,t_0) = \exp\left[\int_{t_0}^{t} \mathbf{A}(\tau)d\tau\right] = \begin{bmatrix} e^{(t_0^2 - t^2)/2} & 1 \\ 1 & e^{(-t_0^2 + t^2)/2} \end{bmatrix} \qquad \blacksquare$$

Some additional properties of $\boldsymbol{\phi}(t,t_0)$ are:

$$\boldsymbol{\phi}(t_0,t_0) = \mathbf{I} \tag{6.27}$$

$$\boldsymbol{\phi}(t_1,t_3) = \boldsymbol{\phi}(t_1,t_2)\boldsymbol{\phi}(t_2,t_3) \tag{6.28}$$

$$\boldsymbol{\phi}(t_1,t_2) = \boldsymbol{\phi}^{-1}(t_2,t_1) \tag{6.29}$$

$$\boldsymbol{\phi}(t,t_0) = \mathbf{P}(t)\mathbf{P}^{-1}(t_0) \tag{6.30}$$

where the *fundamental matrix* $\mathbf{P}(t)$

$$\mathbf{P}(t) = [\mathbf{x}^1(t) \vdots \mathbf{x}^2(t) \vdots \cdots \vdots \mathbf{x}^n(t)] \tag{6.31}$$

is formed by the n linearly independent vectors $\mathbf{x}^i(t)$, $i = 1, \ldots, n$, which are solutions to the homogeneous state equation

$$\dot{\mathbf{x}} = \mathbf{A}(t)\mathbf{x}(t) \tag{6.20}$$

The total solution to the state equation

$$\dot{\mathbf{x}}(t) = \mathbf{A}(t)\mathbf{x}(t) + \mathbf{B}(t)\mathbf{u}(t) \tag{6.32}$$

is given for $t \geq t_0$ by

$$\mathbf{x}(t) = \boldsymbol{\phi}(t,t_0)\mathbf{x}(t_0) + \int_{t_0}^{t} \boldsymbol{\phi}(t,\tau)\mathbf{B}(\tau)\mathbf{u}(\tau)d\tau \tag{6.33}$$

That it is indeed the solution can be established in two steps:

1. The initial conditions are satisfied, since Equation 6.33 is reduced to an identity when $t = t_0$.
2. When Equation 6.33 is differentiated with respect to t we obtain

$$\dot{\mathbf{x}} = \dot{\boldsymbol{\phi}}(t,t_0)\mathbf{x}(t_0) + \boldsymbol{\phi}(t,\tau)\mathbf{B}(\tau)\mathbf{u}(\tau)]_{\tau=t} + \int_{t_0}^{t} \dot{\boldsymbol{\phi}}(t,\tau)\mathbf{B}(\tau)\mathbf{u}(\tau)d\tau \tag{6.34}$$

After rearrangement and use of the previous properties of $\boldsymbol{\phi}(t,t_0)$, this reduces to Equation 6.32.

Two final notes are in order:

1. Since the network is linear (though time varying), Equation 6.33 represents the superposition principle: The zero-input part of the solution is added to the zero-state part. The latter, represented by the integral in that equation, can be thought of as a generalized convolution.
2. Although Equation 6.33 is the form of the solution, explicit solutions depend on finding the explicit expression for $\boldsymbol{\phi}(t,t_0)$ in closed form. This general problem is still unsolved.

Discrete time systems were discussed in Chapter 5, together with the Z-transform method of solution. Here we present an example that illustrates the derivation of the discrete state equation and its state transition matrix.

Example 6.11 Consider the second-order difference equation

$$a_2 y(k + 2) + a_1 y(k + 1) + a_0 y(k) = 0$$

In a way similar to the procedure outlined in Chapter 1 (Equations 1.95–1.107), let us define two state variables as follows:

$$x_1(k) = y(k)$$
$$x_2(k) = y(k + 1)$$

Then the given equation can be rewritten as

$$x_1(k + 1) = x_2(k)$$

$$x_2(k + 1) = -\frac{a_1}{a_2} y(k + 1) - \frac{a_0}{a_2} y(k) = -\frac{a_1}{a_2} x_2(k) - \frac{a_0}{a_2} x_1(k)$$

that is,

$$\begin{bmatrix} x_1(k+1) \\ x_2(k+1) \end{bmatrix} = \begin{bmatrix} 0 & 1 \\ -\dfrac{a_0}{a_2} & -\dfrac{a_1}{a_2} \end{bmatrix} \begin{bmatrix} x_1(k) \\ x_2(k) \end{bmatrix}$$

that is,

$$\mathbf{x}(k+1) = \mathbf{A}\mathbf{x}(k)$$

The generalization to higher order equations follows similar lines.

The corresponding state transition matrix, derived in Equation 5.50 via the Z-transform, may be obtained easily by successive substitutions: Starting with the given initial state $\mathbf{x}(0_-)$, we have

$$\mathbf{x}(1) = \mathbf{A}\mathbf{x}(0_-)$$
$$\mathbf{x}(2) = \mathbf{A}\mathbf{x}(1) = \mathbf{A}^2\mathbf{x}(0_-)$$
$$\mathbf{x}(3) = \mathbf{A}\mathbf{x}(2) = \mathbf{A}^3\mathbf{x}(0_-)$$
$$\vdots$$
$$\mathbf{x}(k) = \mathbf{A}^k\mathbf{x}(0_-)$$

thus exhibiting the state transition matrix

$$\boldsymbol{\phi}(k) = \mathbf{A}^k$$

Compare with Equation 5.50. ∎

As in the case of the continuous time-varying state transition matrix, Equation 6.19 ff., the discrete time-varying transition matrix is defined by the relation

$$\mathbf{x}(k) = \boldsymbol{\phi}(k,l)\mathbf{x}(l), \qquad k \geq l \tag{6.35}$$

expressing the transition from an initial state $\mathbf{x}(l)$ to a subsequent state $\mathbf{x}(k)$. Using the recursion method in the previous example, we can derive the following expression, with $k > l$,

$$\boldsymbol{\phi}(k,l) = \mathbf{A}(k-1)\mathbf{A}(k-2)\ldots\mathbf{A}(l+1)\mathbf{A}(l) \tag{6.36}$$

Also, we have

$$\boldsymbol{\phi}(l,l) = \mathbf{I} \tag{6.37}$$

and

$$\boldsymbol{\phi}(k+1,l) = \mathbf{A}(k)\boldsymbol{\phi}(k,l) \tag{6.38}$$

If we can find n linearly independent vectors $\mathbf{x}^1(k), \mathbf{x}^2(k), \ldots, \mathbf{x}^n(k)$ of the state equation

$$\mathbf{x}(k+1) = \mathbf{A}(k)\mathbf{x}(k) \tag{6.39}$$

i.e., each vector $\mathbf{x}^i(k)$ satisfies

$$\mathbf{x}^i(k+1) = \mathbf{A}(k)\mathbf{x}^i(k) \tag{6.40}$$

then the fundamental matrix here is

$$\mathbf{P}(k) = [\mathbf{x}^1(k) \vdots \mathbf{x}^2(k) \vdots \cdots \vdots \mathbf{x}^n(k)] \tag{6.41}$$

and

$$\boldsymbol{\phi}(k,l) = \mathbf{P}(k)\mathbf{P}^{-1}(l) \qquad (6.42)$$

The total solution to the non-homogeneous linear difference state equation

$$\mathbf{x}(k + 1) = \mathbf{A}(k)\mathbf{x}(k) + \mathbf{B}(k)\mathbf{u}(k) \qquad (6.43)$$

can be written as

$$\mathbf{x}(k) = \boldsymbol{\phi}(k,l)\mathbf{x}(l) + \sum_{j=l}^{k-1} \boldsymbol{\phi}(k,j + 1)\mathbf{B}(j)\mathbf{u}(j), \qquad k \geq l + 1 \qquad (6.44)$$

Again, we recognize here the superposition of the initial state solution given in Equation 6.35, and the summation (convolution) due to the input.

6.5 INPUT–OUTPUT RELATIONS; SIMULATION DIAGRAMS

Knowing the state, $\mathbf{x}(t)$, at every instant provides complete information about the network. In particular, let $\mathbf{y}(t)$ be the vector of desired outputs. These outputs then will depend on $\mathbf{x}(t)$ and possibly also on the input $\mathbf{u}(t)$. Therefore,

$$\mathbf{y}(t) = \mathbf{C}\mathbf{x}(t) + \mathbf{D}\mathbf{u}(t) \qquad (6.45)$$

for linear constant networks. Equation 6.45 is called the *output equation*.

Example 6.12   In the network shown in Figure 6.7, the desired output is i_R. We have

$$i_R(t) = \frac{v_{\text{in}} - v_C}{R}$$

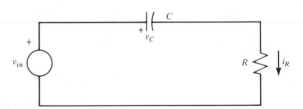

FIGURE 6.7   Example 6.12.

or in the notation of Equation 6.45

$$y(t) = -\frac{1}{R} x(t) + \frac{1}{R} u(t)$$

where $y(t) = i_R(t)$, $x(t) = v_C$, $u(t) = v_{\text{in}}$ are scalars in this simple case.   ∎

The input–output relationship can be obtained from the Laplace transform of the state equation and the output equation for linear constant networks. These transforms are, respectively,*

*The reader should have no trouble in distinguishing, throughout the discussion, the unit matrix $\mathbf{I}$ from the input vector $\mathbf{u}(t)$ and its Laplace transform $\mathbf{U}(s)$.

$$sX(s) - x(0_-) = AX(s) + BU(s) \tag{6.46}$$

and

$$Y(s) = CX(s) + DU(s) \tag{6.47}$$

The algebraic elimination of $X(s)$ between these equations yields the desired input–output relation

$$Y(s) = [C\Phi(s)B + D]U(s) + C\Phi(s)x(0_-) \tag{6.48}$$

where, as before, $\Phi(s) = (sI - A)^{-1}$, the transform of the state transition matrix.

The common definition of a transfer function relates $Y(s)$ to $U(s)$ under zero initial conditions, i.e., it relates the zero-state response to the input. From Equation 6.48 we have then

$$Y(s) = H(s)U(s) \tag{6.49}$$

where $H(s)$, the matrix transfer function, is

$$H(s) = C\Phi(s)B + D \tag{6.50}$$

Example 6.13   For the network in the previous example, we have the (scalar) state equation

$$\frac{dv_C}{dt} = -\frac{1}{RC}v_C + \frac{1}{RC}v_{in}$$

that is,

$$\dot{x} = ax + bu$$

Therefore,

$$\Phi(s) = (s - a)^{-1} = \left(s + \frac{1}{RC}\right)^{-1}$$

and, with i_R as the output, we have

$$H(s) = -\frac{1}{R}\left(s + \frac{1}{RC}\right)^{-1}\frac{1}{RC} + \frac{1}{R} = \frac{Cs}{RCs + 1}$$

which can be readily verified by writing a loop equation.   ∎

Simulation diagrams for analog computers are very useful also in the overall conception of state equations. The three basic operations involved in simulation are

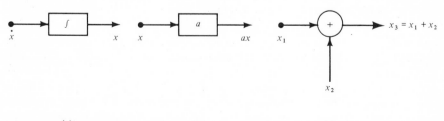

(a)   (b)   (c)

FIGURE 6.8   Basic operations in simulation.

(1) integration, (2) multiplication by a constant, and (3) summation. These are shown symbolically in Figure 6.8. The simulation of the state equation and of the output equation for constant networks is shown in Figure 6.9. Note that, typically, the outputs of the integrators are the state variables.

Example 6.14   Consider the first-order differential equation

$$a_1 \frac{dy}{dt} + a_0 y = u(t)$$

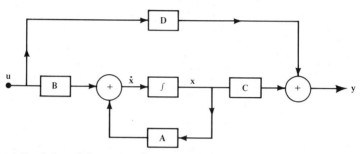

FIGURE 6.9   Simulation of the state and output equations.

Choose the state variable $x = y$, and then

$$\frac{dx}{dt} = \frac{dy}{dt} = -\frac{a_0}{a_1} y + \frac{1}{a_1} u(t)$$

that is,

$$\frac{dx}{dt} = -\frac{a_0}{a_1} x + \frac{1}{a_1} u(t)$$

The simulation diagram is shown in Figure 6.10.   ∎

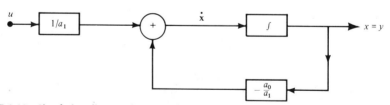

FIGURE 6.10   Simulation diagram for Example 6.14.

Example 6.15   Consider an extension of the method outlined at the end of Chapter 1 (Equations 1.104–1.107). Specifically, let the scalar differential equation be

$$\frac{d^2 y}{dt^2} + a_1 \frac{dy}{dt} + a_0 y = b_2 \frac{d^2 u}{dt^2} + b_1 \frac{du}{dt} + b_0 u$$

describing the relationship between the output $y(t)$ and the input $u(t)$. We have conveniently set the coefficient of $d^2 y/dt^2$ to unity. As in Equations 1.105–1.107 we wish to find the equivalent state equations. Because of the nonzero terms on the right-hand side, we modify slightly our choice of state variables, by comparison with Equation 1.107, as follows: First, let

$$x_1 = y - b_2 u$$

With this choice, the given differential equation becomes

$$\frac{d^2 x_1}{dt^2} + a_1 \frac{dx_1}{dt} + a_0 x_1 = (b_1 - a_1 b_2) \frac{du}{dt} + (b_0 - a_0 b_2) u$$

thus eliminating $d^2 u/dt^2$. As a second state variable, let us choose

$$x_2 = \frac{dx_1}{dt} - (b_1 - a_1 b_2) u$$

and substitute. The result is

$$\frac{dx_2}{dt} = -a_0 x_1 - a_1 x_2 + [(b_0 - a_0 b_2) - a_1(b_1 - a_1 b_2)] u$$

These last two equations are the desired state equations,

$$\begin{bmatrix} \dfrac{dx_1}{dt} \\ \dfrac{dx_2}{dt} \end{bmatrix} = \begin{bmatrix} 0 & 1 \\ -a_o & -a_1 \end{bmatrix} \begin{bmatrix} x_1 \\ x_2 \end{bmatrix} + \begin{bmatrix} (b_1 - a_1 b_2) \\ (b_0 - a_0 b_2) - a_1(b_1 - a_1 b_2) \end{bmatrix} u(t)$$

i.e., $\dot{\mathbf{x}} = \mathbf{Ax} + \mathbf{Bu}$, and the output equation is

$$y = \begin{bmatrix} 1 & 0 \end{bmatrix} \begin{bmatrix} x_1 \\ x_2 \end{bmatrix} + b_2 u$$

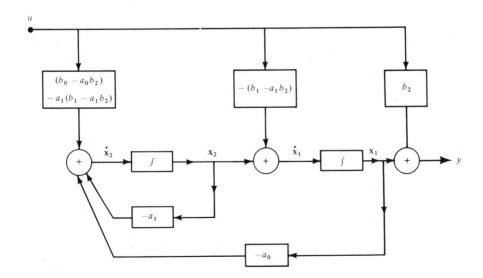

FIGURE 6.11   Simulation diagram for Example 6.15.

that is,

$$y = Cx + Du$$

A simulation diagram for this system is shown in Figure 6.11. A generalization of this method is given as a problem at the end of this chapter.   ∎

Let us consider another aspect of the state equations and the equivalent input–output relationship. More specifically, for a single-input, single-output case, Equation 6.49 yields a scalar transfer function $H(s)$. For constant linear networks described by total differential equations, $H(s)$ will be a ratio of two polynomials,

$$H(s) = \frac{P(s)}{Q(s)} \tag{6.51}$$

with $P(s)$ of degree m and $Q(s)$ of degree n, with $n > m$ in most cases. Assume further that there are no common factors between $P(s)$ and $Q(s)$ and that all of the roots of $Q(s) = 0$ are distinct. Then by the Heaviside inversion theorem of Chapter 3, the unit impulse response of the system is

$$h(t) = \mathcal{L}^{-1}\{H(s)\} = \sum_{k=1}^{n} \frac{P(p_k)}{Q'(p_k)} e^{p_k t} \tag{6.52}$$

where the p_k ($k = 1, \ldots, n$) are the distinct roots of $Q(s) = 0$, the poles of $H(s)$. Also, $Q'(Pk) = [dQ(s)/ds]_{s=p_k}$. It is clear that $h(t)$ can be written as

$$h(t) = \sum_{k=1}^{n} h_k(t) \tag{6.53}$$

where each $h_k(t)$ satisfies the differential equation

$$\frac{dh_k}{dt} = p_k h_k(t) \tag{6.54}$$

Therefore, in matrix notation we have

$$\frac{d\mathbf{h}}{dt} = p_k \mathbf{Ih} \tag{6.55}$$

where $\mathbf{h} = [h_1, h_2, \ldots, h_n]^T$. Equation 6.55 is a homogeneous state equation, with the impulse response vector $\mathbf{h}$ replacing $\mathbf{x}$.

Example 6.16   Let

$$H(s) = \frac{(s + 1/2)}{(s + 1)(s + 2)(s + 3)} \quad \therefore h(t) = -\frac{1}{4} e^{-t} + \frac{3}{2} e^{-2t} - \frac{5}{4} e^{-3t} = \sum_{k=1}^{3} h_k(t)$$

where each $h_k(t)$, ($k = 1,2,3$), satisfies, respectively, the differential equations

$$\frac{dh_1}{dt} + h_1 = 0$$

$$\frac{dh_2}{dt} + 2h_2 = 0$$

and

$$\frac{dh_3}{dt} + 3h_3 = 0$$

In matrix form, these can be written as

$$\frac{d\mathbf{h}}{dt} = p_k \, \mathbf{I} \mathbf{h}$$

where $\mathbf{h}(t) = [h_1 \quad h_2 \quad h_3]^T$ and the matrix $p_k \, \mathbf{I}$ is diagonal with the poles of $H(s)$ on the diagonal:

$$p_k \, \mathbf{I} = \begin{bmatrix} -1 & 0 & 0 \\ 0 & -2 & 0 \\ 0 & 0 & -3 \end{bmatrix}$$

∎

Example 6.17 Consider

$$F(s) = \frac{1}{(s + c)} + \frac{\omega_0}{(s + a)^2[(s + b)^2 + \omega_0^2]}$$

Then

$$f(t) = e^{-ct} + \int_{0_-}^{t} \tau e^{-a\tau} e^{-b(t - \tau)} \sin \omega_0(t - \tau)d\tau$$

We set

$$f(t) = f_1(t) + f_2(t) + f_3(t)$$

where

$$f_1(t) = e^{-ct}$$

$$f_2(t) = e^{-bt} \sin \omega_0 t \int_{0_-}^{t} \tau e^{-a\tau} e^{b\tau} \cos \omega_0 \tau \, d\tau$$

and

$$f_3(t) = -e^{-bt} \cos \omega_0 t \int_{0_-}^{t} e^{-a\tau} e^{b\tau} \sin \omega_0 \tau \, d\tau$$

Then

$$\frac{df_1}{dt} + cf_1 = 0$$

$$\frac{df_2}{dt} + bf_2(t) + \omega_0 f_3(t) = \frac{1}{2} te^{-at} \sin 2\omega_0 t$$

and

$$\frac{df_3}{dt} + bf_3(t) - \omega_0 f_2(t) = -\frac{1}{2} te^{-at} \sin 2\omega_0 t$$

so that

$$\frac{d\mathbf{f}}{dt} = \mathbf{Af} + \mathbf{Bu}$$ ∎

The partial fraction expansion of $H(s)$, used in the previous discussion, provides another approach to simulation diagrams. Again, assume that $m \le n$ and all the poles of $H(s)$ are simple. Then the partial fraction expansion of $H(s)$ will be

$$H(s) = \frac{K_1}{s - p_1} + \frac{K_2}{s - p_2} + \cdots + \frac{K_n}{s - p_n} + K_\infty \tag{6.56}$$

Consider again the first-order network in Example 6.13. There the network function is $H(s) = 1/(a_1 s + a_0)$, essentially the same form as the term $K_n/(s - p_n)$ in our partial fraction expansion. In other words, Figure 6.10 is the basic building block for our purpose here. The resulting simulation diagram (called a *parallel decomposition*) is shown in Figure 6.12. The state variables are the outputs of the integrators, and we can write by inspection

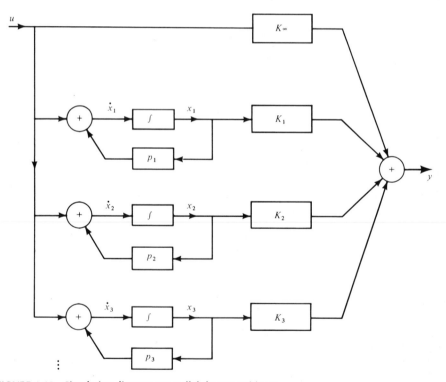

FIGURE 6.12   Simulation diagram ("parallel decomposition").

$$\begin{aligned}
\dot{x}_1 &= p_1 x_1 + u \\
\dot{x}_2 &= p_2 x_2 + u \\
&\;\;\vdots \\
\dot{x}_n &= p_n x_n + u
\end{aligned} \tag{6.57}$$

and

$$y = K_1x_1 + K_2x_2 + \cdots + K_\infty u \qquad (6.58)$$

In matrix form these equations read

$$\dot{\mathbf{x}} = \mathbf{Ax} + \mathbf{Bu} \qquad (6.59)$$

and

$$\mathbf{y} = \mathbf{Cx} + \mathbf{Du} \qquad (6.60)$$

where **A** is diagonal, with the (simple) poles as its elements, **B** is a column unit matrix, **C** is a row column of the residues K_i, and **D** = K_∞. An extension of this method to the case of repeated (multiple) poles is given as a problem at the end of the chapter.

More advanced discussions and further developments of these topics can be found in some of the references listed in the bibliography.

PROBLEMS

6-1 Determine the order n of the network shown.

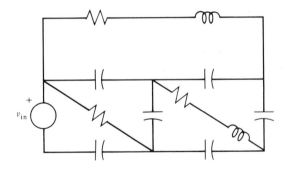

FIGURE 6.13 **Problem 6-1.**

Hint How many independent all-capacitive loops are there?

6-2 Determine the order of each network shown.

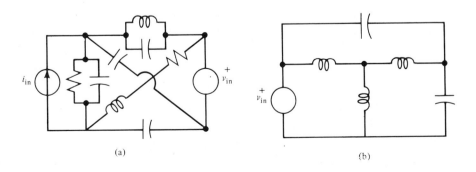

(a)

(b)

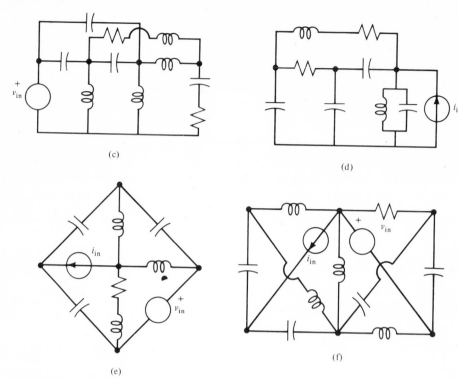

FIGURE 6.14   Problem 6-2.

6-3   The following procedure is suggested for the counting of n_C, the independent all-capacitive loops, and of n_L, the independent all-inductive cut-sets:

(1) To count n_C, *open-circuit* all the resistors, inductors, and current sources in the network. The remaining subnetwork consists only of capacitors and voltage sources forming all-capacitive loops. Then

$$n_C = \hat{b} - (\hat{n} - 1)$$

where $\hat{b}$ is the number of branches and $\hat{n}$ is the number of nodes in this subnetwork.

(2) To determine n_L, *short-circuit* all the resistors, capacitors, and voltage sources. The remaining subnetwork consists only of inductors and current sources forming all-inductive cut-sets. Then

$$n_L = \bar{n} - 1$$

where $\bar{n}$ is the number of nodes in this subnetwork.

Verify this procedure for Problems 6-1 and 6-2.

6-4   In Example 6.2 let the resistor be nonlinear, as follows:

$$i_R(t) = v_R^3(t) - v_R(t)$$

(a) With $C_1 = C_2 = 1$ farad and with the current source $i(t) = 10$ amperes, obtain the state matrix differential equation.

(b) Repeat, if the nonlinear resistor is given by

$$v_R(t) = i_R^3(t) - i_R(t)$$

What difficulty are you encountering?
Hint Sketch the v-i curve of the resistor in cases (a) and (b), and consider the uniqueness of a solution.

6-5 A series RLC circuit is shown in Figure 6.15, with constant L and C, and with a nonlinear resistor whose v-i relation is $v_R = i^3/3 - i$. Compare also with Problem 6-4(b).
(a) Write Kirchhoff's voltage law around the loop, and show that it is the classical van der Pol's equation

$$\frac{d^2i}{dt^2} + \epsilon(i^2 - 1)\frac{di}{dt} + \omega^2 i = 0$$

(b) Formulate the state matrix equation for this circuit, using the capacitor's charge and the inductor's flux as state variables.

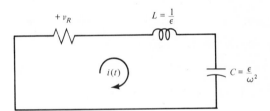

FIGURE 6.15 Problem 6-5.

6-6 Complete the calculations for Example 6.3 in the following steps:
(a) Obtain a single differential equation for V_e by eliminating I_e. Show that it is

$$\frac{d^2 V_e}{dx^2} + k_e^2 V_e = 0$$

with $k_e^2 = \omega^2 LC$. Show that a similar equation holds for V_0.
(b) Set $dV_e/dx = U_e$ and $dV_0/dx = U_0$ and define a new vector

$$\mathbf{Y}(x) = \begin{bmatrix} V_e \\ U_e \\ V_0 \\ U_0 \end{bmatrix}$$

and show that $\mathbf{Y}$ obeys the state equation

$$\frac{d\mathbf{Y}}{dx} = \mathbf{A}\mathbf{Y}$$

Identify $\mathbf{A}$ and, using Laplace transform methods, find the state transition matrix.

6-7 In Example 6.4 both transition probabilities were set equal to λ. Repeat this example, with λ being the probability per unit time of a transition from state n to $(n + 1)$, and μ the corresponding quantity for the transition from $(n - 1)$ to n. Assume that $\mu < \lambda$ and find your answer in terms of a Poisson distribution.

6-8   Prove that the state transition matrix $\boldsymbol{\phi}(t)$ is nonsingular for all finite t. Specifically, show that

$$\det \boldsymbol{\phi}(t) = e^{\text{Tr } \mathbf{A}}$$

where Tr $\mathbf{A}$ = trace of $\mathbf{A} = \sum_{j=1}^{n} a_{jj}$.

6-9   Prove the *semigroup property* of $\boldsymbol{\phi}(t,t_0)$ given by Equation 6.28, i.e.,

$$\boldsymbol{\phi}(t_1,t_3) = \boldsymbol{\phi}(t_1,t_2)\boldsymbol{\phi}(t_2,t_3)$$

by considering the zero-input state equation $\dot{\mathbf{x}} = \mathbf{A}(t)\mathbf{x}$, and the transition from the state $\mathbf{x}(t_2)$ to the state $\mathbf{x}(t_1)$, and then the transition from $\mathbf{x}(t_3)$ to $\mathbf{x}(t_2)$.

6-10   If the commutative condition on $\mathbf{A}(t)$ and $\int_{t_0}^{t} \mathbf{A}(\tau)d\tau$ is not satisfied, the state transition matrix $\boldsymbol{\phi}(t,t_0)$ may be evaluated as follows[4]: Express $\mathbf{A}(t)$ as a sum of two matrices

$$\mathbf{A}(t) = \mathbf{A}_0(t) + \overline{\mathbf{A}}(t)$$

where $\mathbf{A}_0(t)$ satisfies the commutative condition. Therefore, the homogeneous state equation

$$\dot{\mathbf{x}}(t) = \mathbf{A}(t)\mathbf{x}(t)$$

becomes the non-homogeneous equation

$$\dot{\mathbf{x}}(t) = \mathbf{A}_0(t)\mathbf{x}(t) + \overline{\mathbf{A}}(t)\mathbf{x}(t)$$

where $\overline{\mathbf{A}}(t)\mathbf{x}(t)$ plays the role of an "input." The state transition matrix for $\mathbf{A}_0(t)$ is

$$\boldsymbol{\phi}_0(t,t_0) = \exp\left[\int_{t_0}^{t} \mathbf{A}_0(\tau)d\tau\right]$$

The solution to the non-homogeneous equation is then, according to Equation 6.33,

$$\mathbf{x}(t) = \boldsymbol{\phi}_0(t,t_0)\mathbf{x}(t_0) + \int_{t_0}^{t} \boldsymbol{\phi}_0(t,\tau)\overline{\mathbf{A}}(\tau)\mathbf{x}(\tau)d\tau$$

This is an integral (Volterra) equation for $\mathbf{x}(t)$. Its solution is found by successive iterations:

$$\mathbf{x}_p(t) = \boldsymbol{\phi}_0(t,t_0)\mathbf{x}(t_0) + \int_{t_0}^{t} \boldsymbol{\phi}_0(t,\tau)\mathbf{A}(\tau)\mathbf{x}_{p-1}(\tau)d\tau, \quad p = 0,1,2, \ldots$$

(a) Carry out such an iterative solution for the scalar case

$$\dot{x} = (1 + \alpha e^{-t})x$$

where $\alpha \ll 1$ and $x(t_0) = K$, given.[3]
(b) Compare your iterations with the *exact* solution, obtained by separating the variables and then integrating.

6-11   Verify that the commutative condition on $\mathbf{A}(t)$ is satisfied if $\mathbf{A}(t)$ can be written as a product of a *constant* matrix and a scalar time function

$$\mathbf{A}(t) = \mathbf{A}f(t)$$

Hence, obtain the state transition matrix for[3]

$$\dot{\mathbf{x}} = \begin{bmatrix} -2t & -t \\ 2t & -5t \end{bmatrix}\mathbf{x}(t)$$

6-12 Solve by successive iterations, as in Problem 6-10, the state equation

$$\dot{\mathbf{x}} = \begin{bmatrix} t + \alpha e^{-t} & t \\ -t & t \end{bmatrix} \mathbf{x} \qquad \mathbf{x}(t_0) = \begin{bmatrix} 1 \\ 0 \end{bmatrix}$$

6-13 Generalize the homogeneous state difference equation to the case when $\mathbf{A}$ is not constant, that is,

$$\mathbf{x}(k + 1) = \mathbf{A}(k)\mathbf{x}(k)$$

Obtain, by recursion and substitution, the state transition matrix $\boldsymbol{\phi}(k,l)$ such that

$$\mathbf{x}(k) = \boldsymbol{\phi}(k,l)\mathbf{x}(l), \qquad k \geq l$$

where $\mathbf{x}(l)$ is the initial state, not necessarily at zero.

6-14 Let

$$H(s) = \frac{b_0 s^n + b_1 s^{n-1} + \cdots + b_{n-1} s + b_n}{s^n + a_1 s^{n-1} + \cdots + a_{n-1} s + a_n}$$

(a) Obtain the state matrix equation.
(b) Obtain a simulation diagram, generalized from the one in Example 6.14.

6-15 Extend the method of parallel decomposition, Equations 6.56–6.60, to the case of multiple poles. Specifically, let

$$H(s) = \frac{P(s)}{(s - p_1)^r Q_1(s)}$$

where p_1 is of multiplicity $r > 1$ and $Q_1(s)$ has only simple roots. Write the corresponding partial fraction expansion and, from it, draw a simulation diagram.

SELECTED BIBLIOGRAPHY

1. P. M. DeRusso, R. J. Roy, and C. M. Close, *State Variables for Engineers*. New York: John Wiley & Sons, Inc., 1965.
2. T. Kailath, *Linear Systems*. Englewood Cliffs, N.J.: Prentice-Hall, Inc., 1980.
3. S. Karni, *Intermediate Network Analysis*. Boston: Allyn & Bacon, Inc., 1971.
4. B. K. Kinariwala, "Analysis of Time Varying Networks," *IRE International Convention Record*, part 4, pp. 268–276 March 1961.
5. B. J. Leon, *Lumped Systems*. New York: Holt, Rinehart & Winston, Inc., 1968.
6. D. G. Luenberger, *Introduction to Dynamic Systems*. New York: John Wiley & Sons, Inc., 1979.
7. W. J. Rugh, *Mathematical Description of Linear Systems*. New York: Marcel Dekker, Inc., 1975.
8. L. A. Zadeh and C. A. Desoer, *Linear System Theory*. New York: McGraw-Hill Book Company, Inc., 1963.

The
Delta
(Impulse)
Function

It is customary in engineering sciences to define the Dirac delta, or impulse, function according to the following properties:

$$\delta(t - t_0) = 0 \qquad \text{for } t \neq t_0 \qquad (A.1)$$

$$\lim_{t \mapsto t_0} \delta(t - t_0) \rightarrow \infty \qquad (A.2)$$

$$\int_{-\infty}^{\infty} \delta(t - t_0) \, dt = 1 \qquad (A.3)$$

$$\int_{-\infty}^{\infty} f(t)\delta(t - t_0) \, dt = f(t_0) \qquad (A.4)$$

Equation A.3 ascribes to $\delta(t - t_0)$ a probabilistic distribution that is normalizable, whereas A.4 is the "sifting" property whereby $\delta(t - t_0)$ sifts out one value of the continuous function $f(t)$, namely, $f(t_0)$. At $t = t_0$, according to Equation A.2, there is an infinite discontinuity in $\delta(t - t_0)$.

In a strict mathematical sense, $\delta(t - t_0)$ is not a function at all, but must be defined as the limit of a continuous sequence of functions. The theory of distributions has done much, since Laurent Schwartz's pioneering work in the 1950s, to place the delta function on a firm mathematical foundation. It is not our intention in this brief appendix to attempt an exposition of the theory of distributions, but rather to place the properties of the delta function on a firmer footing by choosing continuous functions that represent the delta function.

Consider the Gaussian function

$$f(t - t_0) = \frac{1}{\sqrt{2\pi}\sigma} e^{-(t-t_0)^2/2\sigma^2} \qquad (A.5)$$

As σ becomes smaller, the width of the function $f(t - t_0)$ decreases, while the height increases. However, we have

$$\int_{-\infty}^{\infty} f(t - t_0) \, dt \equiv 1 \qquad \text{for all } \sigma \tag{A.6}$$

To prove this statement, let

$$I = \frac{1}{\sqrt{2\pi}\sigma} \int_{-\infty}^{\infty} e^{-(t-t_0)^2/2\sigma^2} \, dt \tag{A.7}$$

and change variables by setting $(t - t_0)/\sqrt{2}\sigma = x$, so that $dt = \sqrt{2}\sigma \, dx$. Then the integral I becomes

$$I = \frac{1}{\sqrt{\pi}} \int_{-\infty}^{\infty} e^{-x^2} \, dx \tag{A.8}$$

In order to evaluate it, we form its square:

$$I^2 = \frac{1}{\pi} \int_{-\infty}^{\infty} \int_{-\infty}^{\infty} e^{-(x^2+y^2)} \, dx \, dy \tag{A.9}$$

and convert to the polar coordinates (ρ, ϕ), with $x = \rho \cos \phi$ and $y = \rho \sin \phi$, so that $dx \, dy = \rho \, d\rho \, d\phi$. We have, then,

$$I^2 = \frac{1}{\pi} \int_{0}^{2\pi} d\phi \int_{0}^{\infty} e^{-\rho^2} \rho \, d\rho \tag{A.10}$$

Integration with respect to ϕ yields

$$I^2 = 2 \int_{0}^{\infty} e^{-\rho^2} \rho \, d\rho \tag{A.11}$$

With $\rho^2 = r$, so that $2\rho \, d\rho = dr$, we get

$$I^2 = \int_{0}^{\infty} e^{-r} \, dr = 1 \tag{A.12}$$

Thus,

$$I = \frac{1}{\sqrt{2\pi}\sigma} \int_{-\infty}^{\infty} e^{-(t-t_0)^2/2\sigma^2} \, dt \equiv 1 \tag{A.13}$$

This result is standard in engineering and probability theory, where the Gaussian probability density function enters into problems concerned with Brownian motion and random noise, as well as being a fundamental solution to the equation of heat flow and to the diffusion equation of semiconductor theory. The latter are considered in detail in Chapter 3.

We now examine the integral

$$I = \frac{1}{\sqrt{2\pi}\sigma} \int_{-\infty}^{\infty} f(t)e^{-(t-t_0)^2/2\sigma^2} \, dt \tag{A.14}$$

for a continuous function $f(t)$. If σ is small, we can expand $f(t)$ in a Taylor series about the point $t = t_0$ so that

$$f(t) = f(t_0) + \left(\frac{df}{dt}\right)_{t=t_0} (t - t_0) + \frac{1}{2!}\left(\frac{d^2f}{dt^2}\right)_{t=t_0} (t - t_0)^2 + \cdots \qquad (A.15)$$

Then

$$I = \frac{1}{\sqrt{2\pi}\sigma}\left[f(t_0) \int_{-\infty}^{\infty} e^{-(t-t_0)^2/2\sigma^2}\, dt + \left(\frac{df}{dt}\right)_{t=t_0} \int_{-\infty}^{\infty} (t - t_0)e^{-(t-t_0)^2/2\sigma^2}\, dt + \cdots \right]$$

$$(A.16)$$

or

$$I = f(t_0) + \left(\frac{1}{\sqrt{\pi}}\frac{df}{dt}\right)_{t=t_0} \int_{-\infty}^{\infty} x e^{-x^2}\, dx + \cdots \qquad (A.17)$$

But

$$\int_{-\infty}^{\infty} x e^{-x^2}\, dx \equiv 0$$

and the remaining terms are of order σ^2 or higher. Thus,

$$I \equiv f(t_0) \qquad \text{as } \sigma \to 0 \qquad (A.18)$$

The function $f_\sigma(t - t_0)$ thus defined by

$$f_\sigma(t - t_0) \equiv \lim_{\sigma \to 0} \frac{1}{\sqrt{2\pi}\sigma} e^{-(t-t_0)^2/2\sigma^2} \qquad (A.19)$$

is such that

$$\int_{-\infty}^{\infty} f_\sigma(t - t_0)\, dt = 1 \qquad (A.20)$$

and

$$\int_{-\infty}^{\infty} f(t)f_\sigma(t - t_0)\, dt = f(t_0) \qquad (A.21)$$

These two relations, when compared with properties A.3 and A.4 of the delta function, allow us to write

$$\delta(t - t_0) = \lim_{\sigma \to 0} \frac{1}{\sqrt{2\pi}\sigma} e^{-(t-t_0)^2/2\sigma^2} \qquad (A.22)$$

Also, property A.2 of the delta function is satisfied by this representation.

Of more importance in our work is the following possible representation of the delta function:

$$\delta(t - t_0) = \frac{1}{2\pi} \int_{-\infty}^{\infty} e^{-j\omega(t-t_0)}\, d\omega \qquad (A.23)$$

We now establish that the integral

$$I \equiv \lim_{\Omega \to \infty} \frac{1}{2\pi} \int_{-\Omega}^{\Omega} e^{-j\omega(t-t_0)} \, d\omega \tag{A.24}$$

has the properties of the delta function. We have

$$I = \lim_{\Omega \to \infty} \frac{1}{\pi} \frac{\sin \Omega(t - t_0)}{(t - t_0)} \tag{A.25}$$

As $\Omega \to \infty$ for $t \neq t_0$, $I \to 0$. As $t \to t_0$ and $\Omega \to \infty$,

$$I \to \Omega \to \infty \tag{A.26}$$

Thus property A.2 of the delta function is shared by the integral I. We now form

$$\lim_{\Omega \to \infty} \frac{1}{\pi} \int_{-\infty}^{\infty} \frac{\sin \Omega(t - t_0)}{t - t_0} \, dt \equiv J \tag{A.27}$$

and change variables by letting $t - t_0 = x$. Then

$$J = \lim_{\Omega \to \infty} \frac{1}{\pi} \int_{-\infty}^{\infty} \frac{\sin \Omega x}{x} \, dx = \lim_{\Omega \to \infty} \frac{1}{\pi} \, \mathrm{Im} \int_{-\infty}^{\infty} \frac{e^{j\Omega x}}{x} \, dx \tag{A.28}$$

But by Example 2.33 of Chapter 2, the integral has the value of π. Thus,

$$J = 1 \tag{A.29}$$

and property A.3 of the delta function is shared by I.

Finally, we show that

$$\lim_{\Omega \to \infty} \frac{1}{\pi} \int_{-\infty}^{\infty} f(t) \frac{\sin \Omega(t - t_0)}{t - t_0} \, dt = f(t_0) \tag{A.30}$$

Now we must show that

$$\lim_{\Omega \to \infty} \frac{1}{2\pi} \int_{-\infty}^{\infty} f(t) \int_{-\Omega}^{\Omega} e^{-j\omega(t-t_0)} \, d\omega \, dt = f(t_0) \tag{A.31}$$

Although the validity of interchange of the order of integration should be established, we assume that it is a valid step, so that

$$f(t_0) = \frac{1}{2\pi} \lim_{\Omega \to \infty} \int_{-\Omega}^{\Omega} e^{+j\omega t_0} \int_{-\infty}^{\infty} f(t) e^{-j\omega t} \, dt \, d\omega \tag{A.32}$$

Then, since $F(\omega) \equiv \int_{-\infty}^{\infty} e^{-j\omega t} f(t) \, dt$,

$$f(t_0) = \frac{1}{2\pi} \int_{-\infty}^{\infty} e^{j\omega t_0} F(\omega) \, d\omega \tag{A.33}$$

But this is the definition of the Fourier integral representation of $f(t_0)$. Thus property A.4 of the delta function is shared by the quantity I, and we may write

$$\delta(t - t_0) = \frac{1}{2\pi} \int_{-\infty}^{\infty} e^{-j\omega(t-t_0)} \, d\omega \tag{A.34}$$

A careful examination will show that either the representation

$$\delta(t - t_0) = \lim_{\sigma \to 0} \frac{1}{\sqrt{2\pi}\sigma} e^{-(t-t_0)^2/2\sigma^2} \tag{A.35}$$

or that given in Equation A.34 establishes the fact that $\delta(t - t_0)$ is an even function of its argument.

We now examine further properties of the delta function. Consider the integral

$$I(a) = \int_{-\infty}^{\infty} f(t)\delta(at - t_0)\ dt \tag{A.36}$$

where a is a real constant. Set $at = u$, so that $I(a)$ becomes

$$I(a) = \frac{1}{|a|} \int_{-\infty}^{\infty} f\left(\frac{u}{a}\right)\delta(u - t_0)\ du \tag{A.37}$$

or

$$I(a) = \frac{1}{|a|} f\left(\frac{t_0}{a}\right) \tag{A.38}$$

This is often written as

$$\delta(at - t_0) \to \frac{1}{|a|} \delta\left(t - \frac{t_0}{|a|}\right) \tag{A.39}$$

Examine the integral

$$\int_{-\infty}^{\infty} f(x)\delta(x - a)\ dx = f(a) \int_{-\infty}^{\infty} \delta(x - a)\ dx \tag{A.40}$$

This is often written as

$$f(x)\delta(x - a) = f(a)\delta(x - a) \tag{A.41}$$

but must always be understood in the sense of the integral in Equation A.40. In particular, if $f(x) = x$, then

$$x\delta(x - a) = a\delta(x - a) \tag{A.42}$$

and if $a = 0$, then

$$x\delta(x) = 0 \tag{A.43}$$

Other properties of the delta function are listed here without proof:

$$\int_{-\infty}^{\infty} \delta'(t - t_0)f(t)\ dt = -f'(t_0) \tag{A.44}$$

where the prime (') indicates the first derivative. Also, for the nth derivative, we have

$$\int_{-\infty}^{\infty} \delta^{(n)}(t - t_0)f(t)\ dt = (-1)^n f^{(n)}(t_0) \tag{A.45}$$

SELECTED BIBLIOGRAPHY

1. M. J. Lighthill, *Fourier Analysis and Generalized Functions*. New York: Cambridge University Press, 1958.

2. A. Papoulis, *The Fourier Integral and Its Applications*, New York: McGraw-Hill Book Company, Inc., 1962, Appendix I.

3. L. Schwartz, *Théorie des Distributions*, Vols. I and II. Paris: Hermann et Cie, 1957, 1959.

4. B. Van der Pol and H. Bremmer, *Operational Calculus*, 2nd ed. Fair Lawn, N.J.: Oxford University Press, 1955, Chapter 5.

Fourier Series
and the Passage
to the Fourier Integral

As mentioned in the preface, some familiarity with Fourier series is assumed. For that reason we discuss Fourier series only briefly, and examine rather more carefully the passage from a Fourier series representation of a function $f(t)$ to the Fourier integral.

Let $f(t)$ be a periodic function with period T; i.e., let

$$f(t + nT) = f(t) \qquad (B.1)$$

with n an integer. The familiar Fourier series for $f(t)$ is

$$f(t) = \frac{a_0}{2} + \sum_{n=1}^{\infty} (a_n \cos \omega_n t + b_n \sin \omega_n t) \qquad (B.2)$$

where $\omega_n = 2\pi n/T \equiv n\omega_0$, and it will converge uniformly to $f(t)$ for all values of t for which $f(t)$ is continuous. If $f(t)$ is piecewise continuous in $[0,T]$, then the Fourier series will converge to $f(t)$ at all points for which $f(t)$ is continuous, and, at any of the finite number of finite discontinuities of $f(t)$, will converge to the value

$$f(t_0) = \frac{1}{2}[f(t_0^-) + f(t_0^+)] \qquad (B.3)$$

where the discontinuity is at $t = t_0$. See Figure B.1.

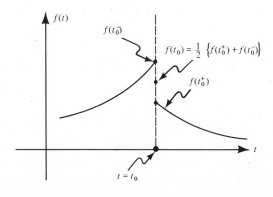

FIGURE B.1 Fourier series behavior in the vicinity of a discontinuity of $f(t)$ at $t=t_0$.

The coefficients of the Fourier series can be found in a straightforward way, and are given as

$$a_0 = \frac{2}{T} \int_0^T f(t) \, dt \tag{B.4}$$

whereas, if $p \neq 0$,

$$a_p = \frac{2}{T} \int_0^T f(t) \cos \omega_p t \, dt \tag{B.5}$$

$$b_p = \frac{2}{T} \int_0^T f(t) \sin \omega_p t \, dt \tag{B.6}$$

In each integral we integrate over one period, i.e., from 0 to T, or from t_0 to $t_0 + T$, whichever is more convenient.

If $f(t)$ is an even function of the variable t, $f(t) = f(-t)$, then all $b_n \equiv 0$ and $f(t)$ can be represented as a cosine series, whereas if $f(t)$ is an odd function, $f(t) = -f(-t)$, then all $a_n \equiv 0$ and $f(t)$ can be written as a sine series.

An alternative form for the Fourier series of $f(t)$ is the following.

$$f(t) = \sum_{n=-\infty}^{\infty} c_n e^{2j\pi n/T} \equiv \sum_{-\infty}^{\infty} c_n e^{j\omega_n t} \tag{B.7}$$

The representation given in Equation B.7 reduces to that of Equation B.2 if $c_n = (a_n - jb_n)/2$ and if $c_n^* = c_{-n}$; i.e., if $c_{-n} = (a_n + jb_n)/2$. The coefficients c_n are found to be

$$c_n = \frac{1}{T} \int_{-T/2}^{T/2} f(\tau) e^{-j\omega_n \tau} \, d\tau \tag{B.8}$$

so that

$$f(t) = \lim_{N \to \infty} \sum_{n=-N}^{N} \frac{1}{T} \int_{-T/2}^{T/2} f(\tau) e^{j\omega_n (t-\tau)} \, d\tau \tag{B.9}$$

To convert this last expression to a Fourier integral representation of $f(t)$, we form the expression

$$f(t) = \lim_{\substack{N \to \infty \\ T \to \infty}} \sum_{n=-N}^{N} \frac{1}{T} \int_{-T/2}^{T/2} f(\tau) e^{j\omega_n (t-\tau)} \, d\tau \tag{B.10}$$

It is important that this double limiting process be performed carefully. To see this fact, we define the integral

$$I = \lim_{T \to \infty} \frac{1}{T} \int_{-T/2}^{T/2} f(\tau) e^{j\omega_n (t-\tau)} \, d\tau \tag{B.11}$$

Now,

$$I \leq \lim_{T \to \infty} \frac{1}{T} \int_{-T/2}^{T/2} f(\tau) \, d\tau \tag{B.12}$$

and if $\int_{-T/2}^{T/2} f(\tau)\, d\tau$ is bounded, then

$$I \to 0 \qquad \text{as } T \to \infty \tag{B.13}$$

Thus, for any finite N, if we permit T to approach infinity first, $f(t) \to 0$.

Now, $\omega_n \equiv n\omega_0$, where $\omega_0 = 2\pi/T$. Thus, as $T \to \infty$,

$$\frac{2\pi}{T} \equiv \omega_{n+1} - \omega_n \equiv \Delta\omega_n \to 0$$

We therefore can write the expression for $f(t)$, given in Equation B.10, in the alternative form

$$f(t) = \lim_{\substack{\Delta\omega_n \to 0 \\ N \to \infty}} \frac{1}{2\pi} \sum_{n=-N}^{N} \int_{-\infty}^{\infty} f(\tau) e^{j\omega_n(t-\tau)} \, d\tau \, \Delta\omega_n \tag{B.14}$$

By the definition of integration, Equation B.14 becomes

$$f(t) = \frac{1}{2\pi} \int_{-\infty}^{\infty} \int_{-\infty}^{\infty} f(\tau) e^{j\omega(t-\tau)} \, d\tau \, d\omega \tag{B.15}$$

In Equation A.23, Appendix A, it is shown that

$$2\pi\delta(t - \tau) = \int_{-\infty}^{\infty} e^{\pm j\omega(t-\tau)} \, d\omega \tag{B.16}$$

so that Equation B.15 is, by the sifting property of the delta function, identically satisfied. Further, on defining

$$F(\omega) \equiv \int_{-\infty}^{\infty} e^{-j\omega\tau} f(\tau) \, d\tau \tag{B.17a}$$

we have that

$$f(t) = \frac{1}{2\pi} \int_{-\infty}^{\infty} F(\omega) e^{j\omega t} \, d\omega \tag{B.17b}$$

Equations B.17a and B.17b constitute the Fourier transform pair.

SELECTED BIBLIOGRAPHY

1. E. O. Brigham, *The Fast Fourier Transform*. Englewood Cliffs, NJ: Prentice-Hall, Inc., 1974.
2. R. V. Churchill, *Fourier Series and Boundary Value Problems*. New York: McGraw-Hill Book Co., 1963.
3. H. F. Davis, *Fourier Series and Orthogonat Functions*. Boston: Allyn and Bacon, Inc., 1963.
4. J. D. Gaskill, *Linear Systems, Fourier Transforms, and Optics*. New York: John Wiley and Sons, Inc., 1978.
5. H. P. Hsu, *Outline of Fourier Analysis*. New York: Unitech Division (Simon and Schuster, Inc.) 1967.
6. W. Kaplan, *Advanced Mathematics for Engineers*. Reading, Mass.: Addison-Wesley Publishing Co., 1981.

7. E. Kreyszig, *Advanced Engineering Mathematics*. New York: John Wiley and Sons, Inc., 1979.

8. M. J. Lighthill, *Introduction to Fourier Analysis and Generalised Functions*. Cambridge: University Press, 1964.

9. A. Papoulis, *The Fourier Integral and Its Applications*. New York: McGraw-Hill Book Co., 1962.

10. L. A. Pipes and L. R. Harvill, *Applied Mathematics for Engineers and Physicists*. New York: McGraw-Hill Book Co., 1970.

11. M. C. Potter, *Mathematical Methods in the Physical Sciences*. Englewood Cliffs, N.J.: Prentice-Hall, Inc., 1978.

12. A. J. M. Spencer et al., *Engineering Mathematics*. New York: Van Nostrand Reinhold Co., 1977.

13. E. C. Titchmarsh, *Introduction to the Theory of Fourier Integrals*. Oxford: University Press, 1948.

APPENDIX C

Bessel

Functions

Bessel functions are solutions of the differential equation

$$\frac{d^2f}{dx^2} + \frac{1}{x}\frac{df}{dx} + \left(1 - \frac{n^2}{x^2}\right)f = 0 \qquad (C.1)$$

where n is some number and $f(x)$ is defined in the interval $(0, \infty)$.

To solve this differential equation, we assume that a series solution exists in the following form

$$f(x) = \sum_{l=0}^{\infty} a_l x^{l+\tau} \qquad (C.2)$$

where the coefficients a_l and the quantity τ are to be found. Upon substituting Equation C.2 into Equation C.1, we find that the latter becomes

$$\sum_{l=0}^{\infty} a_l[(l+\tau)(l+\tau-1) + (l+\tau) - n^2]x^{l+\tau-2} + \sum_{l=0}^{\infty} a_l x^{l+\tau} = 0 \qquad (C.3)$$

We require that the coefficients of each power of x be separately equal to zero. On setting $l = 0$, the coefficient of x^{-2} is $a_0(\tau^2 - n^2)$, which will be zero if $a_0 = 0$ or if $\tau = \pm n$. With the constant a_0 arbitrary but nonzero, choose

$$\tau = n$$

in order that the solution be finite at $x = 0$. When $l = 1$, the coefficient of $x^{\tau-1} = x^{n-1}$ is $a_1[(n+1)^2 - n^2] \equiv 0$. Obviously, $a_1 = 0$. With $\tau = n$, the first terms of Equation C.3 become

$$\sum_{l=0}^{\infty} a_l[(l+n)^2 - n^2]x^{n+l-2}$$

which can be written as

$$\sum_{l=0}^{\infty} a_l(l^2 + 2ln)x^{l+n-2}$$

Set $l - 2 = p$. Then

$$\sum_{p=-2}^{\infty} a_{p+2}\{(p+2)^2 + 2(p+2)n\}x^{p+n}$$

is identically zero when $p = -2$ because the bracketed term disappears. When $p = -1$, $a_{p+2} = a_1 \equiv 0$. Thus,

$$\sum_{p=-2}^{\infty} a_{p+2}[(p + 2)^2 + 2n(p + 2)]x^{p+n} = \sum_{l=0}^{\infty} a_{l+2}[(l + 2)^2 + 2n(l + 2)]x^{l+n}$$

since $p = l$ is a dummy sum index. Equation C.3 is now in the form

$$\sum_{l=0}^{\infty} \{a_{l+2}[(l + 2)(l + 2 + 2n)] + a_l\}x^{l+n} = 0 \tag{C.4}$$

The coefficients therefore must satisfy the recursion relation

$$a_{l+2} = -\frac{a_l}{(l + 2)(l + 2 + 2n)} \tag{C.5}$$

Noting that all odd coefficients are zero, since $a_1 \equiv 0$, we can set $l = 2m$ and sum over all integers m, rather than over even integers l. Then the recursion relation among coefficients is

$$a_{2(m+1)} = \frac{-a_{2m}}{2^2(m + 1)(m + n + 1)} \tag{C.6}$$

With a_0 arbitrary, we have, as the first few coefficients,

$$a_2 = \frac{-a_0}{2^2(n + 1)}$$

$$a_4 = \frac{-a_2}{2^2(2)(n + 2)} = \frac{a_0}{2^4(1 \cdot 2)(n + 1)(n + 2)}$$

$$a_6 = \frac{-a_4}{2^2(3)(n + 3)} = \frac{-a_0}{2^6(1 \cdot 2 \cdot 3)(n + 1)(n + 2)(n + 3)}$$

In general, then,

$$a_{2m} = \frac{(-1)^m a_0}{2^{2m}m!\,(n + 1) \cdots (n + m)} \tag{C.7}$$

We now choose the arbitrary constant $a_0 = (\frac{1}{2})^n n!$, so that

$$a_{2m} = \frac{(-1)^m}{2^{2m+n}m!\,(n + m)!} \tag{C.8}$$

Then

$$f(x) = \sum_{m=0}^{\infty} \frac{(-1)^m \left(\dfrac{x}{2}\right)^{2m+n}}{m!\,(n + m)!} \tag{C.9}$$

This series is defined as the function $J_n(x)$, the Bessel function of integer order n and argument x, i.e.,

$$f(x) = J_n(x) \tag{C.10}$$

Recall that we chose $\tau = n$, discarding the value $\tau = -n$. A second linearly independent solution, usually called the Neumann function, can be generated if we take the value $\tau = -n$. The Neumann function, denoted by $N_n(x)$, is given by

$$N_n(x) = \frac{1}{\sin n\pi} \{J_n(x) \cos n\pi - J_{-n}(x)\} \tag{C.11}$$

Now, from the series solution, it is readily established that, for integer n,

$$J_{-n}(x) = (-1)^n J_n(x) \tag{C.12}$$

so that as n approaches an integer, $N_n(x)$ is indeterminate. Without going into details, it can be shown that, as n approaches an integer, the Neumann function has a logarithmic singularity as $x \to 0$, whereas as $x \to 0$

$$\lim_{x \to 0} J_n(x) \to \frac{1}{n!} \left(\frac{x}{2}\right)^n \tag{C.13}$$

We now examine the behavior of the function $J_n(x)$ as $x \to \infty$. From the differential equation

$$\frac{d^2 J_n}{dx^2} + \frac{1}{x} \frac{dJ_n}{dx} + \left(1 - \frac{n^2}{x^2}\right) J_n = 0 \tag{C.14}$$

we generate, on setting

$$J_n(x) = x^{-1/2} g_n(x) \tag{C.15}$$

a differential equation for $g_n(x)$. It is

$$\frac{d^2 g_n}{dx^2} + \left(1 - \frac{\lambda_n^2}{x^2}\right) g_n = 0 \tag{C.16}$$

where λ_n^2 is a constant depending on n. As $x \to \infty$, $\lambda_n^2 / x^2 \to 0$, so that the function $g_n(x)$ can be written in the form

$$\lim_{x \to \infty} g_n(x) = C_n \cos(x + \phi_n) \tag{C.17}$$

Then

$$\lim_{x \to \infty} J_n(x) = \frac{C_n}{x} \cos(x + \phi_n) \tag{C.18}$$

A careful analysis shows that $\phi_n = -(2n + 1)\pi/4$, and that $C_n = \sqrt{2/\pi}$, so that

$$\lim_{x \to \infty} J_n(x) = \sqrt{\frac{2}{\pi x}} \cos\left(x - (2n + 1)\frac{\pi}{4}\right) \tag{C.19}$$

Similar reasoning applied to the Neuman function yields the result

$$\lim_{x \to \infty} N_n(x) = \sqrt{\frac{2}{\pi x}} \sin\left(x - (2n + 1)\frac{\pi}{4}\right) \tag{C.20}$$

Note that the linear combinations

$$J_n(x) \pm jN_n(x)$$

satisfy the relation

$$\lim_{x \to \infty}(J_n(x) \pm jN_n(x)) = B_n \frac{e^{\pm jx}}{\sqrt{x}} \tag{C.21}$$

where

$$B_n = \sqrt{\frac{2}{\pi}}e^{-j(2n+1)\pi/4}$$

Physically, the terms $e^{\pm jx}/\sqrt{x}$ represent traveling waves that attenuate with distance as $x^{-1/2}$. The quantities $J_n(x) \pm jN_n(x)$ are defined as Hankel functions of order n, of the first or second kind; i.e.,

$$H_n^{(1)}(x) = J_n(x) + jN_n(x)$$

and $\tag{C.22}$

$$H_n^{(2)}(x) = J_n(x) - jN_n(x)$$

Bessel functions of imaginary argument are defined as solutions to the differential equation

$$\frac{d^2g}{dx^2} + \frac{1}{x}\frac{dg}{dx} - \left(1 + \frac{n^2}{x^2}\right)g = 0 \tag{C.23}$$

This equation differs from Equation C.1 only in the sign of the coefficient of g. If we had written

$$\frac{d^2g}{dx^2} + \frac{1}{x}\frac{dg}{dx} + \left(j^2 - \frac{n^2}{x^2}\right)g = 0 \tag{C.24}$$

then it is easily shown, by methods identical to those used in determining the series solution (Equation C.9), that

$$g(x) = J_n(jx) \tag{C.25}$$

A Bessel function of pure imaginary argument, denoted by $I_n(x)$, can now be defined, such that

$$I_n(x) = e^{-jn\pi/2}J_n(jx) \tag{C.26}$$

Since, by Equation C.19,

$$\lim_{x \to \infty} J_n(x) = \sqrt{\frac{2}{\pi x}}\cos\left(x - (2n+1)\frac{\pi}{4}\right) \tag{C.19}$$

we have that

$$\lim_{x \to \infty} J_n(jx) = \sqrt{\frac{2}{j\pi x}}\cos\left(jx - (2n+1)\frac{\pi}{4}\right) \tag{C.27}$$

from which

$$\lim_{x \to \infty} I_n(x) \cong \frac{e^x}{\sqrt{x}} \tag{C.28}$$

That is, the Bessel function of imaginary argument is unbounded as $x \to \infty$. This behavior is used in our discussion of lossy transmission lines in Chapter 3.

There are recursion relations satisfied by Bessel functions. Recall that in Chapter 2, in our discussion of the Laurent expansion, it is established that the generating function for Bessel functions is given by

$$e^{x/2(t - 1/t)} = \sum_{n=-\infty}^{\infty} J_n(x) t^n \tag{C.29}$$

If both sides of this expression are differentiated with respect to x, we have

$$\frac{1}{2}\left(t - \frac{1}{t}\right) \sum_{n=-\infty}^{\infty} J_n(x) t^n = \sum_{n=-\infty}^{\infty} J_n'(x) t^n \tag{C.30}$$

On equating coefficients of like powers of t on both sides of this last equation, the relation

$$\frac{1}{2}(J_{l-1} - J_{l+1}) = J_l'(x) \tag{C.31}$$

is found. We may differentiate Equation C.29 with respect to t, thereby obtaining

$$\frac{x}{2}\left(1 + \frac{1}{t^2}\right) \sum_{n=-\infty}^{\infty} J_n(x) t^n = \sum_{n=-\infty}^{\infty} n J_n(x) t^{n-1} \tag{C.32}$$

Again, on equating coefficients of like powers of t, we have, as coefficients of t^l, the equality

$$\frac{x}{2}(J_l(x) + J_{l+2}(x)) = (l + 1)J_{l+1}(x) \tag{C.33}$$

or, on replacing l by $l - 1$,

$$\frac{x}{2}(J_{l-1}(x) + J_{l+1}(x)) = l J_l(x) \tag{C.34}$$

Equations C.31 and C.34 are recursion relations among Bessel functions of various orders and their derivatives.

Finally, we examine the recursion relation when $t = e^{j\phi}$. Then

$$e^{jx \sin \phi} = \sum_{n=-\infty}^{\infty} J_n(x) e^{jn\phi} \tag{C.35}$$

from which we get the identities

$$\cos (x \sin \phi) = \sum_{n=-\infty}^{\infty} J_n(x) \cos n\phi$$

and $\tag{C.36}$

$$\sin (x \sin \phi) = \sum_{n=-\infty}^{\infty} J_n(x) \sin n\phi$$

Further, if we form

$$\int_0^{2\pi} e^{jx\sin\phi} e^{-jl\phi} \, d\phi = \sum_{n=-\infty}^{\infty} J_n(x) \int_0^{2\pi} e^{j(n-l)\phi} \, d\phi \tag{C.37}$$

we see that the right-hand side of this equation vanishes unless $n = l$, in which case it becomes $2\pi J_l(x)$. Thus we find an integral representation for $J_l(x)$ namely,

$$J_l(x) = \frac{1}{2\pi} \int_0^{2\pi} e^{jx\sin\phi} e^{-jl\phi} \, d\phi \tag{C.38}$$

If $l = 0$,

$$J_0(x) = \frac{1}{2\pi} \int_0^{2\pi} e^{jx\sin\phi} \, d\phi \tag{C.39}$$

Integrals of this kind and for Bessel functions of imaginary argument are encountered in our discussion of the lossy transmission line, as well as in our discussions of frequency modulation and Fourier–Bessel transforms.

SELECTED BIBLIOGRAPHY

1. R. Courant and D. Hilbert, *Methods of Mathematical Physics* (2 vols.). New York: Interscience, 1953 and 1962.
2. A. Erdelyi, Editor, *Higher Transcendental Functions* (3 vols.). New York: McGraw-Hill, 1953–1955.
3. H. Hochstadt, *The Functions of Mathematical Physics*. New York: Wiley, Interscience, 1971.
4. N. W. McLachlan, *Bessel Functions for Engineers*. Oxford: The University Press, 1961.
5. P. M. Morse and H. Feshbach, *Methods of Theoretical Physics*. (parts I and II). New York: McGraw-Hill Book Co., 1953.
6. K. Rektorys, *Survey of Applicable Mathematics*. Cambridge, Mass.: The M.I.T. Press, 1969.
7. G. N. Watson, *Theory of Bessel Functions*. New York: Macmillan, 1954.
8. E. T. Whittaker and G. N. Watson, *Modern Analysis*. Cambridge: Cambridge University Press, 1962.

Short
Tables
of
Transforms

In this appendix there are three separate tables of transforms: Laplace, Fourier (exponential, cosine, and sine), and Z-transforms.

TABLE D.1 Laplace transforms $F(s) = \displaystyle\int_{0_-}^{\infty} f(t)e^{-st}dt$

All time functions are assumed to be multiplied by $u(t)$ appropriately.

$f(t)$	$F(s)$
$a_1f_1(t) + a_2f_2(t)$	$a_1 F_1(s) + a_2 F_2(s)$
$f(t + T) = f(t)$	$(1 - e^{-sT})^{-1} \displaystyle\int_{0_-}^{T} e^{-st}f(t)dt$
$e^{-at}f(t)$	$F(s + a)$
$f(t - a)u(t - a)$	$e^{-as} F(s)$
$t^n f(t)$	$(-1)^n \dfrac{d^n F(s)}{ds^n}$
$t^{-n}f(t)$	$\displaystyle\int_{s}^{\infty}\int_{s}^{\infty} \cdots \int_{s}^{\infty} F(\xi)(d\xi)$
$\dfrac{d^n f(t)}{dt^n} \equiv f^{(n)}(t)$	$s^n F(s) - s^{n-1}f(0_-) - \cdots - f^{(n-1)}(0_-)$
$t^k f^{(n)}(t) \qquad (k \geq n)$	$(-1)^k \dfrac{d^k}{ds^k} (s^n F(s))$

$\dfrac{d^k}{dt^k}(t^n f(t))$ $(n \geq k)$	$(-1)^n s^k F^{(n)}(s)$
$\displaystyle\int_{0_-}^{t} \tau^{-1} f(\tau) d\tau$	$s^{-1} \displaystyle\int_{s}^{\infty} F(\xi) d\xi$
$\displaystyle\int_{0_-}^{t} f_1(\tau) f_2(t - \tau) d\tau$	$F_1(s) F_2(s)$
$\dfrac{1}{a} f\left(\dfrac{t}{a}\right)$ $a > 0$	$F(as)$

The above entries are discussed as theorems in Chapter 3 or are extensions thereof.

$\delta(t)$	1
$u(t)$	$1/s$
t^n $n = 0, 1, 2, \ldots$	$n!/s^{n+1}$
e^{-at} (Re $a > 0$)	$1/(s + a)$
$t^n e^{-at}$ (Re $a > 0$)	$n!/(s + a)^{n+1}$
$\sin \omega t$	$\omega/(s^2 + \omega^2)$
$t^{-1} \sin \omega t$	$\tan^{-1}(\omega/s)$
$t^{-1} \sin \alpha t \sin \beta t$	$\dfrac{1}{4} \ln \dfrac{s^2 + (\alpha + \beta)^2}{s^2 + (\alpha - \beta)^2}$
$\cos \omega t$	$s/(s^2 + \omega^2)$
$\cos^2 \omega t$	$(s^2 + 2\omega^2)/(s^3 + 4\omega^2 s)$
$t^{-1}(\cos \alpha t - \cos \beta t)$	$\dfrac{1}{2} \ln [(\omega^2 + \beta^2)(\omega^2 + \alpha^2)^{-1}]$
$\sinh at$	$a/(s^2 - a^2)$
$\cosh at$	$s/(s^2 - a^2)$
$t^{-1} \sinh at$	$\dfrac{1}{2} \ln \left(\dfrac{s + a}{s - a}\right)$
$\mathrm{erf}(\sqrt{at})$	$\dfrac{\sqrt{a}}{s\sqrt{s + a}}$
$\mathrm{erf}\left(\dfrac{1}{2}\sqrt{\dfrac{a}{t}}\right)$	$\dfrac{1 - e^{-\sqrt{as}}}{s}$

$\operatorname{erfc}\left(\dfrac{1}{2}\sqrt{\dfrac{a}{t}}\right)$	$s^{-1}e^{-\sqrt{as}}$
$J_0(at)$	$(s^2 + a^2)^{-1/2}$
$J_n(at)$ $(\operatorname{Re} n > -1)$	$(s^2 + a^2)^{-1/2}e^{-n\sinh^{-1}(s/a)}$
$J_0(a\sqrt{t^2 - \tau^2})$ $t > \tau$ 0 $0 < t < \tau$	$(s^2 + a^2)^{-1/2}e^{-\tau\sqrt{s^2+a^2}}$
$I_0(at)$	$(s^2 - a^2)^{-1/2}$
$I_n(at)$	$a^n(s^2 - a^2)^{-1/2}(s + \sqrt{s^2 - a^2})^{-n}$

TABLE D.2   Fourier transforms

In this table the notation $F(\omega)$ is the exponential Fourier transform, $F_c(\omega)$ is the Fourier cosine transform, and $F_s(\omega)$ is the Fourier sine transform, of a given function $f(t)$, as defined in Chapter 4.

$f(t)$	$F_c(\omega)$
$\delta(t)$	1
$t^{-1/2}$	$\sqrt{\dfrac{\pi}{2\omega}}$
$(t^2 + \tau^2)^{-1}$ $(\tau\ \text{real}, > 0)$	$\pi e^{-\omega\tau}/2\tau$
$(t^2 + \tau^2)^{-1/2}[(t^2 + \tau^2)^{1/2} + \tau]^{1/2}$	$\left(\dfrac{2\omega}{\pi}\right)^{1/2}e^{-\omega\tau}$
$e^{-\omega_0 t}$ $(\operatorname{Re}\omega_0 > 0)$	$\omega_0/(\omega_0^2 + \omega^2)$
$e^{-\lambda t^2}$ $(\operatorname{Re}\lambda > 0)$	$\dfrac{1}{2}\sqrt{\dfrac{\pi}{\lambda}}\,e^{-\omega^2/4\lambda}$
$t^{-1/2}e^{-\tau/t}$ $(\tau\ \text{real}, > 0)$	$\sqrt{\dfrac{\pi}{2\omega}}\,e^{-(2\omega\tau)^{1/2}}\{\cos(2\omega\tau)^{1/2} - \sin(2\omega\tau)^{1/2}\}$
$t(t^2 + \tau^2)^{-1}\sin\omega_0 t$ $(\omega_0, \tau > 0)$	$\dfrac{\pi}{2}e^{-\omega_0\tau}\cosh\omega\tau$ $\omega < \omega_0$ $-\dfrac{\pi}{2}e^{-\omega_0\tau}\sinh\omega\tau$ $\omega > \omega_0$
$e^{-\lambda t}\sin\omega_0 t$ $(\omega_0 > 0; \lambda > 0)$	$\dfrac{1}{2}\left\{\dfrac{\omega_0 + \omega}{\lambda^2 + (\omega_0 + \omega)^2} + \dfrac{\omega_0 - \omega}{\lambda^2 + (\omega_0 - \omega)^2}\right\}$
$e^{-\lambda t}\cos\omega_0 t$ $(\lambda,\ \omega_0\ \text{real})$	$\dfrac{\lambda}{2}\left\{\dfrac{1}{\lambda^2 + (\omega + \omega_0)^2} + \dfrac{1}{\lambda^2 + (\omega_0 - \omega)^2}\right\}$

$\sin\lambda(\tau^2 - t^2)^{1/2}$ $t < \tau$ $\qquad\qquad 0 \quad t > \tau$	$\dfrac{\pi\lambda\tau}{2\sqrt{\lambda^2 + \omega^2}} J_1(\tau\sqrt{\lambda^2 + \omega^2})$
$J_0(\lambda t)$ $\lambda > 0$	$(\lambda^2 - \omega^2)^{-1/2}$ $0 < \omega < \lambda$ $\qquad\qquad \infty \qquad\qquad \omega = \lambda$ $\qquad\qquad 0 \qquad\qquad \lambda < \omega < \infty$
$f(t)$	$F_s(\omega)$
$\delta(t)$	0
t^{-1}	$\dfrac{\pi}{2}$
$t^{-3/2}$	$\sqrt{2\pi\omega}$
$\dfrac{t}{t^2 + \tau^2}$	$\dfrac{\pi}{2} e^{-\omega\tau}$
$\lambda\left\{\dfrac{1}{\lambda^2 + (\tau - t)^2} - \dfrac{1}{\lambda^2 + (\tau + t)^2}\right\}$ $\qquad\qquad (\lambda > 0, \ \tau \text{ real})$	$\pi e^{-\lambda\omega} \sin \omega\tau$
e^{-at} $(\text{Re } a > 0)$	$\dfrac{\omega}{a^2 + \omega^2}$
$t^{-1}e^{-at}$ $(\text{Re } a > 0)$	$\tan^{-1}\left(\dfrac{\omega}{a}\right)$
$t^{-1/2}e^{-at}$ $(\text{Re } a > 0)$	$\sqrt{\dfrac{\pi}{2}}\left\{\dfrac{(\omega^2 + a^2)^{1/2} - a}{(\omega^2 + a^2)}\right\}^{1/2}$
te^{-at^2}	$\dfrac{1}{4}\dfrac{\sqrt{\pi}\,\omega}{a^{3/2}} e^{-\omega^2/4a}$
$t^{-1}e^{-at^2}$	$\dfrac{\pi}{2} \text{erf}\left(\dfrac{1}{2}\dfrac{\omega}{\sqrt{a}}\right)$
$\ln\left|\dfrac{t + \tau}{t - \tau}\right|$ $(\tau > 0)$	$\dfrac{\pi}{\omega} \sin \omega\tau$
$t^{-1}\sin \lambda t$ $(\lambda > 0)$	$\dfrac{1}{2}\ln\left|\dfrac{\omega + \lambda}{\omega - \lambda}\right|$
$J_0(\lambda t)$ $(\lambda > 0)$	$0 \qquad\qquad\quad 0 < \omega < \lambda$ $(\omega^2 - \lambda^2)^{-1/2} \quad \lambda < \omega < \infty$

$\dfrac{1}{t} J_0(\lambda t) \quad (\lambda > 0)$	$\sin^{-1}\left(\dfrac{\omega}{\lambda}\right) \qquad 0 < \omega < \lambda$ $\dfrac{\pi}{2} \qquad \lambda < \omega < \infty$
$f(t)$	$F(\omega)$
$f(t) = f(-t)$	$2 \displaystyle\int_0^\infty f(t) \cos \omega t \, dt$
$f(t) = -f(-t)$	$-2j \displaystyle\int_0^\infty f(t) \sin \omega t \, dt$
$f(\lambda t)e^{j\beta t} \qquad (\lambda > 0)$	$\dfrac{1}{\lambda} F\left(\dfrac{\omega - \beta}{\lambda}\right)$
$f(\lambda t) \cos \omega_0 t \qquad (\lambda > 0)$	$\dfrac{1}{2\lambda}\left\{ F\left(\dfrac{\omega - \omega_0}{\lambda}\right) + F\left(\dfrac{\omega + \omega_0}{\lambda}\right) \right\}$
$f(\lambda t) \sin \omega_0 t \qquad (\lambda > 0)$	$\dfrac{1}{2j\lambda}\left\{ F\left(\dfrac{\omega - \omega_0}{\lambda}\right) - F\left(\dfrac{\omega + \omega_0}{\lambda}\right) \right\}$
$t^n f(t)$	$j^n \dfrac{d^n F(\omega)}{d\omega^n}$

These entries are discussed as theorems in Chapter 4 or are extensions thereof.

$\delta(t)$	1
$u(t)$	$\pi\delta(\omega) + \dfrac{1}{j\omega}$
$e^{j\omega_0 t}$	$2\pi\delta(\omega - \omega_0)$
$e^{-a|t|} \qquad (\text{Re } a > 0)$	$\dfrac{2a}{a^2 + \omega^2}$
$(t^2 + \tau^2)^{-1} \qquad (\tau > 0)$	$\dfrac{\pi}{\tau} e^{-|\omega|\tau}$
$e^{j\beta \sin \omega_0 t}$	$\displaystyle\sum_{n=-\infty}^{\infty} J_n(\beta)\delta(\omega - n\omega_0)$

TABLE D.3   One-sided Z-transforms, $F(z) = \displaystyle\sum_{n=0}^{\infty} f(n)z^{-n}$

$f(n)$	$F(z)$
$a_1 f_1(n) + a_2 f_2(n)$	$a_1 F_1(z) + a_2 F_2(z)$

$e^{-an}f(n)$	$F(e^a z)$
$n\,f(n)$	$-z\,\dfrac{d}{dz}F(z)$
$f(n-m)$	$z^{-m}F(z)$
$f(n+m)$	$z^m\left\{ F(z) - \displaystyle\sum_{k=0}^{m-1} f(k)z^{-k} \right\}$
$(n-1)(n-2)f(n-2)$	$\dfrac{d^2}{dz^2}F(z)$
$\displaystyle\sum_{k=0}^{n} f_1(k)f_2(n-k)$	$F_1(z)F_2(z)$
$a^{-n}f(n)$	$F(az)$
$\delta(n)$	1
$u(n)$	$\dfrac{z}{z-1}$
$u(n-k)$	$\dfrac{z^{-k+1}}{z-1}$
a^n	$\dfrac{z}{z-a}$
e^{-kn}	$\dfrac{z}{z-e^{-k}}$
$r(n)=n$	$\dfrac{z}{(z-1)^2}$
n^2	$\dfrac{z(z+1)}{(z-1)^3}$
$\sin(\omega_0 n + \beta)$	$\dfrac{z^2 \sin\beta + z\sin(\omega_0 - \beta)}{z^2 - 2z\cos\omega_0 + 1}$
$\cos\omega_0 n$	$\dfrac{z(z-\cos\omega_0)}{z^2 - 2z\cos\omega_0 + 1}$
$\sinh\omega_0 n$	$\dfrac{z\sinh\omega_0\, z(z-\cosh\omega_0)}{z^2 - 2z\cosh\omega_0 + 1}$
$\cosh\omega_0 n$	$\dfrac{z\sinh\omega_0}{z^2 - 2z\cosh\omega_0 + 1}$
$a^n/n!\quad (n = 1,3,5,7,\ldots)$	$\sinh(a/z)$

$a^n/n!$ $(n = 0,2,4,6, \ldots)$	$\cosh(a/z)$
$1/n$ $n > 0$	$\ln \dfrac{z}{z-1}$

SELECTED BIBLIOGRAPHY

1. G. Doetsch, *Guide to the Applications of the Laplace and Z-transforms*. New York: Van Nostrand Reinhold Co., 1971.
2. E. I. Jury, *Theory and Application of the Z-transform Method*. New York: John Wiley and Sons, Inc., 1964.
3. G. A. Korn, *Basic Tables in Electrical Engineering*. New York: McGraw-Hill Book Co., 1965.
4. P. K. F. Kuhfitting, *Introduction to the Laplace Transform*. New York: Plenum Press, 1978.
5. F. E. Nixon, *Handbook of Laplace Transformations, Fundamentals, Applications, Tables and Examples*. Englewood Cliffs, N.J.: Prentice-Hall, 1965.
6. K. B. Wolf, *Integral Transforms in Science and Engineering*. New York: Plenum Press, 1979.

Index